The Elements of
COORDINATE GEOMETRY

Part 1
Cartesian Coordinates

SL LONEY

CLASSIC TEXTS SERIES

The Elements of
COORDINATE GEOMETRY

Part 1
Cartesian Coordinates

SL LONEY

Sydney Luxton Loney

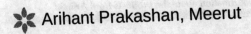

Arihant Prakashan, Meerut

Arihant Prakashan, Meerut

ॐ **Administrative & Production Offices**

Corporate Office
'Ramchhaya' 4577/15, Agarwal Road, Darya Ganj, New Delhi -110002
Tele: 011- 47630600, 43518550; Fax: 011- 2 3280316

Head Office
Kalindi, TP Nagar, Meerut (UP) - 250002
Tele: 0121-2401479, 2512970, 4004199; Fax: 0121-2401648

ॐ **Sales & Support Offices**

Agra, Ahmedabad, Bengaluru, Bhubaneswar, Bareilly, Chennai, Delhi, Guwahati, Haldwani, Hyderabad, Jaipur, Jhansi, Kolkata, Kota, Lucknow, Meerut, Nagpur & Pune

ॐ **ISBN** : 978-93-5176-223-2

ॐ **Price :** ₹140

Typeset by Arihant DTP Unit at Meerut

Printed & Bound By
Arihant Publications (I) Ltd. (Press Unit)

For further information about the products from Arihant,
log on to www.arihantbooks.com *or email to* info@arihantbooks.com

Publishers' Note

In this book, the author has presented the elements of Coordinate Geometry in a manner suitable for beginners and junior students. Cartesian and Polar Coordinates only are used, and the Look forms Part I of the complete work. Part II deals with Trilinear Coordinates, Projection Reciprocation, etc.

The Straight Line and a Circle have treated more fully than the other portions of the subject, since it is generally in the elementary conceptions that beginners find great difficulties.

There are a large number of examples, over 1100 in all, and they are, in general, of an elementary character. The examples are especially numerous in the earlier parts of the book.

CONTENTS

1

INTRODUCTION

SOME ALGEBRAIC RESULTS

➤ **1. Quadratic Equations :** The roots of the quadratic equation

$$ax^2 + bx + c = 0$$

may easily be shewn to be

$$\frac{-b + \sqrt{b^2 - 4ac}}{2a} \quad \text{and} \quad \frac{-b - \sqrt{b^2 - 4ac}}{2a}$$

They are therefore, real and unequal, equal, or imaginary, according as the quantity $b^2 - 4ac$ is positive, zero, or negative, *i.e.*, according as

$$b^2 \gtreqless 4ac$$

➤ **2.** *Relations between the roots of any algebraic equation and the coefficients of the terms of the equation.*

If any equation be written so that the coefficient of the highest term is unity, it is shewn in any treatise on Algebra that:

(i) the sum of the roots is equal to the coefficient of the second term with its sign changed,

(ii) the sum of the products of the roots, taken two at a time, is equal to the coefficient of the third term,

(iii) the sum of their products, taken three at a time, is equal to the coefficient of the fourth term with its sign changed, and so on.

EXAMPLE 1 *If α and β be the roots of the equation,*

$$ax^2 + bx + c = 0, \quad \text{i.e.,} \quad x^2 + \frac{b}{a}x + \frac{c}{a} = 0$$

We have $\qquad \alpha + \beta = -\dfrac{b}{a} \quad \text{and} \quad \alpha\beta = \dfrac{c}{a}$

EXAMPLE 2 *If α, β and γ be the roots of the cubic equation,*

$$ax^3 + bx^2 + cx + d = 0$$

i.e., of $\qquad x^3 + \dfrac{b}{a}x^2 + \dfrac{c}{a}x + \dfrac{d}{a} = 0$

We have
$$\alpha + \beta + \gamma = -\frac{b}{a}$$

$$\beta\gamma + \gamma\alpha + \alpha\beta = \frac{c}{a}$$

and
$$\alpha\beta\gamma = -\frac{d}{a}$$

➤ **3.** It can easily be shewn that the solution of the equations,
$$a_1x + b_1y + c_1z = 0$$
and
$$a_2x + b_2y + c_2z = 0$$
is
$$\frac{x}{b_1c_2 - b_2c_1} = \frac{y}{c_1a_2 - c_2a_1} = \frac{z}{a_1b_2 - a_2b_1}$$

DETERMINANT NOTATION

➤ **4.** The quantity $\begin{vmatrix} a_1, & a_2 \\ b_1, & b_2 \end{vmatrix}$ is called a determinant of the second

order and stands for the quantity $a_1b_2 - a_2b_1$, so that,
$$\begin{vmatrix} a_1, & a_2 \\ b_1, & b_2 \end{vmatrix} = a_1b_2 - a_2b_1$$

EXAMPLE   (i) $\begin{vmatrix} 2, & 3 \\ 4, & 5 \end{vmatrix} = 2 \times 5 - 4 \times 3 = 10 - 12 = -2$

(ii) $\begin{vmatrix} -3, & -4 \\ -7, & -6 \end{vmatrix} = -3 \times (-6) - (-7) \times (-4) = 18 - 28 = -10$

➤ **5.** The quantity $\begin{vmatrix} a_1, & a_2, & a_3 \\ b_1, & b_2, & b_3 \\ c_1, & c_2, & c_3 \end{vmatrix}$

...(1)

is called a determinant of the third order and stands for the quantity.

$$a_1 \times \begin{vmatrix} b_2, & b_3 \\ c_2, & c_3 \end{vmatrix} - a_2 \begin{vmatrix} b_1, & b_3 \\ c_1, & c_3 \end{vmatrix} + a_3 \begin{vmatrix} b_1, & b_2 \\ c_1, & c_2 \end{vmatrix} \qquad \text{...(2)}$$

i.e., by Art. 4, for the quantity,
$$a_1(b_2c_3 - b_3c_2) - a_2(b_1c_3 - b_3c_1) + a_3(b_1c_2 - b_2c_1)$$

i.e
$$a_1(b_2c_3 - b_3c_2) + a_2(b_3c_1 - b_1c_3) + a_3(b_1c_2 - b_2c_1)$$

➤ **6.** A determinant of the third order is therefore, reduced to three determinants of the second order by the following rule:

Take in order the quantities which occur in the first row of the determinant; multiply each of these in turn by the determinant which is obtained by erasing the row and column to which it belongs; prefix the sign + and − alternately to the products thus obtained and add the results.

Thus, if in (1) we omit the row and column to which a_1 belongs, we have left the determinant $\begin{vmatrix} b_2, & b_3 \\ c_2, & c_3 \end{vmatrix}$ and this is the coefficient of a_1 in (2).

Similarly, if in (1), we omit the row and column to which a_2 belongs, we have left the determinant $\begin{vmatrix} b_1, & b_3 \\ c_1, & c_3 \end{vmatrix}$ and this with the − sign prefixed is the coefficient of a_2 in (2).

➤ 7.

EXAMPLE The determinant $= \begin{vmatrix} 1, & -2, & -3 \\ -4, & 5, & -6 \\ -7, & 8, & -9 \end{vmatrix}$

$$= 1 \times \begin{vmatrix} 5, & -6 \\ 8, & -9 \end{vmatrix} - (-2) \times \begin{vmatrix} -4, & -6 \\ -7, & -9 \end{vmatrix} + (-3) \times \begin{vmatrix} -4, & 5 \\ -7, & 8 \end{vmatrix}$$

$$= \{5 \times (-9) - 8 \times (-6)\} + 2 \times \{(-4)(-9) - (-7)(-6)\}$$
$$\qquad - 3 \times \{(-4) \times 8 - (-7) \times 5\}$$

$$= \{-45 + 48\} + 2\{36 - 42\} - 3\{-32 + 35\}$$

$$= 3 - 12 - 9 = -18$$

➤ **8.** The quantity, $\begin{vmatrix} a_1, & a_2, & a_3, & a_4 \\ b_1, & b_2, & b_3, & b_4 \\ c_1, & c_2, & c_3, & c_4 \\ d_1, & d_2, & d_3, & d_4 \end{vmatrix}$

is called a determinant of the fourth order and stands for the quantity.

$$a_1 \times \begin{vmatrix} b_2, & b_3, & b_4 \\ c_2, & c_3, & c_4 \\ d_2, & d_3, & d_4 \end{vmatrix} - a_2 \times \begin{vmatrix} b_1, & b_3, & b_4 \\ c_1, & c_3, & c_4 \\ d_1, & d_3, & d_4 \end{vmatrix}$$

$$+ a_3 \times \begin{vmatrix} b_1, & b_2, & b_4 \\ c_1, & c_2, & c_4 \\ d_1, & d_2, & d_4 \end{vmatrix} - a_4 \times \begin{vmatrix} b_1, & b_2, & b_3 \\ c_1, & c_2, & c_3 \\ d_1, & d_2, & d_3 \end{vmatrix}$$

and its value may be obtained by finding the value of each of these four determinants by the rule of Art. 6.

The rule for finding the value of a determinant of the fourth order in terms of determinants of the third order is clearly the same as that for one of the third order given in Art. 6.

Similarly, for determinants of higher orders.

➤ **9.** A determinant of the second order has two terms. One of the third order has 3×2, *i.e.*, 6 terms. One of the fourth order has $4 \times 3 \times 2$, *i.e.*, 24 terms and so on.

➤ **10.**

Examples *Prove that,*

(1) $\begin{vmatrix} 2, & -3 \\ 4, & 8 \end{vmatrix} = 28$
(2) $\begin{vmatrix} -6, & 7 \\ -4, & -9 \end{vmatrix} = 82$

(3) $\begin{vmatrix} 5, & -3, & 7 \\ -2, & 4, & -8 \\ 9, & 3, & -10 \end{vmatrix} = -98$
(4) $\begin{vmatrix} 9, & 8, & 7 \\ 6, & 5, & 4 \\ 3, & 2, & 1 \end{vmatrix} = 0$

(5) $\begin{vmatrix} -a, & b, & c \\ a, & -b, & c \\ a, & b, & -c \end{vmatrix} = 4abc$

(6) $\begin{vmatrix} a, & h, & g \\ h, & b, & f \\ g, & f, & c \end{vmatrix} = abc + 2fgh - af^2 - bg^2 - ch^2$

ELIMINATION

➤ **11.** Suppose we have the two equations,

$$a_1 x + a_2 y = 0 \qquad \ldots(1)$$
$$b_1 x + b_2 y = 0 \qquad \ldots(2)$$

between the two unknown quantities x and y. There must be some relation holding between the four coefficients $a_1, a_2, b_1,$ and b_2. For, from (1), we have

$$\frac{x}{y} = -\frac{a_2}{a_1}$$

and from (2), we have

$$\frac{x}{y} = -\frac{b_2}{b_1}$$

Equating these two values of $\frac{x}{y}$, we have

$$\frac{b_2}{b_1} = \frac{a_2}{a_1}$$

i.e., $\qquad a_1 b_2 - a_2 b_1 = 0 \qquad \ldots(3)$

The result (3) is the condition that both the equations (1) and (2) should be true for the same values of x and y. The process of finding the condition is called the eliminating of x and y from the equations

(1) and (2), and the result (3) is often called the eliminant of (1) and (2).

Using the notation of Art. 4, the result (3) may be written in the form $\begin{vmatrix} a_1, & a_2 \\ b_1, & b_2 \end{vmatrix} = 0.$

This result is obtained from (1) and (2), by taking the coefficients of x and y in the order in which they occur in the equations, placing them in this order to form a determinant, and equating it to zero.

➤ **12.** Suppose, again, that we have the three equations,

$$a_1x + a_2y + a_3z = 0 \qquad \ldots(1)$$
$$b_1x + b_2y + b_3z = 0 \qquad \ldots(2)$$

and
$$c_1x + c_2y + c_3z = 0 \qquad \ldots(3)$$

between the three unknown quantities x, y, and z.

By dividing each equation by z we have three equations between the two unknown quantities $\dfrac{x}{z}$ and $\dfrac{y}{z}$. Two of these will be sufficient to determine these quantities. By substituting their values in the third equation we shall obtain a relation between the nine coefficients.

Or we may proceed thus. From the equations (2) and (3), we have

$$\frac{x}{b_2c_3 - b_3c_2} = \frac{y}{b_3c_1 - b_1c_3} = \frac{z}{b_1c_2 - b_2c_1}$$

Substituting these values in equations (1), we have

$$a_1(b_2c_3 - b_3c_2) + a_2(b_3c_1 - b_1c_3) + a_3(b_1c_2 - b_2c_1) = 0 \qquad \ldots(4)$$

This is the result of eliminating x, y, and z from the equations (1), (2) and (3).

But, by Art. 5, equation (4), may be written in the form

$$\begin{vmatrix} a_1, & a_2, & a_3 \\ b_1, & b_2, & b_3 \\ c_1, & c_2, & c_3 \end{vmatrix} = 0$$

This eliminant may be written down as in the last article, *viz.*, by taking the coefficients of x, y, and z in the order in which they occur in the equations (1), (2) and (3), placing them to form a determinant, and equating it to zero.

➤ **13.**

EXAMPLE *What is the value of a so that the equations,*

$$ax + 2y + 3z = 0, \quad 2x - 3y + 4z = 0$$

and $\qquad\qquad 5x + 7y - 8z = 0$

may be simultaneously true ?

Eliminating x, y, and z, we have

$$\begin{vmatrix} a & 2 & 3 \\ 2 & -3 & 4 \\ 5 & 7 & -8 \end{vmatrix} = 0$$

i.e., $\qquad a[(-3)(-8) - 4 \times 7] - 2[2 \times (-8) - 4 \times 5] + 3[2 \times 7 - 5 \times (-3)] = 0$

i.e., $\qquad\qquad\qquad\qquad\qquad a[-4] - 2[-36] + 3[29] = 0$

So, that $\qquad\qquad\qquad a = \dfrac{72 + 87}{4} = \dfrac{159}{4}$.

➤ **14.** If again we have the four equations,

$$a_1x + a_2y + a_3z + a_4u = 0$$
$$b_1x + b_2y + b_3z + b_4u = 0$$
$$c_1x + c_2y + c_3z + c_4u = 0$$

and $\qquad\qquad d_1x + d_2y + d_3z + d_4u = 0$

it could be shewn that the result of eliminating the four quantities x, y, z, and u is the determinant

$$\begin{vmatrix} a_1, & a_2, & a_3, & a_4 \\ b_1, & b_2, & b_3, & b_4 \\ c_1, & c_2, & c_3, & c_4 \\ d_1, & d_2, & d_3, & d_4 \end{vmatrix} = 0$$

A similar theorem could be shewn to be true for n equations of the first degree, such as the above, between n unknown quantities.

It will be noted that the right-hand member of each of the above equations is zero.

■

2

COORDINATES, LENGTHS OF STRAIGHT LINES AND AREAS OF TRIANGLES

➤ **15. Coordinates :** Let OX and OY be two fixed straight lines in the plane of the paper. The line OX is called the axis of x, the line OY the axis of y, whilst the two together are called the axes of coordinates.

The point O is called the origin of coordinates or, more shortly, the origin.

From any point P in the plane draw a straight line parallel to OY to meet OX in M.

The distance OM is called the Abscissa, and the distance MP the Ordinate of the point P, whilst the abscissa and the ordinate together are called its Coordinates.

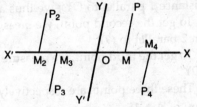

Distances measured parallel to OX are callled x, with or without a suffix, (*e.g.*, $x_1, x_2 \ldots x', x'', \ldots$) and distances measured parallel to OY are called y, with or without a suffix, (*e.g.*, $y_1, y_2, \ldots y', y'', \ldots$).

If the distances OM and MP be respectively x and y, the-coordinates of P are, for brevity, denoted by the symbol (x, y).

Conversely, when we are given that the coordinates of a point P are (x, y) we know its position. For from O we have only to measure a distance $OM (= x)$ along OX and then from M measure a distance $MP (= y)$ parallel to OY and we arrive at the position of the point P. For example, in the figure, if OM be equal to the unit of length and $MP = 2OM$, then P is the point $(1, 2)$.

➤ **16.** Produce XO backwards to form the line OX' and YO backwards to become OY'. In Analytical Geometry we have the same rule as to signs that the student has already met with in Trigonometry.

Lines measured parallel to OX are positive whilst those measured parallel to OX' are negative; lines measured parallel to OY are positive and those parallel to OY' are negative.

If P_2 be in the quadrant YOX' and P_2M_2, drawn parallel to the axis of y, meet OX' in M_2, and if the numerical values of the quantities OM_2 and M_2P_2 be a and b, the coordinates of P are ($-a$ and b) and the position of P_2 is given by the symbol $(-a, b)$.

Similarly, if P_3 be in the third quadrant $X'OY'$, both of its coordinates are negative, and if the numerical lengths of OM_3 and M_3P_3 be c and d, then P_3 is denoted by the symbol $(-c, -d)$.

Finally, if P_4 lie in the fourth quadrant its abscissa is positive and its ordinate is negative.

➤ **17.** <u>EXAMPLE</u>. *Lay down on paper the position of the points*
  (i) $(2, -1)$, (ii) $(-3, 2)$ and (iii) $(-2, -3)$

To get the first point we measure a distance 2 along OX and then a distance 1 parallel to OY'; we thus arrive at the required point.

To get the second point, we measure a distance 3 along OX', and then 2 parallel to OY.

To get the third point, we measure 2 along OX' and then 3 parallel to OY'.

These three points are respectively the points P_4, P_2 and P_3 in the figure of Art. 15.

➤ **18.** When the axes of coordinates are as in the figure of Art. 15, not at right angles, they are said to be Oblique Axes, and the angle between their two positive directions OX and OY, i.e., the angle XOY, is generally denoted by the Greek letter ω.

In general, it is however, found to be more convenient to take the axes OX and OY at right angles. They are then said to be Rectangular Axes.

It may always be assumed throughout this book that the axes are rectangular unless it is otherwise stated.

➤ **19.** The system of coordinates spoken of in the last few articles is known as the Cartesian System of Coordinates. It is so called because this system was first introduced by the philosopher

Des Cartes. There are other systems of coordinates in use, but the Cartesian system is by far the most important.

➤ **20.** *To find the distance between two points whose coordinates are given.*

Let P_1 and P_2 be the two given points, and let their coordinates be respectively (x_1, y_1) and (x_2, y_2).

Draw P_1M_1 and P_2M_2 parallel to OY, to meet OX in M_1 and M_2. Draw P_2R parallel to OX to meet M_1P_1 in R.

Then,

$$P_2R = M_2M_1 = OM_1 - OM_2 = x_1 - x_2$$

$$RP_1 = M_1P_1 - M_2P_2 = y_1 - y_2$$

and $\qquad \angle P_2RP_1 = \angle OM_1P_1 = 180° - P_1M_1X = 180° - \omega$

We therefore, have [*Trigonometry*, Art. 164]

$$P_1P_2{}^2 = P_2R^2 + RP_1{}^2 - 2P_2R \cdot RP_1 \cos P_2RP_1$$

$$= (x_1 - x_2)^2 + (y_1 - y_2)^2 - 2(x_1 - x_2)(y_1 - y_2) \cos (180° - \omega)$$

$$= (x_1 - x_2)^2 + (y_1 - y_2)^2 + 2(x_1 - x_2)(y_1 - y_2) \cos \omega \qquad \dots(1)$$

If the axes be, as is generally the case, at right angles, we have $\omega = 90°$ and hence, $\cos \omega = 0$.

The formula (1), then becomes

$$P_1P_2{}^2 = (x_1 - x_2)^2 + (y_1 - y_2)^2$$

so that in rectangular coordinates the distance between the two points (x_1, y_1) and (x_2, y_2) is,

$$\sqrt{(x_1 - x_2)^2 + (y_1 - y_2)^2} \qquad \dots(2)$$

Cor.: The distance of the point (x_1, y_1) from the origin is $\sqrt{x_1{}^2 + y_1{}^2}$, the axes being rectangular. This follows from (2) by making both x_2 and y_2 equal to zero.

➤ **21.** The formula of the previous article has been proved for the case when the coordinates of both the points are all positive.

Due regard being had to the signs of the coordinates, the formula will be found to be true for all points.

As a numerical example, let P_1 be the point (5, 6) and P_2 be the point (–7, – 4), so that we have

$$x_1 = 5, y_1 = 6, x_2 = -7,$$

and $\qquad y_2 = -4$

then, $\qquad P_2R = M_2O + OM_1 = 7 + 5$

$$= -x_2 + x_1$$

and $\qquad RP_1 = RM_1 + M_1P_1 = 4 + 6$

$$= -y_2 + y_1$$

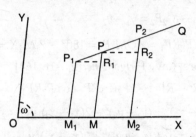

The rest of the proof is as in the last article.

Similarly, any other case could be considered.

➤ **22.** *To find the coordinates of the point which divides in a given ratio* $(m_1 : m_2)$ *the line joining two given points* (x_1, y_1) *and* (x_2, y_2).

Let P_1 be the point (x_1, y_1), P_2 be the point (x_2, y_2) and P be the required point, so that we have

$$P_1P : PP_2 :: m_1 : m_2$$

Let P be the point (x, y) so that if P_1M_1, PM and P_2M_2 be drawn parallel to the axis of y to meet the axis of x in M_1, M and M_2, we have

$$OM_1 = x_1, M_1P_1 = y_1, OM = x, MP = y, OM_2 = x_2,$$

and $\qquad\qquad\qquad M_2P_2 = y_2$

Draw P_1R_1 and PR_2, parallel to OX, to meet MP and M_2P_2 in R_1 and R_2 respectively.

Then, $\qquad\qquad P_1R_1 = M_1M = OM - OM_1 = x - x_1,$

$$PR_2 = MM_2 = OM_2 - OM = x_2 - x,$$

$$R_1P = MP - M_1P_1 = y - y_1,$$

and $\qquad\qquad R_2P_2 = M_2P_2 - MP = y_2 - y.$

From the similar triangles P_1R_1P and PR_2P_2, we have

$$\frac{m_1}{m_2} = \frac{P_1P}{PP_2} = \frac{P_1R_1}{PR_2} = \frac{x - x_1}{x_2 - x}$$

$\therefore$ $$m_1(x_2 - x) = m_2(x - x_1),$$

i.e., $$x = \frac{m_1 x_2 + m_2 x_1}{m_1 + m_2}$$

Again, $$\frac{m_1}{m_2} = \frac{P_1 P}{P P_2} = \frac{R_1 P}{R_2 P_2} = \frac{y - y_1}{y_2 - y},$$

So that, $$m_1(y_2 - y) = m_2(y - y_1)$$

and hence, $$y = \frac{m_1 y_2 + m_2 y_1}{m_1 + m_2}$$

The coordinates of the point which divides $P_1 P_2$ internally in the given ratio $m_1 : m_2$ are therefore,

$$\frac{m_1 x_2 + m_2 x_1}{m_1 + m_2} \quad \text{and} \quad \frac{m_1 y_2 + m_2 y_1}{m_1 + m_2}$$

If the point Q divide the line $P_1 P_2$ *externally* in the same ratio, i.e., so that $P_1 Q : Q P_2 :: m_1 : m_2$, its coordinates would be found to be,

$$\frac{m_1 x_2 - m_2 x_1}{m_1 - m_2} \quad \text{and} \quad \frac{m_1 y_2 - m_2 y_1}{m_1 - m_2}$$

The proof of this statement is similar to that of the preceding article and is left as an exercise for the student.

Cor : The coordinates of the middle point of the line joining (x_1, y_1) to (x_2, y_2) are:

$$\frac{x_1 + x_2}{2} \quad \text{and} \quad \frac{y_1 + y_2}{2}$$

➤ **23.**

Example 1 *In any triangle ABC prove that:*
$$AB^2 + AC^2 = 2(AD^2 + DC^2)$$
where D is the middle point of BC.

Take B as origin, BC as the axis of x and a line through B perpendicular to BC as the axis of y.

Let $BC = a$, so that C is the point $(a, 0)$, and let A be the point (x_1, y_1).

Then D is the point $\left(\dfrac{a}{2}, 0\right)$

Hence, $$AD^2 = \left(x_1 - \frac{a}{2}\right)^2 + y_1^2 \quad \text{and} \quad DC^2 = \left(\frac{a}{2}\right)^2$$

Hence, $$2(AD^2 + DC^2) = 2\left[x_1^2 + y_1^2 - ax_1 + \frac{a^2}{2}\right]$$

$$= 2x_1^2 + 2y_1^2 - 2ax_1 + a^2$$

Also, $AC^2 = (x_1 - a)^2 + y_1^2,$

and $AB^2 = x_1^2 + y_1^2$

Therefore, $AB^2 + AC^2 = 2x_1^2 + 2y_1^2 - 2ax_1 + a^2$

Hence, $AB^2 + AC^2 = 2(AD^2 + DC^2)$

EXAMPLE 2 *ABC is a triangle and D, E, and F are the middle points of the sides* $\overline{BC}$, CA, *and AB; prove that the point which divides AD internally in the ratio* 2 : 1 *also divides the lines BE and CF in the same ratio.*

Hence, prove that the medians of a triangle meet in a point.

Let the coordinates of the vertices A, B and C be (x_1, y_1), (x_2, y_2) and (x_3, y_3) respectively.

The coordinates of D are therefore,

$$\frac{x_2 + x_3}{2} \quad \text{and} \quad \frac{y_2 + y_3}{2}$$

Let G be the point that divides internally AD in the ratio 2 : 1, and let its coordinates be $\overline{x}$ and $\overline{y}$.

By the last article

$$\overline{x} = \frac{2 \times \dfrac{x_2 + x_3}{2} + 1 \times x_1}{2 + 1} = \frac{x_1 + x_2 + x_3}{3}$$

So, $\overline{y} = \dfrac{y_1 + y_2 + y_3}{3}$

In the same manner we could shew that these are the coordinates of the points that divide BE and CF in the ratio 2 : 1.

Since, the point whose coordinates are:

$$\frac{x_1 + x_2 + x_3}{3} \quad \text{and} \quad \frac{y_1 + y_2 + y_3}{3}$$

lies on each of the lines AD, BE and CF, it follows that these three lines meet in a point.

This point is called the Centroid of the triangle.

EXAMPLES I

Find the distances between the following pairs of points
1. (2, 3) and (5, 7)
2. (4, −7) and (−1, 5).
3. (−3, −2) and (−6, 7), the axes being inclined at 60°.
4. $(a, 0)$ and $(0, b)$
5. $(b + c, c + a)$ and $(c + a, a + b)$

6. $(a \cos \alpha, a \sin \alpha)$ and $(a \cos \beta, a \sin \beta)$

7. $(am_1^2, 2am_1)$ and $(am_2^2, 2am_2)$.

8. Lay down in a figure the positions of the points $(1, -3)$ and $(-2, 1)$, and prove that the distance between them is 5.

9. Find the value of x_1 if the distance between the points $(x_1, 2)$ and $(3, 4)$ be 8.

10. A line is of length 10 and one end is at the point $(2, -3)$; if the abscissa of the other end be 10, prove that its ordinate must be 3 or -9.

11. Prove that the points $(2a, 4a)$, $(2a, 6a)$ and $(2a + \sqrt{3}a, 5a)$ are the vertices of an equilateral triangle whose side is $2a$.

12. Prove that the points $(-2, -1)$, $(1, 0)$, $(4, 3)$, and $(1, 2)$ are at the vertices of a parallelogram.

13. Prove that the points $(2, -2)$, $(8, 4)$, $(5, 7)$ and $(-1, 1)$ are at the angular points of a rectangle.

14. Prove that the point $\left(-\dfrac{1}{14}, \dfrac{39}{14}\right)$ is the centre of the circle circumscribing the triangle whose angular points are $(1, 1)$, $(2, 3)$, and $(-2, 2)$.

Find the coordinates of the point which

15. divides the line joining the points $(1, 3)$ and $(2, 7)$ in the ratio $3 : 4$.

16. divides the same line in the ratio $3 : -4$.

17. divides, internally and externally, the line joining $(-1, 2)$ to $(4, -5)$ in the ratio $2 : 3$.

18. divides, internally and externally, the line joining $(-3, -4)$ to $(-8, 7)$ in the ratio $7 : 5$.

19. The line joining the points $(1, -2)$ and $(-3, 4)$ is trisected; find the coordinates of the points of trisection.

20. The line joining the points $(-6, 8)$ and $(8, -6)$ is divided into four equal parts; find the coordinates of the points of section.

21. Find the coordinates of the points which divide, internally and externally, the line joining the point $(a + b, a - b)$ to the point $(a - b, a + b)$ in the ratio $a : b$.

22. The coordinates of the vertices of a triangle are (x_1, y_1), (x_2, y_2) and (x_3, y_3). The line joining the first two is divided in the ratio $l : k$, and the line joining this point of division to the opposite angular point is then divided in the ratio $m : k + l$. Find the coordinates of the latter point of section.

23. Prove that the coordinates, x and y, of the middle point of the line joining the point $(2, 3)$ to the point $(3, 4)$ satisfy the equation,

$$x - y + 1 = 0$$

24. If G be the centroid of a triangle ABC and O be any other point, prove that,

$$3(GA^2 + GB^2 + GC^2) = BC^2 + CA^2 + AB^2$$

and $\qquad OA^2 + OB^2 + OC^2 = GA^2 + GB^2 + GC^2 + 3GO^2$

25. Prove that the lines joining the middle points of opposite sides of a quadrilateral and the line joining the middle points of its diagonals meet in a point and bisect one another.

26. $A, B, C, D \ldots$ are n points in a plane whose coordinates are $(x_1, y_1), (x_2, y_2), (x_3, y_3), \ldots AB$ is bisected in the point G_1; $G_1 C$ is divided at G_2 in the ratio $1 : 2$; $G_2 D$ is divided at G_3 in the ratio $1 : 3$; $G_3 E$ at G_4 in the ratio $1 : 4$, and so on until all the points are exhausted. Shew that the coordinates of the final point so obtained are,

$$\frac{x_1 + x_2 + x_3 + \ldots + x_n}{n} \quad \text{and} \quad \frac{y_1 + y_2 + y_3 + \ldots + y_n}{n}$$

[This point is called the **Centre of Mean Position** of the n given points.]

27. Prove that a point can be found which is at the same distance from each of the four points:

$$\left(am_1, \frac{a}{m_1} \right), \left(am_2, \frac{a}{m_2} \right), \left(am_3, \frac{a}{m_3} \right) \text{ and } \left(\frac{a}{m_1 m_2 m_3}, am_1 m_2 m_3 \right)$$

➤ **24.** *To prove that the area of a trapezium, i.e., a quadrilateral having two sides parallel, is one half the sum of the two parallel sides multiplied by the perpendicular distance between them.*

Let $ABCD$ be the trapezium having the sides AD and BC parallel.

Join AC and draw AL perpendicular to BC and CN perpendicular to AD, produced if necessary.

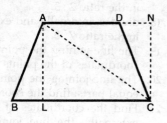

Since, the area of a triangle is one half the product of any side and the perpendicular drawn from the opposite angle, we have

$$\text{area } ABCD = \triangle ABC + \triangle ACD$$

$$= \frac{1}{2} \cdot BC \cdot AL + \frac{1}{2} \cdot AD \cdot CN$$

$$= \frac{1}{2} (BC + AD) \times AL$$

➤ **25.** *To find the area of the triangle, the coordinates of whose angular points are given, the axes being rectangular.*

Let ABC be the triangle and let the coordinates of its angular points A, B and C be (x_1, y_1), (x_2, y_2) and (x_3, y_3).

Draw AL, BM and CN perpendicular to the axis of x, and let Δ denote the required area.

Then,

$\Delta =$ trapezium $ALNC +$ trapezium $CNMB -$ trapezium $ALMB$

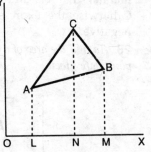

$$= \frac{1}{2} LN(LA + NC) + \frac{1}{2} NM(NC + MB)$$

$$- \frac{1}{2} LM(LA + MB)$$

by the last article,

$$= \frac{1}{2} [(x_3 - x_1)(y_1 + y_3) + (x_2 - x_3)(y_2 + y_3) - (x_2 - x_1)(y_1 + y_2)]$$

On simplifying we easily have

$$\Delta = \frac{1}{2}(x_1 y_2 - x_2 y_1 + x_2 y_3 - x_3 y_2 + x_3 y_1 - x_1 y_3)$$

or the equivalent form,

$$\Delta = \frac{1}{2} [x_1(y_2 - y_3) + x_2(y_3 - y_1) + x_3(y_1 - y_2)]$$

If we use the determinant notation this may be written (as in Art. 5).

$$\Delta = \frac{1}{2} \begin{vmatrix} x_1, & y_1, & 1 \\ x_2, & y_2, & 1 \\ x_3, & y_3, & 1 \end{vmatrix}$$

Cor. : The area of the triangle whose vertices are the origin $(0, 0)$ and the points (x_1, y_1), (x_2, y_2) is $\frac{1}{2}(x_1 y_2 - x_2 y_1)$.

▶ **26.** In the preceding article, if the axes be oblique, the perpendiculars AL, BM, and CN, are not equal to the ordinates y_1, y_2, and y_3 but are equal respectively to $y_1 \sin \omega$, $y_2 \sin \omega$, and $y_3 \sin \omega$. The area of the triangle in this case becomes,

$$\frac{1}{2} \sin \omega \{x_1 y_2 - x_2 y_1 + x_2 y_3 - x_3 y_2 + x_3 y_1 - x_1 y_3\}$$

i.e., $\qquad \dfrac{1}{2} \sin \omega \times \begin{vmatrix} x_1, & y_1, & 1 \\ x_2, & y_2, & 1 \\ x_3, & y_3, & 1 \end{vmatrix}$

▶ **27.** In order that the expression for the area in Art. 25 may be a positive quantity (as all areas necessarily are) the points A, B and C must be taken in the order in which they would be met by a person starting from A and walking round the triangle in such a manner that *the area of the triangle is always on his left hand.* Otherwise the expressions of Art. 25 would be found to be negative.

➤ **28.** *To find the area of a quadrilateral the coordinates of whose angular points are given.*

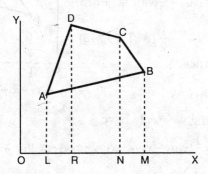

Let the angular points of the quadrilateral, taken in order, be $A, B, C,$ and D and let their coordinates be respectively (x_1, y_1), (x_2, y_2), (x_3, y_3) and (x_4, y_4).

Draw AL, BM, CN and DR perpendicular to the axis of x.

Then the area of the quadrilateral

$$= \text{trapezium } ALRD + \text{trapezium } DRNC + \text{trapezium } CNMB$$
$$- \text{trapezium } ALMB$$

$$= \frac{1}{2} LR(LA + RD) + \frac{1}{2} RN\,(RD + NC) + \frac{1}{2} NM(NC + MB)$$
$$- \frac{1}{2} LM(LA + MB)$$

$$= \frac{1}{2} \{(x_4 - x_1)(y_1 + y_4) + (x_3 - x_4)(y_3 + y_4) + (x_2 - x_3)(y_3 + y_2)$$
$$- (x_2 - x_1)(y_1 + y_2)\}$$

$$= \frac{1}{2} \{(x_1 y_2 - x_2 y_1) + (x_2 y_3 - x_3 y_2) + (x_3 y_4 - x_4 y_3) + (x_4 y_1 - x_1 y_4)\}$$

➤ **29.** The above formula may also be obtained by drawing the lines $OA, OB, OC,$ and OD. For the quadrilateral $ABCD$.
$$= \triangle OBC + \triangle OCD - \triangle OBA - \triangle OAD$$

But the coordinates of the vertices of the triangle OBC are $(0, 0)$, (x_2, y_2) and (x_3, y_3); hence, by Art. 25, its area is $\frac{1}{2}(x_2 y_3 - x_3 y_2)$.

So for the other triangles.

The required area therefore,

$$= \frac{1}{2} \left[(x_2 y_3 - x_3 y_2) + (x_3 y_4 - x_4 y_3) - (x_2 y_1 - x_1 y_2) - (x_1 y_4 - x_4 y_1) \right]$$

$$= \frac{1}{2} \left[(x_1 y_2 - x_2 y_1) + (x_2 y_3 - x_3 y_2) + (x_3 y_4 - x_4 y_3) + (x_4 y_1 - x_1 y_4) \right]$$

In a similar manner it may be shewn that the area of a polygon of n sides the coordinates of whose angular points, taken in order, are:

$$(x_1, y_1), \ (x_2, y_2), \ (x_3, y_3), \ldots (x_n, y_n)$$

is $\dfrac{1}{2} \left[(x_1 y_2 - x_2 y_1) + (x_2 y_3 - x_3 y_2) + \ldots + (x_n y_1 - x_1 y_n) \right]$

EXAMPLES II

Find the areas of the triangles the coordinates of whose angular points are respectively:

1. $(1, 3)$, $(-7, 6)$ and $(5, -1)$.
2. $(0, 4)$, $(3, 6)$ and $(-8, -2)$.
3. $(5, 2)$, $(-9, -3)$ and $(-3, -5)$.
4. $(a, b + c)$, $(a, b - c)$ and $(-a, c)$.
5. $(a, c + a)$, (a, c) and $(-a, c - a)$.
6. $(a \cos \phi_1, b \sin \phi_1)$, $(a \cos \phi_2, b \sin \phi_2)$ and $(a \cos \phi_3, b \sin \phi_3)$.
7. $(am_1^2, 2am_1)$, $(am_2^2, 2am_2)$ and $(am_3^2, 2am_3)$.
8. $\{am_1 m_2, a(m_1 + m_2)\}$, $\{am_2 m_3, a(m_2 + m_3)\}$ and $\{am_3 m_1, a(m_3 + m_1)\}$
9. $\left\{ am_1, \dfrac{a}{m_1} \right\}$, $\left\{ am_2, \dfrac{a}{m_2} \right\}$ and $\left\{ am_3, \dfrac{a}{m_3} \right\}$.

Prove (by shewing that the area of the triangle formed by them is ꝫ that the following sets of three points are in a straight line:

10. $(1, 4)$, $(3, -2)$, and $(-3, 16)$.

11. $\left(-\dfrac{1}{2}, 3 \right)$ $(-5, 6)$ and $(-8, 8)$.

12. $(a, b + c)$, $(b, c + a)$, and $(c, a + b)$.

Find the areas of the quadrilaterals the coordinates of whose angular points, taken in order, are:

13. $(1, 1)$, $(3, 4)$, $(5, -2)$ and $(4, -7)$.
14. $(-1, 6)$, $(-3, -9)$, $(5, -8)$ and $(3, 9)$.
15. If O be the origin, and if the coordinates of any two points P_1 and P_2 be respectively (x_1, y_1) and (x_2, y_2), prove that:

$$OP_1 \cdot OP_2 \cdot \cos P_1 O P_2 = x_1 x_2 + y_1 y_2.$$

➤ **30. Polar Coordinates :** There is another method, which is often used, for determining the position of a point in a plane.

Suppose, O to be a fixed point, called the **origin** or **pole**, and OX a fixed line, called the **initial line.**

Take any other point P in the plane of the paper and join OP. The position of P is clearly known when the angle XOP and the length OP are given.

[For giving the angle XOP shews the direction in which OP is drawn, and giving the distance OP tells the distance of P along this direction.]

The angle XOP which would be traced out by the line OP in revolving from the initial line OX is called the vectorial angle of P and the length OP is called its radius vector. The two taken together are called the polar coordinates of P.

If the vectorial angle be θ and the radius vector be r, the position of P is denoted by the symbol (r, θ).

The radius vector is positive if it be measured from the origin O along the line bounding the vectorial angle; if measured in the opposite direction it is negative.

➤ **31.** EXAMPLE *Construct the positions of the points* (i) $(2, 30°)$, (ii) $(3, 150°)$, (iii) $(-2, 45°)$, (iv) $(-3, 330°)$, (v) $(3, -210°)$ and (vi) $(-3, -30°)$.

(i) To construct the first point, let the radius vector revolve from OX through an angle of $30°$, and then mark off along it a distance equal to two units of length. We thus, obtain the point P_1.

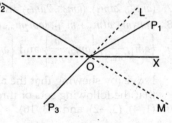

(ii) For the second point, the radius vector revolves from OX through $150°$ and is then in the position OP_2; measuring a distance 3 along it we arrive at P_2.

(iii) For the third point, let the radius vector revolve from OX through $45°$ into the position OL. We have now to measure along OL a distance -2, *i.e.*, we have to measure a distance 2 not along OL but in the *opposite* direction. Producing LO to P_3, so that OP_3 is 2 units of length, we have the required point P_3.

(iv) To get the fourth point, we let the radius vector rotate from OX through $330°$ into the position OM and measure on it a distance -3, *i.e.*, 3 in the direction MO produced. We thus, have the point P_2, which is the same as the point given by (ii).

(v) If the radius vector rotate through $-210°$, it will be in the position OP_2, and the point required is P_2.

(vi) For the sixth point, the radius vector, after rotating through $-30°$, is in the position OM. We then measure -3 along it, *i.e.*, 3 in the direction MO produced, and once more arrive at the point P_2.

➤ **32.** It will be observed that in the previous example the same point P_2 is denoted by each of the four sets of polar coordinates.

$$(3, 150°), \ (-3, 330°), \ (3, -210°) \text{ and } (-3, -30°).$$

In general it will be found that the same point is given by each of the polar coordinates.

$$(r, \theta), (-r, 180° + \theta), \{r, -(360° - \theta)\} \text{ and } \{-r, -(180° - \theta)\}$$

or expressing the angles in radians, by each of the coordinates.

$$(r, \theta), (-r, \pi + \theta), \{r, -(2\pi - \theta)\} \text{ and } \{-r, -(\pi - \theta)\}$$

It is also clear that adding 360° (or any multiple of 360°) to the vectorial angle does not alter the final position of the revolving line, so that (r, θ) is always the same point as $(r, \theta + n \cdot 360°)$, where n is an integer.

So, adding 180° or any odd multiple of 180° to the vectorial angle and changing the sign of the radius vector gives the same point as before. Thus, the point

$$[-r, \theta + (2n + 1) \ 180°]$$

is the same point as $[-r, \theta + 180°]$, *i.e.*, is the point $[r, \theta]$.

➤ **33.** *To find the length of the straight line joining two points whose polar coordinates are given.*

Let A and B be the two points and let their polar coordinates be (r_1, θ_1) and (r_2, θ_2) respectively, so that,

$$OA = r_1, \ OB = r_2, \ \angle XOA = \theta_1 \text{ and } \angle XOB = \theta_2$$

Then (*Trigonometry*, Art. 164).

$$AB^2 = OA^2 + OB^2 - 2OA \cdot OB \cos AOB$$

$$= r_1^2 + r_2^2 - 2r_1 r_2 \cos (\theta_1 - \theta_2)$$

➤ **34.** *To find the area of a triangle the coordinates of whose angular points are given.*

Let ABC be the triangle and let (r_1, θ_1), (r_2, θ_2) and (r_3, θ_3) be the polar coordinates of its angular points.

We have

$$\Delta ABC = \Delta OBC + \Delta OCA - \Delta OBA \qquad \qquad \text{...(1)}$$

Now,

$$\Delta OBC = \frac{1}{2}\, OB \cdot OC \sin BOC$$

[*Trigonometry*, Art. 198]

$$= \frac{1}{2}\, r_2 r_3 \sin (\theta_3 - \theta_2)$$

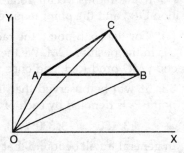

So,

$$\Delta OCA = \frac{1}{2}\, OC \cdot OA \sin COA = \frac{1}{2}\, r_3 r_1 \sin (\theta_1 - \theta_3)$$

and

$$\Delta OAB = \frac{1}{2}\, OA \cdot OB \sin AOB = \frac{1}{2}\, r_1 r_2 \sin (\theta_1 - \theta_2)$$

$$= -\frac{1}{2}\, r_1 r_2 \sin (\theta_2 - \theta_1)$$

Hence, (1), gives

$$\Delta ABC = \frac{1}{2}\, [r_2 r_3 \sin (\theta_3 - \theta_2) + r_3 r_1 \sin (\theta_1 - \theta_3) + r_1 r_2 \sin (\theta_2 - \theta_1)]$$

➤ **35.** *To change from Cartesian Coordinates to Polar Coordinates, and conversely.*

Let P be any point whose Cartesian coordinates, referred to rectangular axes, are x and y, and whose polar coordinates, referred to O as pole and OX as initial line, are (r, θ).

Draw PM perpendicular to OX so that we have

$$OM = x, MP = y, \angle MOP = \theta,$$

and

$$OP = r$$

From the triangle MOP we have

$$x = OM = OP \cos MOP = r \cos \theta \qquad \ldots(1)$$

$$y = MP = OP \sin MOP = r \sin \theta \qquad \ldots(2)$$

$$r = OP = \sqrt{OM^2 + MP^2} = \sqrt{x^2 + y^2} \qquad \ldots(3)$$

and

$$\tan \theta = \frac{MP}{OM} = \frac{y}{x} \qquad \ldots(4)$$

Equations (1) and (2) express the Cartesian coordinates in terms of the polar coordinates.

Equations (3) and (4), express the polar in terms of the Cartesian coordinates.

The same relations will be found to hold if P be in any other of the quadrants into which the plane is divided by XOX' and YOY'.

EXAMPLE *Change to Cartesian coordinates the equations,*

(1) $r = a \sin \theta$, *and* (2) $r^{1/2} = a^{1/2} \cos \dfrac{\theta}{2}$

1. Multiplying the equation by r, it becomes $r^2 = ar \sin \theta$, *i.e.*, by equations (2) and (3), $x^2 + y^2 = ay$.

2. Squaring the equation (2), it becomes

$$r = a \cos^2 \frac{\theta}{2} = \frac{a}{2}(1 + \cos \theta)$$

i.e., $2r^2 = ar + ar \cos \theta$

i.e., $2(x^2 + y^2) = a\sqrt{x^2 + y^2} + ax$

i.e. $(2x^2 + 2y^2 - ax)^2 = a^2(x^2 + y^2)$

EXAMPLES III

Lay down the positions of the points whose polar coordinates are:

1. $(3, 45°)$ **2.** $(-2, -60°)$ **3.** $(4, 135°)$ **4.** $(2, 330°)$

5. $(-1, -180°)$ **6.** $(1, -210°)$ **7.** $(5, -675°)$ **8.** $\left(a, \dfrac{\pi}{2}\right)$

9. $\left(2a, -\dfrac{\pi}{2}\right)$ **10.** $\left(-a, \dfrac{\pi}{6}\right)$ **11.** $\left(-2a, -\dfrac{2\pi}{3}\right)$

Find the lengths of the straight lines joining the pairs of points whose polar coordinates are:

12. $(2, 30°)$ and $(4, 120°)$ **13.** $(-3, 45°)$ and $(7, 105°)$

14. $\left(a, \dfrac{\pi}{2}\right)$ and $\left(3a, \dfrac{\pi}{6}\right)$

15. Prove that the points $(0, 0)$, $\left(3, \dfrac{\pi}{2}\right)$ and $\left(3, \dfrac{\pi}{6}\right)$ form an equilateral triangle.

Find the areas of the triangles the coordinates of whose angular points are:

16. $(1, 30°)$, $(2, 60°)$ and $(3, 90°)$.

17. $(-3, -30°)$, $(5, 150°)$ and $(7, 210°)$.

18. $\left(-a, \dfrac{\pi}{6}\right)$ $\left(a, \dfrac{\pi}{2}\right)$, and $\left(-2a, -\dfrac{2\pi}{3}\right)$.

Find the polar coordinates (drawing the figure in each case) of the points:

19. $x = \sqrt{3}, y = 1$ **20.** $x = -\sqrt{3}, y = 1$ **21.** $x = -1, y = 1$

Find the Cartesian coordinates (drawing a figure in each case) of the points whose polar coordinates are:

22. $\left(5, \dfrac{\pi}{4}\right)$ **23.** $\left(-5, \dfrac{\pi}{3}\right)$ **24.** $\left(5, -\dfrac{\pi}{4}\right)$

Change to polar coordinates the equations:

25. $x^2 + y^2 = a^2$ **26.** $y = x \tan \alpha$ **27.** $x^2 + y^2 = 2ax$

28. $x^2 - y^2 = 2ay$ **29.** $x^3 = y^2(2a - x)$ **30.** $(x^2 + y^2)^2 = a^2(x^2 - y^2)$

Transform to Cartesian coordinates the equations:

31. $r = a$ **32.** $\theta = \tan^{-1} m$ **33.** $r = a \cos \theta$ **34.** $r = a \sin 2\theta$

35. $r^2 = a^2 \cos 2\theta$ **36.** $r^2 \sin 2\theta = 2a^2$ **37.** $r^2 \cos 2\theta = a^2$

38. $r^{1/2} \cos \dfrac{\theta}{2} = a^{1/2}$ **39.** $r^{1/2} = a^{1/2} \sin \dfrac{\theta}{2}$

40. $r(\cos 3\theta + \sin 3\theta) = 5k \sin \theta \cos \theta$.

3

LOCUS. EQUATION TO A LOCUS

> **36.** When a point moves so as always to satisfy a given condition, or conditions, the path it traces out is called its Locus under these conditions.

For example, suppose O to be a given point in the plane of the paper and that a point P is to move on the paper so that its distance from O shall be constant and equal to a. It is clear that all the positions of the moving point must lie on the circumference of a circle whose centre is O and whose radius is a. The circumference of this circle is therefore the "Locus" of P when it moves subject to the condition that its distance from O shall be equal to the constant distance a.

> **37.** Again, suppose A and B to be two fixed points in the plane of the paper and that a point P is to move in the plane of the paper so that its distances from A and B are to be always equal. If we bisect AB in C and through it draw a straight line (of infinite length in both directions) perpendicular to AB, then any point on this straight line is at equal distances from A and B. Also there is no point, whose distances from A and B are the same, which does not lie on this straight line. This straight line is therefore the "Locus" of P subject to the assumed condition.

> **38.** Again, suppose A and B to be two fixed points and that the point P is to move in the plane of the paper so that the angle APB is always a right angle. If we describe a circle on AB as diameter then P may be any point on the circumference of this circle, since the angle in a semi-circle is a right angle; also it could easily be shewn that APB is not a right angle except when P lies on this circumference. The "Locus" of P under the assumed condition is therefore a circle on AB as diameter.

> **39.** One single equation between two unknown quantities x and y,
> e.g.,
$$x + y = 1 \qquad \ldots(1)$$
cannot completely determine the values of x and y.

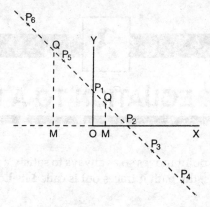

Such an equation has an infinite number of solutions.
Amongst them are the following:

$$\left.\begin{array}{l} x = 0, \\ y = 1 \end{array}\right\}, \quad \left.\begin{array}{l} x = 1, \\ y = 0 \end{array}\right\}, \quad \left.\begin{array}{l} x = 2, \\ y = -1 \end{array}\right\}, \quad \left.\begin{array}{l} x = 3, \\ y = -2 \end{array}\right\} \cdots \left.\begin{array}{l} x = -1, \\ y = 2 \end{array}\right\}, \quad \left.\begin{array}{l} x = -2, \\ y = 3 \end{array}\right\} \cdots$$

Let us mark down on paper a number of points whose coordinates
(as defined in the last chapter) satisfy equation (1).

Let OX and OY be the axes of coordinates.

If we mark off a distance OP_1 (= 1) along, OY, we have a point
P_1 whose coordinates $(0, 1)$ clearly satisfy equation (1).

If we mark off a distance OP_2 (= 1) along OX, we have a point
P_2 whose coordinates $(1, 0)$ satisfy equation (1).

Similarly the point P_3, $(2, -1)$, and P_4, $(3, -2)$, satisfy the equation
(1).

Again, the coordinates $(-1, 2)$ of P_5 and the coordinates $(-2, 3)$ of
P_6 satisfy equation (1).

On making the measurements carefully we should find that all
the points we obtain lie on the line P_1P_2 (produced both ways).

Again, if we took *any* point Q, lying on $P_1 P_2$, and draw a
perpendicular QM to OX, we should find on measurement that the
sum of its x and y (each taken with its proper sign) would be equal
to unity, so that the coordinates of Q would satisfy equation (1).

Also we should find no point, whose coordinates satisfy Eq. (1),
which does not lie on P_1P_2.

All the points, lying on the straight line P_1P_2, and no others are
therefore such that their coordinates satisfy the equation (1).

This result is expressed in the language of Analytical Geometry
by saying that equation (1) is the Equation to the Straight Line P_1P_2.

➤ **40.** Consider again the equation

$$x^2 + y^2 = 4 \qquad \qquad \text{...(1)}$$

Amongst an infinite number of solutions of this equation are the following:

$$\begin{matrix} x = 2, \\ y = 0 \end{matrix} \bigg\}, \quad \begin{matrix} x = \sqrt{3}, \\ y = 1 \end{matrix} \bigg\}, \quad \begin{matrix} x = \sqrt{2}, \\ y = \sqrt{2} \end{matrix} \bigg\}, \quad \begin{matrix} x = 1, \\ y = \sqrt{3} \end{matrix} \bigg\},$$

$$\begin{matrix} x = 0, \\ y = 2 \end{matrix} \bigg\}, \quad \begin{matrix} x = -1, \\ y = \sqrt{3} \end{matrix} \bigg\}, \quad \begin{matrix} x = -\sqrt{2}, \\ y = \sqrt{2} \end{matrix} \bigg\}, \quad \begin{matrix} x = -\sqrt{3}, \\ y = 1 \end{matrix} \bigg\},$$

$$\begin{matrix} x = -2, \\ y = 0 \end{matrix} \bigg\}, \quad \begin{matrix} x = -\sqrt{3}, \\ y = -1 \end{matrix} \bigg\}, \quad \begin{matrix} x = -\sqrt{2}, \\ y = -\sqrt{2} \end{matrix} \bigg\}, \quad \begin{matrix} x = -1, \\ y = -\sqrt{3} \end{matrix} \bigg\},$$

$$\begin{matrix} x = 0, \\ y = -2 \end{matrix} \bigg\}, \quad \begin{matrix} x = 1, \\ y = -\sqrt{3} \end{matrix} \bigg\}, \quad \begin{matrix} x = \sqrt{2}, \\ y = -\sqrt{2} \end{matrix} \bigg\}, \text{ and } \begin{matrix} x = \sqrt{3}, \\ y = -1 \end{matrix} \bigg\}.$$

All these points are respectively represented by the points $P_1, P_2, P_3, ..., P_{16}$, and they will all be found to lie on the dotted circle whose centre is O and radius is 2.

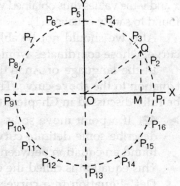

Also, if we take any other point Q on this circle and its ordinate QM, it follows, since $OM^2 + MQ^2 = OQ^2 = 4$, that the x and y of the point Q satisfies (1).

The dotted circle therefore passes through all the points whose coordinates satisfy (1).

In the language of Analytical Geometry the (1) is therefore the equation to the above circle.

➤ **41.** As another example let us trace the locus of the point whose coordinates satisfy the equation,

$$y^2 = 4x \qquad \qquad \text{...(1)}$$

If we give x a negative value we see that y is impossible; for the square of a real quantity cannot be negative.

We see therefore that there are no points lying to the left of OY.

If we give x any positive value we see that y has two real corresponding values which are equal and of opposite signs.

The following values, amongst an infinite number of others, satisfy (1), viz.

$$x = 0, \atop y = 0 \Big\} , \quad x = 1, \atop y = +2 \text{ or } -2 \Big\} , \quad x = 2, \atop y = 2\sqrt{2} \text{ or } -2\sqrt{2} \Big\} ,$$

$$x = 4, \atop y = +4 \text{ or } -4 \Big\} \cdots \quad x = 16, \atop y = 8 \text{ or } -8 \Big\} \cdots \quad x = +\infty, \atop y = +\infty \text{ or } -\infty \Big\} .$$

The origin is the first of these points and P_1 and Q_1, P_2 and Q_2, P_3 and Q_3, ... represent the next pairs of points.

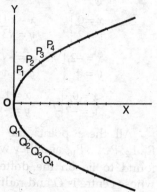

If we took a large number of values of x and the corresponding values of y, the points thus obtained would be found all to lie on the curve in the figure.

Both of its branches would be found to stretch away to infinity towards the right of the figure.

Also, if we took any point on this curve and measured with sufficient accuracy its x and y the values thus obtained would be found to satisfy equation (1).

Also we should not be able to find any point, not lying on the curve, whose coordinates would satisfy (1)

In the language of Analytical Geometry the equation (1) is the equation to the above curve. This curve is called a parabola and will be fully discussed in Chapter 10.

➤ **42.** If a point move so as to satisfy any given condition it will describe some definite curve, or locus, and there can always be found an equation between the x and y of *any* point on the path. This equation is called the equation to the locus or curve. Hence

Def. Equation to a curve : *The equation to a curve is the relation which exists between the coordinates of* **any** *point on the curve, and which holds for no other points except those lying on the curve.*

➤ **43.** Conversely to every equation between x and y it will be found that there is, in general, a definite geometrical locus.

Thus, in Art. 39 the equation is $x + y = 1$, and the definite path, or locus, is the straight line P_1P_2 (produced indefinitely both ways).

In Art. 40 the equation is $x^2 + y^2 = 4$, and the definite path, or locus, is the dotted circle.

Again the equation $y = 1$ states that the moving point is such that its ordinate is always unity, *i.e.*, that it is always at a distance 1 from the axis of x. The definite path, or locus is therefore a straight line parallel to OX and at a distance unity from it.

➤ **44.** In the next chapter it will be found that if the equation be of the first degree (*i.e.*, if it contain no products, squares, or higher powers of x and y) the locus corresponding is always a straight line.

If the equation be of the second or higher degree, the corresponding locus is, in general, a curved line.

➤ **45.** We append a few simple examples of the formation of the equation to a locus.

EXAMPLE 1 *A point moves so that the algebraic sum of its distances from two given perpendicular axes is equal to a constant quantity a; find the equation to its locus.*

Take the two straight lines as the axes of coordinates. Let (x, y) be any point satisfying the given condition. We then have $x + y = a$.

This being the relation connecting the coordinates of any point on the locus is the equation to the locus.

It will be found in the next chapter that this equation represents a straight line.

EXAMPLE 2 *The sum of the squares sof the distances of a moving point from the two fixed points $(a, 0)$ and $(-a, 0)$ is equal to a constant quantity $2c^2$. Find the equation to its locus.*

Let (x, y) be any position of the moving point. Then, by Art. 20, the condition of the question gives

$$\{(x - a)^2 + y^2\} + \{(x + a)^2 + y^2\} = 2c^2,$$

i.e., $$x^2 + y^2 = c^2 - a^2.$$

This being the relation between the coordinates of any, and every, points that satisfies the given condition is, by Art. 42, equation to the required locus.

This equation tells us that the square of the distance of the point (x, y) from the origin is constant and equal to $c^2 - a^2$, and therefore the locus of the point is a circle whose centre is the origin.

EXAMPLE 3 *A point moves so that its distance from the point $(-1, 0)$ is always three times its distance from the point $(0, 2)$.*

Let (x, y) be any point which satisfies the given condition. We then have

$$\sqrt{(x + 1)^2 + (y - 0)^2} = 3\sqrt{(x - 0)^2 + (y - 2)^2}$$

so that, on squaring,

$$x^2 + 2x + 1 + y^2 = 9(x^2 + y^2 - 4y + 4),$$

i.e., $$8(x^2 + y^2) - 2x - 36y + 35 = 0.$$

This being the relation between the coordinates of each, and every, point that satisfies the given relation is, by Art. 42, the required equation.

It will be found, in a later chapter, that this equation represents a circle.

EXAMPLES IV

By taking a number of solutions, as in Arts. 39–41, sketch the loci of the following equations:

1. $2x + 3y = 10$ 2. $4x - y = 7$ 3. $x^2 - 2ax + y^2 = 0$
4. $x^2 - 4ax + y^2 + 3a^2 = 0$ 5. $y^2 = x$ 6. $3x = y^2 - 9$
7. $\dfrac{x^2}{4} + \dfrac{y^2}{9} = 1$

A and B being the fixed points $(a, 0)$ and $(-a, 0)$ respectively, obtain the equations giving the locus of P, when

8. $PA^2 - PB^2 = a$ constant quantity $= 2k^2$.
9. $PA = nPB$, n being constant.
10. $PA + PB = c$, a constant quantity.
11. $PB^2 + PC^2 = 2PA^2$, C being the point $(c, 0)$.
12. Find the locus of a point whose distance from the point $(1, 2)$ is equal to its distance from the axis of y.

Find the equation to the locus of a point which is always equidistant from the points whose coordinates are

13. $(1, 0)$ and $(0, -2)$.
14. $(2, 3)$ and $(4, 5)$.
15. $(a + b, a - b)$ and $(a - b, a + b)$.

Find the equation to the locus of a point which moves so that

16. its distance from the axis of x is three times its distance from the axis of y.
17. its distance from the point $(a, 0)$ is always four times its distance from the axis of y.
18. the sum of the squares of its distances from the axes is equal to 3.
19. the square of its distance from the point $(0, 2)$ is equal to 4.
20. its distance from the point $(3, 0)$ is three times its distance from $(0, 2)$.
21. its distance from the axis of x is always one half its distance from the origin.
22. A fixed point is at a perpendicular distance a from a fixed straight line and a point moves so that its distance from the fixed point is always equal to its distance from the fixed line. Find the equation to its locus, the axes of coordinates being drawn through the fixed point and being parallel and perpendicular to the given line.
23. In the previous question if the first distance be (1), always half, and (2), always twice, the second distance, find the equations to the respective loci.

4

THE STRAIGHT LINE, RECTANGULAR COORDINATES

▶ **46.** *To find the equation to a straight line which is parallel to one of the coordinate axes.*

Let CL be any line parallel to the axis of y and passing through a point C on the axis of x such that $OC = c$.

Let P be any point on this line whose coordinates are x and y.

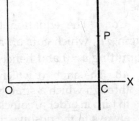

Then the abscissa of the point P is always c, so that

$$x = c \qquad \text{...(1)}$$

This being true for every point on the line CL (produced indefinitely both ways), and for no other point, is, by Art. 42, the equation to the line.

It will be noted that the equation does not contain the coordinate y.

Similarly, the equation to a straight line parallel to the axis of x is $y = d$.

Cor. : The equation to the axis of x is $y = 0$.

The equation to the axis of y is $x = 0$.

▶ **47.** *To find the equation to a straight line which cuts off a given intercept on the axis of y and is inclined at a given angle to the axis of x.*

Let the given intercept be c and let the given angle be α.

Let C be a point on the axis of y such that OC is c.

Through C draw a straight line LCL' inclined at an angle $\alpha (= \tan^{-1} m)$ to the axis of x, so that $\tan \alpha = m$.

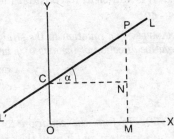

The straight line LCL' is therefore the straight line required, and we have to find the relation between the coordinates of any point P lying on it.

Draw PM perpendicular to OX to meet in N a line through C parallel to OX.

Let the coordinates of P be x and y, so that $OM = x$ and $MP = y$.

Then, $MP = NP + MN = CN \tan \alpha + OC = m \cdot x + c$,

i.e., $y = mx + c.$

This relation being true for *any* point on the given straight line is, by Art. 42, the equation to the straight line.

[In this, and other similar cases, it could be shewn, conversely, that the equation is only true for points lying on the given straight line.]

Cor. : The equation to any straight line passing through the origin, *i.e.*, which cuts off a zero intercept from the axis of y, is found by putting $c = 0$ and hence, is $y = mx$.

➤ **48.** The angle α which is used in the previous article is the angle through which a straight line, originally parallel to OX, would have to turn in order to coincide with the given direction, the rotation being always in the positive direction. Also m is always the tangent of this angle. In the case of such a straight line as AB, in the figure of Art. 50, m is equal to the tangent of the angle XAP (not of the angle PAO). In this case therefore m, being the tangent of an obtuse angle, is a negative quantity.

The student should verify the truth of the equation of the last article for *all* points on the straight line LCL', and also for straight lines in other positions, *e.g.*, for such a straight line as A_2B_2 in the figure of Art. 59. In this latter case both m and c are negative quantities.

A careful consideration of all the possible cases of a few propositions will soon satisfy him that this verification is not always necessary, but that it is sufficient to consider the standard figure.

➤ **49.**

EXAMPLE   *The equation to the straight line cutting off an intercept 3 from the negative direction of the axis of y, and inclined at 120° to the axis of x, is*

$$y = x \tan 120° + (-3),$$

i.e., $y = -x\sqrt{3} - 3,$

i.e., $y + x\sqrt{3} + 3 = 0.$

➤ **50.** *To find the equation to the straight line which cuts off given intercepts a and b from the axes.*

Let A and B be on OX and OY respectively, and be such that $OA = \alpha$ and $OB = b$.

Join AB and produce it indefinitely both ways. Let P be any point (x, y) on this straight line, and draw PM perpendicular to OX.

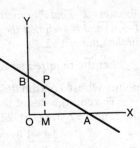

We require the relation that always holds between x and y, so long as P lies on AB.

By geometry, we have

$$\frac{OM}{OA} = \frac{PB}{AB}, \quad \text{and} \quad \frac{MP}{OB} = \frac{AP}{AB}.$$

$\therefore$
$$\frac{OM}{OA} + \frac{MP}{OB} = \frac{PB + AP}{AB} = 1,$$

i.e.,
$$\frac{x}{a} + \frac{y}{b} = 1.$$

This is therefore the required equation; for it is the relation that holds between the coordinates of *any* point lying on the given straight line.

➤ **51.** The equation in the preceding article may be also obtained by expressing the fact that the sum of the areas of the triangles OPA and OPB is equal to OAB, so that

$$\frac{1}{2} a \times y + \frac{1}{2} b \times x = \frac{1}{2} a \times b,$$

and hence,
$$\frac{x}{a} + \frac{y}{b} = 1.$$

➤ **52.**

EXAMPLE 1 *Find the equation to the straight line passing through the point* $(3, -4)$ *and cutting off intercepts, equal but of opposite signs, from the two axes*

Let the intercepts cut off from the two axes be of lengths a and $-a$.

The equation to the straight line is then

$$\frac{x}{a} + \frac{y}{-a} = 1,$$

i.e.,
$$x - y = a \qquad \qquad \text{...(1}$$

Since, in addition, the straight line is to go through the point $(3, -4)$, these coordinates must satisfy (1), so that

$$3 - (-4) = a,$$

and therefore,
$$a = 7.$$

The required equation is therefore,

$$x - y = 7.$$

EXAMPLE 2 *Find the equation to the straight line which passes through the point* (−5, 4) *and is such that the portion of it between the axes is divided by the point in the ratio of* 1 : 2.

Let the required straight line be $\dfrac{x}{a} + \dfrac{y}{b} = 1$. This meets the axes in the points whose coordinates are $(a, 0)$ and $(0, b)$.

The coordinates of the point dividing the line joining these points in the ratio 1 : 2, are (Art. 22).

$$\frac{2 \cdot a + 1 \cdot 0}{2 + 1} \quad \text{and} \quad \frac{2 \cdot 0 + 1 \cdot b}{2 + 1}, \quad i.e., \quad \frac{2a}{3} \quad \text{and} \quad \frac{b}{3}.$$

If this be the point (−5, 4) we have

$$-5 = \frac{2a}{3} \quad \text{and} \quad 4 = \frac{b}{3},$$

So that

$$a = -\frac{15}{2} \quad \text{and} \quad b = 12.$$

The required straight line is therefore

$$\frac{x}{-\dfrac{15}{2}} + \frac{y}{12} = 1,$$

i.e.,

$$5y - 8x = 60.$$

➤ **53.** *To find the equation to a straight line in terms of the perpendicular let fall upon it from the origin and the angle that this perpendicular makes with the axis of x.*

Let *OR* be the perpendicular from *O* and let its length be *p*

Let α be the angle that *OR* makes with *OX*.

Let *P* be any point, whose coordinates are *x* and *y*, lying on *AB*; draw the ordinate *PM*, and also *ML* perpendicular to *OR* and *PN* perpendicular to *ML*.

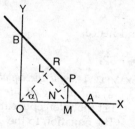

Then,

$$OL = OM \cos \alpha \qquad \qquad \dots(1)$$

and

$$LR = NP = MP \sin NMP.$$

But,

$$\angle NMP = 90° - \angle NMO = \angle MOL = \alpha.$$

∴

$$LR = MP \sin \alpha \qquad \qquad \dots(2)$$

Hence, adding (1) and (2), we have

$$OM \cos \alpha + MP \sin \alpha = OL + LR = OR = p,$$

i.e.,

$$x \cos \alpha + y \sin \alpha = p.$$

This is the required equation.

➤ **54.** In Arts. 47–53 we have found that the corresponding equations are only of the first degree in x and y. We shall now prove that

Any equation of the first degree in x and y always represents a straight line.

For the most general form of such an equation is

$$Ax + By + C = 0 \qquad \text{...(1)}$$

where A, B, and C are constants, *i.e.*, quantities which do not contain x and y and which remain the same for all points on the locus.

Let (x_1, y_1), (x_2, y_2), and (x_3, y_3) be *any* three points on the locus of the (1).

Since, the point (x_1, y_1) lies on the locus, its coordinates when substituted for x and y in equation (1) must satisfy it.

Hence, $\qquad\qquad Ax_1 + By_1 + C = 0 \qquad \text{...(2)}$

So, $\qquad\qquad\quad Ax_2 + By_2 + C = 0 \qquad \text{...(3)}$

and $\qquad\qquad\quad Ax_3 + By_3 + C = 0 \qquad \text{...(4)}$

Since, these three equations hold between the three quantities A, B, and C, we can, as in Art. 12, eliminate them.

The result is

$$\begin{vmatrix} x_1, & y_1, & 1 \\ x_2, & y_2, & 1 \\ x_3, & y_3, & 1 \end{vmatrix} = 0 \qquad \text{...(5)}$$

But, by Art. 25, the relation (5) states that the area of the triangle whose vertices are (x_1, y_1), (x_2, y_2), and (x_3, y_3) is zero.

Also these are any three points on the locus.

The locus must therefore be a straight line; for a curved line could not be such that the triangle obtained by joining *any* three points on it should be zero.

➤ **55.** The proposition of the preceding article may also be deduced from Art. 47. For the equation

$$Ax + By + C = 0$$

may be written $\qquad\qquad y = -\dfrac{A}{B}x - \dfrac{C}{B},$

and this is the same as the straight line

$$y = mx + c,$$

if $\qquad\qquad m = -\dfrac{A}{B} \quad \text{and} \quad c = -\dfrac{C}{B}.$

But in Art. 47 it was shewn that $y = mx + c$ was the equation to a straight line cutting off an intercept c from the axis of y and inclined at an angle $\tan^{-1} m$ to the axis of x.

The equation, $\qquad Ax + By + C = 0$

therefore represents a straight line cutting off an intercept $-\dfrac{C}{B}$ from the axis of y and inclined at an angle $\tan^{-1}\left(-\dfrac{A}{B}\right)$ to the axis of x.

➤ **56.** We can reduce the general equation of the first degree
$$Ax + By + C = 0 \qquad \ldots(1)$$
to the form of Art. 53.

For, if p be the perpendicular from the origin on (1) and α the angle it makes with the axis, the equation to the straight line must be
$$x \cos \alpha + y \sin \alpha - p = 0 \qquad \ldots(2)$$
This equation must therefore be the same as (1).

Hence, $\qquad \dfrac{\cos \alpha}{A} = \dfrac{\sin \alpha}{B} = \dfrac{-p}{C},$

i.e., $\qquad \dfrac{p}{C} = \dfrac{\cos \alpha}{-A} = \dfrac{\sin \alpha}{-B} = \dfrac{\sqrt{\cos^2 \alpha + \sin^2 \alpha}}{\sqrt{A^2 + B^2}} = \dfrac{1}{\sqrt{A^2 + B^2}}.$

Hence, $\cos \alpha = \dfrac{-A}{\sqrt{A^2 + B^2}}$, $\sin \alpha = \dfrac{-B}{\sqrt{A^2 + B^2}}$, and $p = \dfrac{C}{\sqrt{A^2 + B^2}}.$

The equation (1) may therefore be reduced to the form (2) by dividing it by $\sqrt{A^2 + B^2}$ and arranging it so that the constant term is negative.

➤ **57.**

EXAMPLE *Reduce to the perpendicular form the equation*
$$x + y\sqrt{3} + 7 = 0, \qquad \ldots(1)$$
Here, $\qquad \sqrt{A^2 + B^2} = \sqrt{1 + 3} = \sqrt{4} = 2$

Dividing (1) by (2), we have
$$\frac{1}{2} x + y \frac{\sqrt{3}}{2} + \frac{7}{2} = 0,$$

i.e., $\qquad x\left(-\frac{1}{2}\right) + y\left(-\frac{\sqrt{3}}{2}\right) - \frac{7}{2} = 0,$

i.e., $\qquad x \cos 240° + y \sin 240° - \frac{7}{2} = 0.$

➤ **58.** *To trace the straight line given by an equation of the first degree.*
Let the equation be
$$Ax + By + C = 0 \qquad \ldots(1)$$

(α) This can be written in the form

$$\frac{x}{-\dfrac{C}{A}} + \frac{y}{-\dfrac{C}{B}} = 1.$$

Comparing this with the result of Art. 50, we see that it represents a straight line which cuts off intercepts $-\dfrac{C}{A}$ and $-\dfrac{C}{B}$ from the axes. Its position is therefore known.

If C be zero, the equation (1) reduces to the form

$$y = -\frac{A}{B}x,$$

and thus, (by Art. 47, Cor.) represents a straight line passing through the origin inclined at an angle $\tan^{-1}\left(-\dfrac{A}{B}\right)$ to the axis of x. Its position is therefore known.

(β) The straight line may also be traced by finding the coordinates of any two points on it.

If we put $y = 0$ in (1) we have $x = -\dfrac{C}{A}$. The point $\left(-\dfrac{C}{A}, 0\right)$ therefore lies on it.

If we put $x = 0$, we have $y = -\dfrac{C}{B}$, so that the point $\left(0, -\dfrac{C}{B}\right)$ lies on it.

Hence, as before, we have the position of the straight line.

➤ **59.**

EXAMPLE *Trace the straight lines*

1. $3x - 4y + 7 = 0$;   2. $7x + 8y + 9 = 0$;   3. $3y = x$;
4. $x = 2$;   5. $y = -2$

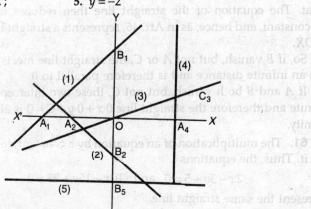

1. Putting $y = 0$, we have $x = -\dfrac{7}{3}$

and putting $x = 0$, we have $y = \dfrac{7}{4}$.

Measuring $OA_1\left(=-\dfrac{7}{3}\right)$ along the axis of x we have one point on the line.

Measuring $OB_1\left(=\dfrac{7}{4}\right)$ along the axis of y we have another point.

Hence, A_1B_1, produced both ways, is the required line.

2. Putting in succession y and x equal to zero, we have the intercepts on the axes equal to $-\dfrac{9}{7}$ and $-\dfrac{9}{8}$.

If then, $OA_2 = -\dfrac{9}{7}$ and $OB_2 = -\dfrac{9}{8}$, we have A_2B_2 the required line.

3. The point $(0, 0)$ satisfies the equation so that the origin is on the line.

Also the point $(3, 1)$, *i.e.*, C_3, lies on it. The required line is therefore OC_3.

4. The line $x = 2$ is, by Art. 46, parallel to the axis of y and passes through the point A_4 on the axis of x such that $OA_4 = 2$.

5. The line $y = -2$ is parallel to the axis of x and passes through the point B_5 on the axis of y, such that $OB_5 = -2$.

➤ **60. Straight line at Infinity.** We have seen that the equation $Ax + By + C = 0$ represents a straight line which cuts off intercepts $-\dfrac{C}{A}$ and $-\dfrac{C}{B}$ from the axes of coordinates.

If A vanish, but not B or C, the intercept on the axis of x is infinitely great. The equation of the straight line then reduces to the form $y =$ constant, and hence, as in Art. 46, represents a straight line parallel to OX.

So, if B vanish, but not A or C, the straight line meets the axis of y at an infinite distance and is therefore parallel to it.

If A and B both vanish, but not C, these two intercepts are both infinite and therefore the straight line $0 \cdot x + 0 \cdot y + C = 0$ is altogether at infinity.

➤ **61.** The multiplication of an equation by a constant does not alter it. Thus, the equations

$$2x - 3y + 5 = 0 \quad \text{and} \quad 10x - 15y + 25 = 0$$

represent the same straight line.

Conversely, if two equations of the first degree represent the same straight line, one equation must be equal to the other multiplied by a constant quantity, so that the ratios of the corresponding coefficients must be the same.

For example, if the equations

$$a_1x + b_1y + c_1 = 0 \quad \text{and} \quad A_1x + B_1y + C_1 = 0$$

represent the same straight line, we must have

$$\frac{a_1}{A_1} = \frac{b_1}{B_1} = \frac{c_1}{C_1}.$$

➤ **62.** *To find the equation to the straight line which passes through the two given points* (x', y') *and* (x'', y').

By Art. 47, the equation to **any** straight line is

$$y = mx + c \qquad \qquad \text{...(1)}$$

By properly determining the quantities m and c we can makes (1) represent any straight line we please.

If (1) pass through the point (x', y'), we have

$$y' = mx' + c \qquad \qquad \text{...(2)}$$

Substituting for c from (2), the equation (1) becomes

$$y - y' = m(x - x') \qquad \qquad \text{...(3)}$$

This is the equation to the line going through (x', y') making an angle $\tan^{-1} m$ with OX. If in addition (3) passes through the point (x'', y''), then,

$$y'' - y' = m(x'' - x'),$$

giving $\qquad\qquad\qquad\qquad m = \dfrac{y'' - y'}{x'' - x'}.$

Substituting this value in (3), we get as the required equation

$$y - y' = \frac{y'' - y'}{x'' - x'}(x - x').$$

➤ **63.**

EXAMPLE *Find the equation to the straight line which passes through the points* $(-1, 3)$ *and* $(4, -2)$.

Let the required equation be

$$y = mx + c \qquad \qquad \text{...(1)}$$

Since, (1) goes through the first point, we have

$$3 = -m + c, \text{ so that } c = m + 3.$$

Hence, (1) becomes

$$y = mx + m + 3 \qquad \qquad \text{...(2)}$$

If in addition the line goes through the second point, we have

$$-2 = 4m + m + 3, \quad \text{so that} \quad m = -1.$$

Hence, (2) becomes

$$y = -x + 2, \quad i.e., \quad x + y = 2.$$

Or, again, using the result of the last article the equation is

$$y - 3 = \frac{-2 - 3}{4 - (-1)} (x + 1) = -x - 1,$$

i.e., $$y + x = 2.$$

➤ **64.** To fix definitely the position of a straight line we must have always two quantities given. Thus, one point on the straight line and the direction of the straight line will determine it; or again two points lying on the straight line will determine it.

Analytically, the general equation to a straight line will contain two arbitrary constants, which will have to be determined so that the general equation may represent any particular straight line.

Thus, in Art. 47, the quantities m and c which remain the same, *so long as we are considering the same straight line*, are the two constants for the straight line.

Similarly, in Art. 50, the quantities a and b are the constants for the straight line.

➤ **65.** If any equation to a locus the quantities x and y, which are the coordinates of any point on the locus are called Current Coordinates; the curve may be conceived as traced out by a point which "runs" along the locus.

EXAMPLES V

Find the equation to the straight line

1. cutting off an intercept unity from the positive direction of the axis of y and inclined at 45° to the axis of x.

2. cutting off an intercept –5 from the axis of y and being equally inclined to the axes.

3. cutting off an intercept 2 from the negative direction of the axis of y and inclined at 30° to OX.

4. cutting off an intercept –3 from the axis of y and inclined at an angle $\tan^{-1} \frac{3}{5}$ to the axis of x.

Find the equation to the straight line

5. cutting off intercepts 3 and 2 from the axes.

6. cutting off intercepts –5 and 6 from the axes.

7. Find the equation to the straight line which passes through the points (5, 6) and has intercepts on the axes
   (i) equal in magnitude and both positive,
   (ii) equal in magnitude but opposite in sign.

8. Find the equations to the straight lines which passes through the point (1, −2) and cut off equal distance from the two axes.

9. Find the equation to the straight line which passes through the given point (x', y') and is such that the given point bisects the part intercepted between the axes.

10. Find the equation to the straight line which passes through the point (−4, 3) and is such that the portion of it between the axes is divided by the point in the ratio 5 : 3.

Trace the straight line whose equation are

11. $x + 2y + 3 = 0$
12. $5x − 7y − 9 = 0$
13. $3x + 7y = 0$
14. $2x − 3y + 4 = 0$

Find the equations to the straight lines passing through the following pairs of points.

15. (0, 0) and (2, −2)
16. (3, 4) and (5, 6)
17. (−1, 3) and (6, −7)
18. (0, −a) and (b, 0).
19. (a, b) and (a + b, a − b)
20. $(at_1{}^2, 2at_1)$ and $(at_2{}^2, 2at_2)$
21. $\left(at_1, \dfrac{a}{t_1}\right)$ and $\left(at_2, \dfrac{a}{t_2}\right)$
22. $(a \cos \phi_1, a \sin \phi_1)$ and $(a \cos \phi_2, a \sin \phi_2)$
23. $(a \cos \phi_1, b \sin \phi_1)$ and $(a \cos \phi_2, b \sin \phi_2)$
24. $(a \sec \phi_1, b \tan \phi_1)$ and $(a \sec \phi_2, b \tan \phi_2)$

Find the equations to the sides of the triangles the coordinates of whose angular points are respectively

25. (1, 4), (2, −3), and (−1, −2)
26. (0, 1), (2, 0), and (−1, −2)

27. Find the equation to the diagonals of the rectangle the equations of whose sides are $x = a, x = a', y = b$, and $y = b'$

28. Find the equation to the straight line which bisects the distance between the points (a, b) and (a', b') and also bisects the distance between the points (−a, b) and (a', −b').

29. Find the equations to the straight lines which go through the origin and trisect the portion of the straight line $3x + y = 12$ which is intercepted between the axes of coordinates.

ANGLES BETWEEN STRAIGHT LINES

➤ **66.** *To find the angle between two given straight lines.*

Let the two straight lines be AL_1 and AL_2, meeting the axis of x in L_1 and L_2.

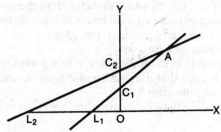

I. Let their equations be

$$y = m_1x + c_1 \quad \text{and} \quad y = m_2x + c_2 \qquad \ldots(1)$$

By Art. 47 we therefore have

$$\tan AL_1X = m_1, \quad \text{and} \quad \tan AL_2X = m_2$$

Now,

$$\angle L_1AL_2 = \angle AL_1X - \angle AL_2X$$

$$\therefore \quad \tan L_1AL_2 = \tan[AL_1X - AL_2X]$$

$$= \frac{\tan AL_1X - \tan AL_2X}{1 + \tan AL_1X \cdot \tan AL_2X} = \frac{m_1 - m_2}{1 + m_1m_2}$$

Hence, the required angle $= \angle L_1AL_2$

$$= \tan^{-1}\frac{m_1 - m_2}{1 + m_1m_2} \qquad \ldots(2)$$

[In any numerical example, if the quantity (2) be a positive quantity it is the tangent of the acute angle between the lines; if negative, it is the tangent of the obtuse angle.]

II. Let the equations of the straight lines be

$$A_1x + B_1y + C_1 = 0,$$

and

$$A_2x + B_2y + C_2 = 0$$

By dividing the equations by B_1 and B_2, they may be written

$$y = -\frac{A_1}{B_1}x - \frac{C_1}{B_1},$$

and

$$y = -\frac{A_2}{B_2}x - \frac{C_2}{B_2}$$

Comparing these with the equations of (I.), we see that

$$m_1 = -\frac{A_1}{B_1}, \text{ and } m_2 = -\frac{A_2}{B_2}$$

Hence, the required angle

$$= \tan^{-1}\frac{m_1 - m_2}{1 + m_1 m_2} = \tan^{-1}\frac{-\dfrac{A_1}{B_1} - \left(-\dfrac{A_2}{B_2}\right)}{1 + \left(-\dfrac{A_1}{B_1}\right)\left(-\dfrac{A_2}{B_2}\right)}$$

$$= \tan^{-1}\frac{B_1 A_2 - A_1 B_2}{A_1 A_2 + B_1 B_2} \qquad \qquad \text{...(3)}$$

III. If the equations be given in the form

$$x \cos \alpha + y \sin \alpha - p_1 = 0 \text{ and } x \cos \beta + y \sin \beta - p_2 = 0,$$

The perpendiculars from the origin make angles α and β with the axis of x.

Now, that angle between two straight lines, in which the origin lies, is the supplement of the angle between the perpendiculars, and the angle between these perpendiculars is $\beta - \alpha$.

[For, if OR_1 and OR_2 be the perpendiculars from the origin upon the two lines, then the points O, R_1, R_2, and A lie on a circle, and hence the angles $R_1 O R_2$ and $R_2 A R_1$ are either equal or supplementary.]

▶ **67.** *To find the condition that two straight lines may be parallel.*

Two straight lines are parallel when the angle between them is zero and therefore the tangent of this angle is zero.

The equation (2) of the last article then gives

$$m_1 = m_2$$

Two straight lines whose equations are given in the "m" form are therefore, parallel when their "m's" are the same, or, in other words, if their equations differ only in the constant term.

The straight line $Ax + By + C' = 0$ is any straight line which is parallel to the straight line $Ax + By + C = 0$. For the "m's" of the two equations are the same.

Again the equation $A(x - x') + B(y - y') = 0$ clearly represents the straight line which passes through the point (x', y') and is parallel to $Ax + By + C = 0$.

The result (3) of the last article gives, as the condition for parallel lines,

$$B_1 A_2 - A_1 B_2 = 0,$$

i.e.,
$$\frac{A_1}{B_1} = \frac{A_2}{B_2}$$

➤ **68.**

EXAMPLE *Find the equation to the straight line, which passes through the point* (4, –5). *and which is parallel to the straight line*

$$3x + 4y + 5 = 0 \qquad \ldots(1)$$

Any straight line which is parallel to (1) has its equation of the form

$$3x + 4y + C = 0 \qquad \ldots(2)$$

[For the "*m*" of both (1) and (2) is the same.]

This straight line will pass through the point (4, –5) if

$$3 \times 4 + 4 \times (-5) + C = 0$$

i.e., if
$$C = 20 - 12 = 8$$

The equation (2) then becomes

$$3x + 4y + 8 = 0$$

➤ **69.** *To find the condition that two straight lines, whose equations are given, may be perpendicular.*

Let the straight lines be

$$y = m_1 x + c_1,$$

and
$$y = m_2 x + c_2$$

If θ be the angle between them we have, by Art. 66,

$$\tan \theta = \frac{m_1 - m_2}{1 + m_1 m_2} \qquad \ldots(1)$$

If the lines be perpendicular, then θ = 90°, and therefore, tan θ = ∞.

The right-hand member of equation (1) must therefore, be infinite, and this can only happen when its denominator is zero.

The condition of perpendicularity is therefore that

$$1 + m_1 m_2 = 0,$$

i.e.,
$$m_1 m_2 = -1$$

The straight line $y = m_2 x + c_2$ is therefore, perpendicular to $y = m_1 x + c_1$, if $m_2 = -\dfrac{1}{m_1}$.

It follows that the straight lines

$$A_1 x + B_1 y + C_1 = 0 \quad \text{and} \quad A_2 x + B_2 y + C_2 = 0$$

for which $m_1 = -\dfrac{A_1}{B_1}$ and $m_2 = -\dfrac{A_2}{B_2}$, are at right angles if

$$\left(-\frac{A_1}{B_1}\right)\left(-\frac{A_2}{B_2}\right) = -$$

i.e., if $\qquad\qquad A_1A_2 + B_1B_2 = 0$

➤ **70.** *From the preceding article it follows that the two straight lines*

$$A_1x + B_1y + C_1 = 0 \qquad\qquad\qquad ...(1)$$

and $\qquad\qquad B_1x - A_1y + C_2 = 0 \qquad\qquad\qquad ...(2)$

are at right angles; for the product of their m's

$$= -\frac{A_1}{B_1} \times \frac{B_1}{A_1} = -1$$

Also (2) is derived from (1) by interchanging the coefficients of x and y, changing the sign of one of them, and changing the constant into any other constant.

Example *The straight line through (x', y') perpendicular to (1) is (2).*

where $\qquad\qquad B_1x' - A_1y' + C_2 = 0$, *so that* $C_2 = A_1y' - B_1x'$

This straight line is therefore,

$$B_1(x - x') - A_1(y - y') = 0$$

➤ **71.**

Example 1 *Find the equation to the straight line which passes through the point* $(4, -5)$ *and is perpendicular to the straight line*

$$3x + 4y + 5 = 0 \qquad\qquad\qquad ...(1)$$

First Method : Any straight line perpendicular to (1) is by the last article

$$4x - 3y + C = 0 \qquad\qquad\qquad ...(2)$$

[We should expect an arbitrary constant in (2) because there are an infinite number of straight lines perpendicular to (1)]

The straight line (2) passes through the point $(4, -5)$ if

$$4 \times 4 - 3 \times (-5) + C = 0,$$

i.e., if $\qquad\qquad C = -16 - 15 = -31$

The required equation is therefore

$$4x - 3y = 31$$

Second Method : Any straight line passing through the given point is

$$y - (-5) = m(x - 4)$$

This straight line is perpendicular to (1) if the product of their m's is -1

i.e., if
$$m \times \left(-\frac{3}{4}\right) = -1,$$

i.e., if
$$m = \frac{4}{3}$$

The required equation is therefore,
$$y + 5 = \frac{4}{3}(x - 4)$$

i.e.,
$$4x - 3y = 31$$

Third Method. Any straight line is $y = mx + c$. It passes through the point $(4, -5)$, if
$$-5 = 4m + c \qquad \qquad \qquad \dots(3)$$

It is perpendicular to (1) if
$$m \times \left(-\frac{3}{4}\right) = -1 \qquad \qquad \dots(4)$$

Hence, $m = \frac{4}{3}$ and then (3) gives $c = -\frac{31}{3}$.

The required equation is therefore, $y = \frac{4}{3}x - \frac{31}{3}$,

i.e.,
$$4x - 3y = 31$$

[In the first method, we start with any straight line which is perpendicular to the given straight line and pick out that particular straight line which goes through the given point.

In the second method, we start with any straight line passing through the given point and pick out that particular one which is perpendicular to the given straight line.

In the third method, we start with any straight line whatever and determine its constants, so that it may satisfy the two given conditions.

The student should illustrate by figures.]

EXAMPLE 2 *Find the equation to the straight line which passes through the point (x', y') and is perpendicular to the given straight line*
$$yy' = 2a(x + x')$$

The given straight line is
$$yy' - 2ax - 2ax' = 0$$

Any straight line perpendicular to it is (Art. 70)
$$2ay + xy' + C = 0 \qquad \qquad \dots(1)$$

This will pass through the point (x', y') and therefore, will be the straight line required if the coordinates x' and y' satisfy it,

i.e., if
$$2ay' + x'y' + C = 0,$$

i.e., if
$$C = -2ay' - x'y'$$

Substituting in (1) for C the required equation is therefore,

$$2a(y - y') + y'(x - x') = 0$$

➤ **72.** *To find the equations to the straight lines which pass through a given point (x', y') and make a given angle α with the given straight line $y = mx + c$.*

Let P be the given point and let the given straight line be LMN, making an angle θ with the axis of x such that

$$\tan \theta = m.$$

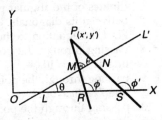

In general (*i.e.*, except when α is a right angle or zero) there are two straight lines PMR and PNS making an angle α with the given line.

et these lines meet the axis of x in R and S and let them make ang:es ϕ and ϕ' with the positive direction of the axis of x.

The equations to the two required straight lines are therefore, (by Art. 62)

$$y - y' = \tan \phi \times (x - x') \qquad \qquad \text{...(1)}$$

and $$y - y' = \tan \phi' \times (x - x') \qquad \qquad \text{...(2)}$$

Now, $$\phi = \angle LMR + \angle RLM = \alpha + \theta,$$

and $$\phi' = \angle LNS + \angle SLN = (180° - \alpha) + \theta$$

Hence, $\tan \phi = \tan (\alpha + \theta) = \dfrac{\tan \alpha + \tan \theta}{1 - \tan \alpha \tan \theta} = \dfrac{\tan \alpha + m}{1 - m \tan \alpha}$,

and $$\tan \phi' = \tan (180° + \theta - \alpha)$$

$$= \tan (\theta - \alpha) = \frac{\tan \theta - \tan \alpha}{1 + \tan \theta \tan \alpha} = \frac{m - \tan \alpha}{1 + m \tan \alpha}$$

On substituting these values in (1) and (2), we have as the required equations

$$y - y' = \frac{m + \tan \alpha}{1 - m \tan \alpha} (x - x'),$$

and $$y - y' = \frac{m - \tan \alpha}{1 + m \tan \alpha} (x - x')$$

EXAMPLES VI

Find the angles between the pairs of straight lines:
1. $x - y\sqrt{3} = 5$ and $\sqrt{3}x + y = 7$
2. $x - 4y = 3$ and $6x - y = 11$

3. $y = 3x + 7$ and $3y - x = 8$

4. $y = (2 - \sqrt{3})x + 5$ and $y = (2 + \sqrt{3})x - 7$

5. $(m^2 - mn)y = (mn + n^2)x + n^3$ and $(mn + m^2)y = (mn - n^2)x + m^3$

6. Find the tangent of the angle between the lines whose intercepts on the axes are respectively a, $-b$ and b, $-a$.

7. Prove that the points $(2, -1)$, $(0, 2)$, $(2, 3)$, and $(4, 0)$ are the coordinates of the angular points of a parallelogram and find the angle between its diagonals.

Find the equation to the straight line

8. passing through the point $(2, 3)$ and perpendicular to the straight line $4x - 3y = 10$.

9. passing through the point $(-6, 10)$ and perpendicular to the straight line $7x + 8y = 5$.

10. passing through the point $(2, -3)$ and perpendicular to the straight line joining the points $(5, 7)$ and $(-6, 3)$.

11. passing through the point $(-4, -3)$ and perpendicular to the straight line joining $(1, 3)$ and $(2, 7)$.

12. Find the equation to the straight line drawn at right angles to the straight line $\dfrac{x}{a} - \dfrac{y}{b} = 1$ through the point where it meets the axis of x.

13. Find the equation to the straight line which bisects, and is perpendicular to the straight line joining the points (a, b) and (a', b').

14. Prove that the equation to the straight line which passes through the point $(a \cos^3 \theta, a \sin^3 \theta)$ and is perpendicular to the straight line $x \sec \theta + y \csc \theta = a$ is $x \cos \theta - y \sin \theta = a \cos 2\theta$.

15. Find the equations to the straight lines passing through (x', y') and respectively perpendicular to the straight lines

$$xx' + yy' = a^2,$$

$$\frac{xx'}{a^2} + \frac{yy'}{b^2} = 1,$$

and

$$x'y + xy' = a^2$$

16. Find the equations to the straight lines which divide, internally and externally, the line joining $(-3, 7)$ to $(5, -4)$ in the ratio $4 : 7$ and which are perpendicular to this line.

17. Through the point $(3, 4)$ are drawn two straight lines each inclined at $45°$ to the straight line $x - y = 2$. Find their equations and find also the area included by the three lines.

18. Shew that the equations to the straight lines passing through the point $(3, -2)$ and inclined at $60°$ to the line
$\sqrt{3}x + y = 1$ are $y + 2 = 0$ and $y - \sqrt{3}x + 2 + 3\sqrt{3} = 0$

19. Find the equations to the straight lines which pass through the origin and are inclined at $75°$ to the straight line

$$x + y + \sqrt{3}(y - x) = a$$

20. Find the equations to the straight lines which pass through the point (h, k) and are inclined at an angle $\tan^{-1} m$ to the straight line

$$y = mx + c.$$

21. Find the angle between the two straight lines $3x = 4y + 7$ and $5y = 12x + 6$ and also the equations to the two straight lines which pass through the point $(4, 5)$ and make equal angles with the two given lines.

➤ **73.** *To shew that the point (x', y') is on one side or the other of the straight line $Ax + By + C = 0$ according as the quantity $Ax' + By' + C$ is positive or negative.*

Let LM be the given straight line and P any point (x', y').

Through P draw PQ, parallel to the axis of y, to meet the given straight line in Q, and let the co-ordinates of Q be (x', y'').

Since Q lies on the given line, we have

$$Ax' + By'' + C = 0,$$

so that $\qquad y'' = -\dfrac{Ax' + C}{B}$ \qquad ...(1)

It is clear from the figure that PQ is drawn parallel to the positive or negative direction of the axis of y according as P is on one side, or the other, of the straight line LM,

i.e., according as y'' is $>$ or $< y'$,

i.e., according as $y'' - y'$ is positive or negative.

Now, by (1),

$$y'' - y' = -\frac{Ax' + C}{B} - y' = -\frac{1}{B}\,[Ax' + By' + C].$$

The point (x', y') is therefore, on one side or the other of LM according as the quantity $Ax' + By' + C$ is negative or positive.

Cor. : The point (x', y') and the origin are on the same side of the given line if $Ax' + By' + C$ and $A \times 0 + B \times 0 + C$ have the same signs, i.e., if $Ax' + By' + C$ has the same sign as C.

If these two quantities have opposite signs, then the origin and the point (x', y') are on opposite sides of the given line.

➤ **74.** The condition that two points may lie on the same or opposite sides of a given line may also be obtained by considering the ratio in which the line joining the two points is cut by the given line.

For let the equation to the given line be

$$Ax + By + C = 0 \qquad ...(1)$$

and let the coordinates of the two given points be (x_1, y_1) and (x_2, y_2).

The coordinates of the point which divides in the ratio $m_1 : m_2$ the line joining these points are, by Art. 22,

$$\frac{m_1 x_2 + m_2 x_1}{m_1 + m_2} \quad \text{and} \quad \frac{m_1 y_2 + m_2 y_1}{m_1 + m_2} \qquad \text{...(2)}$$

If this point lie on the given line we have

$$A \frac{m_1 x_2 + m_2 x_1}{m_1 + m_2} + B \frac{m_1 y_2 + m_2 y_1}{m_1 + m_2} + C = 0,$$

So that, $$\frac{m_1}{m_2} = -\frac{A x_1 + B y_1 + C}{A x_2 + B y_2 + C} \qquad \text{...(3)}$$

If the point (2) be *between* the two given points (x_1, y_1) and (x_2, y_2), *i.e.*, if these two points be on *opposite* sides of the given line, the ratio $m_1 : m_2$ is positive.

In this case, by (3) the two quantities $A x_1 + B y_1 + C$ and $A x_2 + B y_2 + C$ have opposite signs.

The two points (x_1, y_1) and (x_2, y_2) therefore lie on the opposite (or the same) sides of the straight line $A x + B y + C = 0$ according as the quantities $A x_1 + B y_1 + C$ and $A x_2 + B y_2 + C$ have opposite (or the same) signs.

LENGTHS OF PERPENDICULARS

➤ **75.** *To find the length of the perpendicular let fall from a given point upon a given straight line.*

(i) Let the equation of the straight line be

$x \cos \alpha + y \sin \alpha - p = 0$ ...(1)

so that, if p be the perpendicular on it, we have

$ON = p$ and $\angle XON = \alpha$.

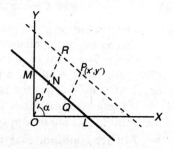

Let the given point P be (x', y').

Through P draw PR parallel to the given line to meet ON produced in R and draw PQ the required perpendicular.

If OR be p', the equation to PR is, by Art. 53,

$$x \cos \alpha + y \sin \alpha - p' = 0$$

Since, this passes through the point (x', y'), we have

$$x' \cos \alpha + y' \sin \alpha - p' = 0,$$

So that, $p' = x' \cos \alpha + y' \sin \alpha$

But the required perpendicular

$$= PQ = NR = OR - ON = p' - p$$
$$= x' \cos \alpha + y' \sin \alpha - p \qquad \ldots(2)$$

The length of the required perpendicular is therefore, obtained by substituting x' and y' for x and y in the given equation.

(ii) Let the equation to the straight line be

$$Ax + By + C = 0 \qquad \ldots(3)$$

the equation being written so that C is a negative quantity.

As in Art. 56 this equation is reduced to the form (1) by dividing it by $\sqrt{A^2 + B^2}$. It then becomes

$$\frac{Ax}{\sqrt{A^2 + B^2}} + \frac{By}{\sqrt{A^2 + B^2}} + \frac{C}{\sqrt{A^2 + B^2}} = 0$$

Hence,

$$\cos \alpha = \frac{A}{\sqrt{A^2 + B^2}}, \quad \sin \alpha = \frac{B}{\sqrt{A^2 + B^2}}, \quad \text{and} \quad -p = \frac{C}{\sqrt{A^2 + B^2}}.$$

The perpendicular from the point (x', y') therefore,

$$= x' \cos \alpha + y' \sin \alpha - p$$
$$= \frac{Ax' + By' + C}{\sqrt{A^2 + B^2}}$$

The length of the perpendicular from (x', y') on (3) is therefore, obtained by substituting x' and y' for x and y in the left-hand member of (3), and dividing the result so obtained by the square root of the sum of the squares of the coefficients of x and y.

Cor. 1 : The perpendicular from the origin

$$= C \div \sqrt{A^2 + B^2}$$

Cor. 2 : The length of the perpendicular is, by Art. 73, positive or negative according as (x', y') is on one side or the other of the given line.

➤ **76.** The length of the perpendicular may also be obtained as follows:

As in the figure of the last article let the straight line meet the axes in L and M, so that

$$OL = -\frac{C}{A} \quad \text{and} \quad OM = -\frac{C}{B}$$

Let PQ be the perpendicular from $P(x', y')$ on the given line and PS and PT the perpendiculars on the axes of coordinates.

We then have
$$\Delta PML + \Delta MOL = \Delta OLP + \Delta OPM,$$

i.e., since the area of a triangle is one half the product of its base and perpendicular height,
$$PQ \cdot LM + OL \cdot OM = OL \cdot PS + OM \cdot PT$$

But, $\quad LM = \sqrt{\left(-\dfrac{C}{A}\right)^2 + \left(-\dfrac{C}{B}\right)^2} = \dfrac{\sqrt{A^2+B^2}}{AB} \times (-C),$

since C is a negative quantity.

Hence, $\quad PQ \times \dfrac{\sqrt{A^2+B^2}}{AB} \times (-C) + \dfrac{C}{A} \cdot \dfrac{C}{B} = -\dfrac{C}{A} \times y' + \left(-\dfrac{C}{B}\right) \times x',$

so that
$$PQ = \dfrac{Ax' + By' + C}{\sqrt{A^2+B^2}}$$

EXAMPLES VII

Find the length of the perpendicular drawn from

1. the point $(4, 5)$ upon the straight line $3x + 4y = 10$.

2. the origin upon the straight line $\dfrac{x}{3} - \dfrac{y}{4} = 1$.

3. the point $(-3, -4)$ upon the straight line
$$12(x + 6) = 5(y - 2)$$

4. the point (b, a) upon the straight line $\dfrac{x}{a} - \dfrac{y}{b} = 1$.

5. Find the length of the perpendicular from the origin upon the straight line joining the two points whose coordinates are
$$(a \cos \alpha, a \sin \alpha) \quad \text{and} \quad (a \cos \beta, a \sin \beta)$$

6. Shew that the product of the perpendiculars drawn from the two points $(\pm \sqrt{a^2 - b^2}, 0)$ upon the straight line
$$\dfrac{x}{a} \cos \theta + \dfrac{y}{b} \sin \theta = 1 \text{ is } b^2$$

7. If p and p' be the perpendiculars from the origin upon the straight lines whose equations are $x \sec \theta + y \operatorname{cosec} \theta = a$ and
$$x \cos \theta - y \sin \theta = a \cos 2\theta,$$
prove that $\qquad 4p^2 + p'^2 = a^2$

8. Find the distance between the two parallel straight lines
$$y = mx + c \quad \text{and} \quad y = mx + d$$

9. What are the points on the axis of x whose perpendicular distance from the straight line $\dfrac{x}{a} + \dfrac{y}{b} = 1$ is a?

10. Show that the perpendiculars let fall from any point of the straight line $2x + 11y = 5$ upon the two straight lines $24x + 7y = 20$ and $4x - 3y = 2$ are equal to each other.

11. Find the perpendicular distance from the origin of the perpendicular from the point $(1, 2)$ upon the straight line

$$x - \sqrt{3}y + 4 = 0$$

➤ **77.** *To find the coordinates of the point of intersection of two given straight lines.*

Let the equations of the two straight lines be

$$a_1x + b_1y + c_1 = 0 \qquad \qquad \dots(1)$$

and $\qquad \qquad a_2x + b_2y + c_2 = 0 \qquad \qquad \dots(2)$

and let the straight lines be AL_1 and AL_2 as in the figure of Art. 66.

Since, (1) is the equation of AL_1, the coordinates of *any* point on it must satisfy the (1). So the coordinates of any point on AL_2 satisfy (2).

Now, the only point which is common to these two straight lines is their point of intersection A.

The coordinates of this point must therefore, satisfy both (1) and (2).

If therefore, A be the point (x_1, y_1), we have

$$a_1x_1 + b_1y_1 + c_1 = 0 \qquad \qquad \dots(3)$$

and $\qquad \qquad a_2x_1 + b_2y_1 + c_2 = 0 \qquad \qquad \dots(4)$

Solving (3) and (4) we have (as in Art. 3)

$$\frac{x_1}{b_1c_2 - b_2c_1} = \frac{y_1}{c_1a_2 - c_2a_1} = \frac{1}{a_1b_2 - a_2b_1},$$

So that, the coordinates of the required common point are

$$\frac{b_1c_2 - b_2c_1}{a_1b_2 - a_2b_1} \quad \text{and} \quad \frac{c_1a_2 - c_2a_1}{a_1b_2 - a_2b_1}$$

➤ **78.** The coordinates of the point of intersection found in the last article are infinite if

$$a_1b_2 - a_2b_1 = 0$$

But from Art. 67 we know that the two straight lines are parallel if this condition holds.

Hence, parallel lines must be looked upon as lines whose point of intersection is at an infinite distance.

➤ **79.** *To find the condition that three straight lines may meet in a point.*
Let their equations be

$$a_1x + b_1y + c_1 = 0 \qquad \ldots(1)$$

$$a_2x + b_2y + c_2 = 0 \qquad \ldots(2)$$

ar d $$a_3x + b_3y + c_3 = 0 \qquad \ldots(3)$$

By Art. 77 the coordinates of the point of intersection of (1) and (2) are

$$\frac{b_1c_2 - b_2c_1}{a_1b_2 - a_2b_1} \quad \text{and} \quad \frac{c_1a_2 - c_2a_1}{a_1b_2 - a_2b_1} \qquad \ldots(4)$$

If the three straight lines meet in a point, the point of intersection of (1) and (2) must lie on (3). Hence, the values (4) must satisfy (3), so that

$$a_3 \times \frac{b_1c_2 - b_2c_1}{a_1b_2 - a_2b_1} + b_3 \times \frac{c_1a_2 - c_2a_1}{a_1b_2 - a_2b_1} + c_3 = 0,$$

i.e., $\quad a_3(b_1c_2 - b_2c_1) + b_3(c_1a_2 - c_2a_1) + c_3(a_1b_2 - a_2b_1) = 0,$

i.e., $\quad a_1(b_2c_3 - b_3c_2) + b_1(c_2a_3 - c_3a_2) + c_1(a_2b_3 - a_3b_2) = 0 \qquad \ldots(5)$

Aliter : If the three straight lines meet in a point let it be (x_1, y_1), so that the values x_1 and y_1 satisfy the equations (1), (2), and (3), and hence,

$$a_1x_1 + b_1y_1 + c_1 = 0,$$

$$a_2x_1 + b_2y_1 + c_2 = 0,$$

and $$a_3x_1 + b_3y_1 + c_3 = 0$$

The condition that these three equations should hold between the two quantities x_1 and y_1 is, as in Art. 12,

$$\begin{vmatrix} a_1, & b_1, & c_1 \\ a_2, & b_2, & c_2 \\ a_3, & b_3, & c_3 \end{vmatrix} = 0,$$

which is the same as equation (5).

➤ **80.** Another criterion as to whether the three straight lines of the previous article meet in a point is the following.
If any three quantities $p, q,$ and r can be found so that

$$p(a_1x + b_1y + c_1) + q(a_2x + b_2y + c_2) + r(a_3x + b_3y + c_3) = 0$$

identically, then the three straight lines meet in a point.

For in this case we have

$$a_3x + b_3y + c_3 = -\frac{p}{r}(a_1x + b_1y + c_1) - \frac{q}{r}(a_2x + b_2y + c_2) \qquad \dots(1)$$

Now, the coordinates of the point of intersection of the first two of the lines make the right-hand side of (1) vanish. Hence, the same coordinates make the left-hand side vanish. The point of intersection of the first two therefore satisfies the equation to the third line and all three therefore meet in a point.

➤ **81.**

EXAMPLE 1 *Shew that the three straight lines* $2x - 3y + 5 = 0$, $3x + 4y - 7 = 0$, *and* $9x - 5y + 8 = 0$ *meet in a point.*

If we multiply these three equations by 3, 1, and –1 we have *identically*

$$3(2x - 3y + 5) + (3x + 4y - 7) - (9x - 5y + 8) = 0$$

The coordinates of the point of intersection of the first two lines make the first two brackets of this equation vanish and hence, make the third vanish. The common point of intersection of the first two therefore, satisfies the third equation. The three straight lines therefore, meet in a point.

EXAMPLE 2 *Prove that the three perpendiculars drawn from the vertices of a triangle upon the opposite sides all meet in a point.*

Let the triangle be ABC and let its angular points be the points (x_1, y_1), (x_2, y_2), and (x_3, y_3).

The equation to BC is $\quad y - y_2 = \dfrac{y_3 - y_2}{x_3 - x_2}(x - x_2)$.

The equation to the perpendicular from A on this straight line is

$$y - y_1 = -\frac{x_3 - x_2}{y_3 - y_2}(x - x_1)$$

i.e., $\quad y(y_3 - y_2) + x(x_3 - x_2) = y_1(y_3 - y_2) + x_1(x_3 - x_2) \qquad \dots(1)$

So, the perpendiculars from B and C on CA and AB are

$$y(y_1 - y_3) + x(x_1 - x_3) = y_2(y_1 - y_3) + x_2(x_1 - x_3) \qquad \dots(2)$$

and $\quad y(y_2 - y_1) + x(x_2 - x_1) = y_3(y_2 - y_1) + x_3(x_2 - x_1) \qquad \dots(3)$

On adding these three equations their sum identically vanishes. The straight lines represented by them therefore meet in a point.

This point is called the **orthocentre** of the triangle.

➤ **82.** *To find the equation to any straight line which passes through the intersection of the two straight lines*

$$a_1x + b_1y + c_1 = 0 \qquad \dots(1)$$

and $\quad\quad\quad a_2x + b_2y + c_2 = 0 \qquad \dots(2)$

If (x_1, y_1) be the common point of the equations (1) and (2) we may, as in Art. 77, find the values of x_1 and y_1, and then the equation to any straight line through it is

$$y - y_1 = m(x - x_1)$$

where m is any quantity whatever.

Aliter : If A be the common point of the two straight lines, then both equations (1) and (2) are satisfied by the coordinates of the point A.

Hence, the equation

$$a_1x + b_1y + c_1 + \lambda(a_2x + b_2y + c_2) = 0 \qquad \text{...(3)}$$

is satisfied by the coordinates of the common point A, where λ is any arbitrary constant.

But, (3), being of the first degree in x and y, always represents a straight line.

It therefore, represents a straight line passing through A.

Also the arbitrary constant λ may be so chosen that (3) may fulfil any other condition. It therefore represents any straight line passing through A.

➤ **83.**

EXAMPLE *Find the equation to the straight line which passes through the intersection of the straight lines*

$$2x - 3y + 4 = 0, \quad 3x + 4y - 5 = 0 \qquad \text{...(1)}$$

and is perpendicular to the straight line

$$6x - 7y + 8 = 0 \qquad \text{...(2)}$$

Solving the equations (1), the coordinates x_1, y_1 of their common point are given by

$$\frac{x_1}{(-3)(-5) - 4 \times 4} = \frac{y_1}{4 \times 3 - 2 \times (-5)} = \frac{1}{2 \times 4 - 3 \times (-3)} = \frac{1}{17}$$

so that

$$x_1 = -\frac{1}{17} \quad \text{and} \quad y_1 = \frac{22}{17}.$$

The equation of any straight line through this common point is therefore,

$$y - \frac{22}{17} = m\left(x + \frac{1}{17}\right)$$

This straight line is, by Art. 69, perpendicular to (2) if

$$m \times \frac{6}{7} = -1, \quad i.e., \quad \text{if } m = -\frac{7}{6}$$

The required equation is therefore,

$$y - \frac{22}{17} = -\frac{7}{6}\left(x + \frac{1}{17}\right)$$

i.e., $\qquad 119x + 102y = 125.$

Aliter: Any straight line through the intersection of the straight lines (1) is

$$2x - 3y + 4 + \lambda(3x + 4y - 5) = 0$$

i.e., $$(2 + 3\lambda)x + y(4\lambda - 3) + 4 - 5\lambda = 0 \qquad \qquad ...(3)$$

This straight line is perpendicular to (2), if

$$6(2 + 3\lambda) - 7(4\lambda - 3) = 0 \qquad \text{(Art. 69)}$$

i.e., if $$\lambda = \frac{33}{10}$$

The equation (3) is therefore,

$$x\left(2 + \frac{99}{10}\right) + y\left(\frac{132}{10} - 3\right) + 4 - \frac{165}{10} = 0$$

i.e.., $$119x + 102y - 125 = 0$$

BISECTORS OF ANGLES BETWEEN STRAIGHT LINES

➤ **84.** *To find the equations of the bisectors of the angles between the straight lines*

$$a_1x + b_1y + c_1 = 0 \qquad \qquad ...(1)$$

and $$a_2x + b_2y + c_2 = 0 \qquad \qquad ...(2)$$

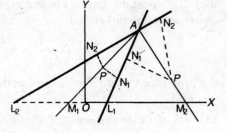

Let the two straight lines be AL_1 and AL_2, and let the bisectors of the angles between them be AM_1 and AM_2.

Let P be any point on either of these bisectors and draw PN_1 and PN_2 perpendicular to the given lines.

The triangles PAN_1 and PAN_2 are equal in all respects, so that the perpendiculars PN_1 and PN_2 are equal in magnitude.

Let the equations to the straight lines be written so that c_1 and c_2 are both negative, and to the quantities $\sqrt{a_1{}^2 + b_1{}^2}$ and $\sqrt{a_2{}^2 + b_2{}^2}$ let the positive sign be prefixed.

If P be the point (h, k), the numerical values of PN_1 and PN_2 are (by Art. 75)

$$\frac{a_1h + b_1k + c_1}{\sqrt{a_1{}^2 + b_1{}^2}} \quad \text{and} \quad \frac{a_2h + b_2k + c_2}{\sqrt{a_2{}^2 + b_2{}^2}} \qquad \qquad ...(1)$$

If P lie on AM_1, *i.e.,* on the bisector of the angle between the two straight lines in which the origin lies, the point P and the origin lie on the same side of each of the two lines. Hence, (by Art. 73, Cor.) the two quantities (1) have the same sign as c_1 and c_2 respectively.

In this case, since c_1 and c_2 have the same sign, the quantities (1) have the same sign, and hence,

$$\frac{a_1h + b_1k + c_1}{\sqrt{a_1^2 + b_1^2}} = +\frac{a_2h + b_2k + c_2}{\sqrt{a_2^2 + b_2^2}}$$

But this is the condition that the point (h, k) may lie on the straight line

$$\frac{a_1x + b_1y + c_1}{\sqrt{a_1^2 + b_1^2}} = \frac{a_2x + b_2y + c_2}{\sqrt{a_2^2 + b_2^2}}$$

which is therefore the equation to AM_1.

If, however, P lie on the other bisector AM_2, the two quantities (1) will have opposite signs, so that the equation to AM_2 will be

$$\frac{a_1x + b_1y + c_1}{\sqrt{a_1^2 + b_1^2}} = -\frac{a_2x + b_2y + c_2}{\sqrt{a_2^2 + b_2^2}}$$

The equations to the original lines being therefore, arranged so that the constant terms are both positive (or both negative) the equation to the bisectors is

$$\frac{a_1x + b_1y + c_1}{\sqrt{a_1^2 + b_1^2}} = \pm\frac{a_2x + b_2y + c_2}{\sqrt{a_2^2 + b_2^2}}$$

the upper sign giving the bisector of the angle in which the origin lies.

➤ **85.**

EXAMPLE *Find the equations to the bisectors of the angles between the straight lines*

$$3x - 4y + 7 = 0 \quad \text{and} \quad 12x - 5y - 8 = 0$$

Writing the equations so that their constant terms are both positive they are

$$3x - 4y + 7 = 0 \quad \text{and} \quad -12x + 5y + 8 = 0$$

The equation to the bisector of the angle in which the origin lies is therefore,

$$\frac{3x - 4y + 7}{\sqrt{3^2 + 4^2}} = \frac{-12x + 5y + 8}{\sqrt{12^2 + 5^2}}$$

i.e., $$13(3x - 4y + 7) = 5(-12x + 5y + 8)$$

i.e., $$99x - 77y + 51 = 0$$

The equation to the other bisector is

$$\frac{3x - 4y + 7}{\sqrt{3^2 + 4^2}} = -\frac{-12x + 5y + 8}{\sqrt{12^2 + 5^2}}$$

i.e., $\qquad$ $13(3x - 4y + 7) + 5(-12x + 5y + 8) = 0$

i.e., $\qquad$ $21x + 27y - 131 = 0$

➤ **86.** It will be found useful in a later chapter to have the equation to a straight line, which passes through a given point and makes a given angle θ with a given line, in a form different from that of Art. 62.

Let A be the given point (h, k) and $L'AL$ a straight line through it inclined at an angle θ to the axis of x.

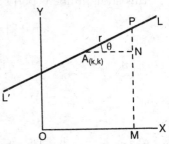

Take any point P, whose coordinates are (x, y), lying on this line, and let the distance AP be r.

Draw PM perpendicular to the axis of x and AN perpendicular to PM.

Then, $\qquad$ $x - h = AN = AP \cos \theta = r \cos \theta,$

and $\qquad$ $y - k = NP = AP \sin \theta = r \sin \theta$

Hence, $\qquad$ $\dfrac{x-h}{\cos \theta} = \dfrac{y-k}{\sin \theta} = r$ $\qquad$ ...(1)

This being the relation holding between the coordinates of any point P on the line is the equation required.

Cor. 1 : From (1) we have

$$x = h + r \cos \theta \quad \text{and} \quad y = k + r \sin \theta$$

The coordinates of any point on the given line are therefore

$$h = r \cos \theta \quad \text{and} \quad k + r \sin \theta$$

➤ **87.** *To find the length of the straight line drawn through a given point in a given direction to meet a given straight line.*

Let the given straight line be

$$Ax + By + C = 0 \qquad ...(1)$$

Let the given point A be (h, k) and the given direction one making an angle θ with the axis of x.

Let the line drawn through A meet the straight line (1) in P and let AP be r.

By the corollary to the last article the coordinates of P are

$$h + r \cos \theta \quad \text{and} \quad k + r \sin \theta$$

Since, these coordinates satisfy (1) we have

$$A(h + r \cos \theta) + B(k + r \sin \theta) + C = 0$$

∴ $\qquad$ $r = -\dfrac{Ah + Bk + C}{A \cos \theta + B \sin \theta}$ $\qquad$ ...(2)

giving the length AP which is required.

Cor. : From the preceding may be deduced the length of the perpendicular drawn from (h, k) upon (1).

For the "m" of the straight line drawn through A is $\tan \theta$ and the "m" of (1) is $-\dfrac{A}{B}$.

This straight line is perpendicular to (1) if

$$\tan \theta \times \left(-\frac{A}{B}\right) = -1$$

i.e., if

$$\tan \theta = \frac{B}{A}$$

so that

$$\frac{\cos \theta}{A} = \frac{\sin \theta}{B} = \frac{1}{\sqrt{A^2 + B^2}}$$

and hence,

$$A \cos \theta + B \sin \theta = \frac{A^2 + B^2}{\sqrt{A^2 + B^2}} = \sqrt{A^2 + B^2}$$

Substituting this value in (2) we have the magnitude of the required perpendicular.

EXAMPLES VIII

Find the coordinates of the points of intersection of the straight lines whose equations are

1. $2x - 3y + 5 = 0$ and $7x + 4y = 3$

2. $\dfrac{x}{a} + \dfrac{y}{b} = 1$ and $\dfrac{x}{b} + \dfrac{y}{a} = 1$

3. $y = m_1 x + \dfrac{a}{m_1}$ and $y = m_2 x + \dfrac{a}{m_2}$

4. $x \cos \phi_1 + y \sin \phi_1 = a$ and $x \cos \phi_2 + y \sin \phi_2 = a$

5. Two straight lines cut the axis of x at distances a and $-a$ and the axis of y at distances b and b' respectively; find the coordinates of their point of intersection.

6. Find the distance of the point of intersection of the two straight lines
$$2x - 3y + 5 = 0 \quad \text{and} \quad 3x + 4y = 0$$
from the straight line
$$5x - 2y = 0$$

7. Shew that the perpendicular from the origin upon the straight line joining the points
$$(a \cos \alpha, a \sin \alpha) \quad \text{and} \quad (a \cos \beta, a \sin \beta)$$
bisects the distance between them.

8. Find the equations of the two straight lines drawn through the point

$(0, a)$ on which the perpendicular let fall from the point $(2a, 2a)$ are each of length a.

Prove also that the equation of the straight line joining the feet of these perpendiculars is $y + 2x = 5a$

9. Find the point of intersection and the inclination of the two lines

$$Ax + By = A + B \quad \text{and} \quad A(x - y) + B(x + y) = 2B$$

10. Find the coordinates of the point in which the line

$$2y - 3x + 7 = 0$$

meets the line joining the two points $(6, -2)$ and $(-8, 7)$. Find also the angle between them.

11. Find the coordinates of the feet of the perpendiculars let fall from the point $(5, 0)$ upon the sides of the triangle formed by joining the three points $(4, 3)$, $(-4, 3)$, and $(0, -5)$; prove also that the points so determined lie on a straight line.

12. Find the coordinates of the point of intersection of the straight lines

$$2x - 3y = 1 \quad \text{and} \quad 5y - x = 3$$

and determine also the angle at which they cut one another.

13. Find the angle between the two lines

$$3x + y + 12 = 0 \quad \text{and} \quad x + 2y - 1 = 0$$

Find also the coordinates of their point of intersection and the equations of lines drawn perpendicular to them from the point $(3, -2)$.

14. Prove that the points whose coordinates are respectively $(5, 1)$, $(1, -1)$, and $(11, 4)$ lie on a straight line, and find its intercepts on the axes.

Prove that the following sets of three lines meet in a point.

15. $2x - 3y = 7$, $3x - 4y = 13$, and $8x - 11y = 33$

16. $3x + 4y + 6 = 0$, $6x + 5y + 9 = 0$, and $3x + 3y + 5 = 0$

17. $\dfrac{x}{a} + \dfrac{y}{b} = 1$, $\dfrac{x}{b} + \dfrac{y}{a} = 1$, and $y = x$.

18. Prove that the three straight lines whose equations are $15x - 18y + 1 = 0$, $12x + 10y - 3 = 0$, and $6x + 66y - 11 = 0$ all meet in a point.

Shew also that the third line bisects the angle between the other two.

19. Find the conditions that the straight lines

$$y = m_1x + a_1, \; y = m_2x + a_2, \text{ and } y = m_3x + a_3$$

may meet in a point.

Find the coordinates of the orthocentre of the triangles whose angular points are

20. $(0, 0)$, $(2, -1)$, and $(-1, 3)$.

21. $(1, 0)$, $(2, -4)$, and $(-5, -2)$.

22. In any triangle ABC, prove that
    (i) the bisectors of the angles $A, B,$ and C meet in a point,
    (ii) the medians, *i.e.*, the lines joining each vertex to the middle point of the opposite side, meet in a point.

and (iii) the straight lines through the middle points of the sides perpendicular to the sides meet in a point.

Find the equation to the straight line passing through

23. the point $(3, 2)$ and the point of intersection of the lines
$$2x + 3y = 1 \quad \text{and} \quad 3x - 4y = 6.$$

24. the point $(2, -9)$ and the intersection of the lines
$$2x + 5y - 8 = 0 \quad \text{and} \quad 3x - 5y = 35$$

25. the origin and the point of intersection of
$$x - y - 4 = 0 \quad \text{and} \quad 7x + y + 20 = 0$$
proving that it bisects the angles between them.

26. the origin and the point of intersection of the lines
$$\frac{x}{a} + \frac{y}{b} = 1 \quad \text{and} \quad \frac{x}{b} + \frac{y}{a} = 1$$

27. the point (a, b) and the intersection of the same two lines.

28. the intersection of the lines
$$x - 2y - a = 0 \quad \text{and} \quad x + 3y - 2a = 0$$
and parallel to the straight line
$$3x + 4y = 0$$

29. The intersection of the lines
$$x + 2y + 3 = 0 \quad \text{and} \quad 3x + 4y + 7 = 0$$
and perpendicular to the straight line
$$y - x = 8.$$

30. The intersection of the lines
$$3x - 4y + 1 = 0 \quad \text{and} \quad 5x + y - 1 = 0$$
and cutting off equal intercepts from the axes.

31. The intersection of the lines
$$2x - 3y = 10 \quad \text{and} \quad x + 2y = 6$$
and the intersection of the lines
$$16x - 10y = 33 \quad \text{and} \quad 12x + 14y + 29 = 0$$

32. If through the angular points of a triangle straight lines be drawn parallel to the sides, and if the intersections of these lines be joined to the opposite angular points of the triangle, shew that the joining lines so obtained will meet in a point.

33. Find the equations to the straight lines passing through the point of intersection of the straight lines
$$Ax + By + C = 0 \quad \text{and} \quad A'x + B'y + C' = 0 \text{ and}$$

(i) passing through the origin.

(ii) parallel to the axis of y,

(iii) cutting off a given distance a from the axis of y,

and (iv) passing through a given point (x', y').

34. Prove that the diagonals of the parallelogram formed by the four straight lines

$$\sqrt{3}x + y = 0, \quad \sqrt{3}y + x = 0, \quad \sqrt{3}x + y = 1, \quad \text{and} \quad \sqrt{3}y + x = 1$$

are at right angles to one another.

35. Prove the same property for the parallelogram whose sides are

$$\frac{x}{a} + \frac{y}{b} = 1, \frac{x}{b} + \frac{y}{a} = 1, \frac{x}{a} + \frac{y}{b} = 2, \text{ and } \frac{x}{b} + \frac{y}{a} = 2$$

36. One side of a square is inclined to the axis of x at an angle α and one of its extremities is at the origin; prove that the equations to its diagonals are

$$y(\cos \alpha - \sin \alpha) = x(\sin \alpha + \cos \alpha)$$

and $\qquad y(\sin \alpha + \cos \alpha) + x(\cos \alpha - \sin \alpha) = a$

where a is the length of the side of the square.

Find the equations to the straight lines bisecting the angles between the following pairs of straight lines, placing first the bisector of the angle in which the origin lies.

37. $x + y\sqrt{3} = 6 + 2\sqrt{3}$ and $x - y\sqrt{3} = 6 - 2\sqrt{3}$

38. $12x + 5y - 4 = 0$ and $3x + 4y + 7 = 0$

39. $4x + 3y - 7 = 0$ and $24x + 7y - 31 = 0$

40. $2x + y = 4$ and $y + 3x = 5$

41. Find the bisectors of the angles between the straight lines

$$y - b = \frac{2m}{1 - m^2}(x - a) \quad \text{and} \quad y - b = \frac{2m'}{1 - m'^2}(x - a)$$

Find the equations to the bisectors of the internal angles of the triangles the equations of whose sides are respectively

42. $3x + 4y = 6$, $12x - 5y = 3$, and $4x - 3y + 12 = 0$

43. $3x + 5y = 15$, $x + y = 4$, and $2x + y = 6$

44. Find the equations to the straight lines passing through the foot of the perpendicular from the point (h, k) upon the straight line $Ax + By + C = 0$ and bisecting the angles between the perpendicular and the given straight line.

45. Find the direction in which a straight line must be drawn through the point $(1, 2)$, so that its point of intersection with the line $x + y = 4$ may be at a distance $\frac{1}{3}\sqrt{6}$ from this point.

5

THE STRAIGHT LINE (CONTINUED)

POLAR EQUATIONS. OBLIQUE COORDINATES. MISCELLANEOUS PROBLEMS. LOCI.

► **88.** *To find the general equation to a straight line in polar coordinates.*

Let p be the length of the perpendicular OY from the origin upon the straight line, and let this perpendicular make an angle α with the initial line.

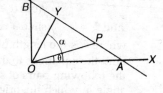

Let P be any point on the line and let its coordinates be r and θ.

The equation required will then be the relation between r, θ, p and α.

From the triangle OYP we have

$$p = r \cos YOP = r \cos (\alpha - \theta) = r \cos (\theta - \alpha)$$

The required equation is therefore

$$r \cos (\theta - \alpha) = p$$

[On transforming to Cartesian coordinates this equation becomes the equation of Art. 53.]

► **89.** *To find the polar equation of the straight line joining the points whose coordinates are (r_1, θ_1) and (r_2, θ_2).*

Let A and B be the two given points and P any point on the line joining them whose coordinates are r and θ.

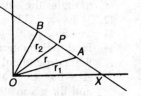

Then, since

$\Delta AOB = \Delta AOP + \Delta POB$, we have

$$\frac{1}{2} r_1 r_2 \sin AOB = \frac{1}{2} r_1 r \sin AOP + \frac{1}{2} r r_2 \sin POB,$$

i.e., $\quad r_1 r_2 \sin (\theta_2 - \theta_1) = r_1 r \sin (\theta - \theta_1) + r r_2 \sin (\theta_2 - \theta)$

i.e., $\quad \dfrac{\sin (\theta_2 - \theta_1)}{r} = \dfrac{\sin (\theta - \theta_1)}{r_2} + \dfrac{\sin (\theta_2 - \theta)}{r_1}$

OBLIQUE COORDINATES

➤ **90.** In the previous chapter we took the axes to be rectangular. In the great majority of cases rectangular axes are employed but in some cases oblique axes may be used with advantage.

In the following articles we shall consider the propositions in which the results for oblique axes are different from those for rectangular axes. The propositions of Arts. 50 and 62 are true for oblique, as well as rectangular, coordinates.

➤ **91.** *To find the equation to a straight line referred to axes inclined at an angle ω.*

Let LPL' be a straight line which cuts the axis of Y at a distance c from the origin and is inclined at an angle θ to the axis of x.

Let P be any point on the straight line. Draw PNM parallel to the axis of y to meet OX in M, and let it meet the straight line through C parallel to the axis of x in the point N.

Let P be the point (x, y), so that

$$CN = OM = x, \text{ and } NP = MP - OC = y - c$$

Since, $\angle CPN = \angle PNN' - \angle PCN' = \omega - \theta$, we have

$$\frac{y - c}{x} = \frac{NP}{CN} = \frac{\sin NCP}{\sin CPN} = \frac{\sin \theta}{\sin (\omega - \theta)}$$

Hence, $y = x \dfrac{\sin \theta}{\sin (\omega - \theta)} + c$ ...(1)

This equation is of the form

$$y = mx + c,$$

where $m = \dfrac{\sin \theta}{\sin (\omega - \theta)} = \dfrac{\sin \theta}{\sin \omega \cos \theta - \cos \omega \sin \theta} = \dfrac{\tan \theta}{\sin \omega - \cos \omega \tan \theta}$

and therefore, $\tan \theta = \dfrac{m \sin \omega}{1 + m \cos \omega}$

In oblique coordinates the equation

$$y = mx + c$$

therefore represents a straight line which is inclined at an angle

$$\tan^{-1} \frac{m \sin \omega}{1 + m \cos \omega}$$

to the axis of x.

Cor. : From (1), by putting in succession θ equal to 90° and 90° + ω, we see that the equation to the straight lines, passing through the origin and perpendicular to the axes of x and y, are respectively

$$y = -\frac{x}{\cos \omega} \text{ and } y = -x \cos \omega.$$

➤ **92.** *The axes being oblique, to find the equation to the straight line, such that the perpendicular on it from the origin is of length p and makes angles α and β with the axes of x and y.*

Let LM be the given straight line and OK the perpendicular on it from the origin.

Let P be any point on the straight line; draw the ordinate PN and draw NR perpendicular to OK and PS perpendicular to NR.

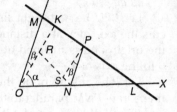

Let P be the point (x, y), so that,

$$ON = x \text{ and } NP = y$$

The lines NP and OY are parallel.

Also OK and SP are parallel, each being perpendicular to NR.

Thus, $\angle SPN = \angle KOM = \beta$

We therefore have

$$p = OK = OR + SP = ON \cos \alpha + NP \cos \beta = x \cos \alpha + y \cos \beta$$

Hence, $x \cos \alpha + y \cos \beta - p = 0,$

being the relation which holds between the coordinates of any point on the straight line, is the required equation.

➤ **93.** *To find the angle between the straight lines*

$$y = mx + c \text{ and } y = m'x + c'$$

the axes being oblique.

If these straight lines be respectively inclined at angles θ and θ' to the axis of x, we have, by the last article,

$$\tan \theta = \frac{m \sin \omega}{1 + m \cos \omega} \text{ and } \tan \theta' = \frac{m' \sin \omega}{1 + m' \cos \omega}$$

The angle required is $\theta \sim \theta'$.

Now, $\tan (\theta - \theta') = \dfrac{\tan \theta - \tan \theta'}{1 + \tan \theta \cdot \tan \theta'}$

$$= \frac{\dfrac{m \sin \omega}{1 + m \cos \omega} - \dfrac{m' \sin \omega}{1 + m' \cos \omega}}{1 + \dfrac{m \sin \omega}{1 + m \cos \omega} \cdot \dfrac{m' \sin \omega}{1 + m' \cos \omega}}$$

$$= \frac{m \sin \omega (1 + m' \cos \omega) - m' \sin \omega (1 + m \cos \omega)}{(1 + m \cos \omega)(1 + m' \cos \omega) + mm' \sin^2 \omega}$$

$$= \frac{(m - m') \sin \omega}{1 + (m + m') \cos \omega + mm'}$$

The required angle is therefore

$$\tan^{-1} \frac{(m - m') \sin \omega}{1 + (m + m') \cos \omega + mm'}$$

Cor. 1 : The two given lines are parallel if $m = m'$.

Cor. 2 : The two given lines are perpendicular if

$$1 + (m + m') \cos \omega + mm' = 0$$

➤ **94.** If the straight lines have their equations in the form

$$Ax + By + C = 0 \quad \text{and} \quad A'x + B'y + C' = 0$$

then, $$m = -\frac{A}{B} \quad \text{and} \quad m' = -\frac{A'}{B'}$$

Substituting these values in the result of the last article the angle between the two lines is easily found to be

$$\tan^{-1} \frac{A'B - AB'}{AA' + BB' - (AB' + A'B) \cos \omega} \sin \omega$$

The given lines are therefore parallel if

$$A'B - AB' = 0$$

They are perpendicular if

$$AA' + BB' = (AB' + A'B) \cos \omega.$$

➤ **95.**

EXAMPLE *The axes being inclined at an angle of* 30°, *obtain the equations to the straight lines which pass through the origin and are inclined at* 45° *to the straight line* $x + y = 1$.

Let either of the required straight lines be $y = mx$.

The given straight line is $y = -x + 1$, so that $m' = -1$

We therefore have

$$\frac{(m - m') \sin \omega}{1 + (m + m') \cos \omega + mm'} = \tan (\pm 45°)$$

where $m' = -1$ and $\omega = 30°$.

This equation gives $\dfrac{-m+1}{2+(m-1)\sqrt{3}-2m}=\pm 1$

Taking the upper sign we obtain $m=-\dfrac{1}{\sqrt{3}}$

Taking the lower sign we have $m=-\sqrt{3}$

The required equations are therefore,

$$y=-\sqrt{3}x \quad \text{and} \quad y=-\dfrac{1}{\sqrt{3}}x,$$

i.e., $y+\sqrt{3}x=0 \quad \text{and} \quad \sqrt{3}y+x=0$

➤ **96.** *To find the length of the perpendicular from the point (x', y') upon the straight line $Ax+By+C=0$, the axes being inclined at an angle ω, and the equation being written so that C is a negative quantity.*

Let the given straight line meet the axis in L and M, so that

$$OL=-\dfrac{C}{A} \quad \text{and} \quad OM=-\dfrac{C}{B}.$$

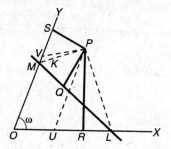

Let P be the given point (x', y'). Draw the perpendiculars PQ, PR and PS on the given line and the two axes.

Taking O and P on opposite sides of the given line, we then have

$$\Delta LPM + \Delta MOL = \Delta OLP + \Delta\, OPM$$

i.e., $\quad PQ \cdot LM + OL \cdot OM \sin \omega = OL \cdot PR + OM \cdot PS$ ...(1)

Draw PU and PV parallel to the axes of y and x, so that $PU=y'$ and $PV=x'$.

Hence, $PR = PU \sin PUR = y' \sin \omega$

and $PS = PV \sin PVS = x' \sin \omega$

Also, $LM = \sqrt{OL^2 + OM^2 - 2OL \cdot OM \cos \omega}$

$$= \sqrt{\dfrac{C^2}{A^2}+\dfrac{C^2}{B^2}-2\dfrac{C^2}{AB}\cos\omega} = -C\sqrt{\dfrac{1}{A^2}+\dfrac{1}{B^2}-\dfrac{2\cos\omega}{AB}}$$

since, C is a negative quantity.

On substituting these values in (1), we have

$$PQ \times (-C) \times \sqrt{\dfrac{1}{A^2}+\dfrac{1}{B^2}-\dfrac{2\cos\omega}{AB}+\dfrac{C^2}{AB}\sin\omega}$$

$$=-\dfrac{C}{A}\cdot y' \sin \omega-\dfrac{C}{B}\cdot x' \sin \omega$$

So that, $$PQ = \frac{Ax' + By' + C}{\sqrt{A^2 + B^2 - 2AB \cos \omega}} \cdot \sin \omega.$$

Cor. : If $\omega = 90°$, *i.e.*, if the axes be rectangular, we have the result of Art. 75.

EXAMPLES IX

1. The axes being inclined at an angle of 60°, find the inclination to the axis of x of the straight lines whose equations are
   (i) $\qquad y = 2x + 5,$
   (ii) $\qquad 2y = (\sqrt{3} - 1)\, x + 7$

2. The axes being inclined at an angle of 120°, find the tangent of the angle between the two straight lines
   $$8x + 7y = 1 \quad \text{and} \quad 28x - 73y = 101$$

3. With oblique coordinates find the tangent of the angle between the straight lines
   $$y = mx + c \quad \text{and} \quad my + x = d.$$

4. If $y = x \tan \dfrac{11\pi}{24}$ and $y = x \tan \dfrac{19\pi}{24}$ represent two straight lines at right angles, prove that the angle between the axes is $\dfrac{\pi}{4}$.

5. Prove that the straight lines $y + x = c$ and $y = x + d$ are at right angles, whatever be the angle between the axes.

6. Prove that the equation to the straight line which passes through the point (h, k) and is perpendicular to the axis of x is
   $$x + y \cos \omega = h + k \cos \omega.$$

7. Find the equation to the sides and diagonals of a regular hexagon, two of its sides, which meet in a corner, being the axes of coordinates.

8. From each corner of a parallelogram a perpendicular is drawn upon the diagonal which does not pass through that corner and these are produced to form another parallelogram; shew that its diagonals are perpendicular to the sides of the first parallelogram and that they both have the same centre.

9. If the straight line $y = m_1 x + c_1$ and $y = m_2 x + c_2$ make equal angles with the axis of x and be not parallel to one another, prove that $m_1 + m_2 + 2m_1 m_2 \cos \omega = 0$.

10. The axes being inclined at an angle of 30°, find the equation to the straight line which passes through the point $(-2, 3)$ and is perpendicular to the straight line $y + 3x = 6$.

11. Find the length of the perpendicular drawn from the point $(4, -3)$ upon the straight line $6x + 3y - 10 = 0$, the angle between the axes being 60°.

12. Find the equation to, and the length of the perpendicular drawn from the point (1, 1) upon the straight line $3x + 4y + 5 = 0$, the angle between the axes being 120°.

13. The coordinates of a point P referred to axes meeting at an angle ω are (h, k); prove that the length of the straight line joining the feet of the perpendiculars from P upon the axes is

$$\sin \omega \sqrt{h^2 + k^2 + 2hk \cos \omega}$$

14. From a given point (h, k) perpendiculars are drawn to the axes, whose inclination is ω, and their feet are joined. Prove that the length of the perpendicular drawn from (h, k) upon this line is

$$\frac{hk \sin^2 \omega}{\sqrt{h^2 + k^2 + 2hk \cos \omega}}$$

and that its equation is $hx - ky = h^2 - k^2$.

STRAIGHT LINE PASSING THROUGH FIXED POINTS

➤ **97.** *If the equation to a straight line be of the form*

$$ax + by + c + \lambda (a'x + b'y + c') = 0 \qquad \ldots(1)$$

where λ is any arbitrary constant, it always passes through one fixed point whatever be the value of λ.

For the equation (1) is satisfied by the coordinates of the point which satisfies both of the equations

$$ax + by + c = 0$$

and $$a'x + b'y + c' = 0$$

This point is, by Art. 77,

$$\left(\frac{bc' - b'c}{ab' - a'b}, \ \frac{ca' - c'a}{ab' - a'b} \right),$$

and these coordinates are independent of λ.

EXAMPLE *Given the vertical angle of a triangle is magnitude and position, and also the sum of the reciprocals of the sides which contain it; shew that the base always passes through a fixed point.*

Take the fixed angular point as origin and the directions of the sides containing it as axes; let the lengths of these sides in any such triangle be a and b, which are not therefore given.

We have $$\frac{1}{a} + \frac{1}{b} = \text{constant} = \frac{1}{k} \text{ (say)} \qquad \ldots(1)$$

The equation to the base is

$$\frac{x}{a} + \frac{y}{b} = 1$$

i.e., by (1),
$$\frac{x}{a} + y\left(\frac{1}{k} - \frac{1}{a}\right) = 1$$

i.e.,
$$\frac{1}{a}(x - y) + \frac{y}{k} - 1 = 0$$

Whatever be the value of a this straight line always passes through the point given by

$$x - y = 0 \quad \text{and} \quad \frac{y}{k} - 1 = 0$$

i.e., through the fixed point (k, k).

➤ **98.** *Prove that the coordinates of the centre of the circle inscribed in the triangle, whose vertices are the points (x_1, y_1), (x_2, y_2), and (x_3, y_3), are*

$$\frac{ax_1 + bx_2 + cx_3}{a + b + c} \quad \text{and} \quad \frac{ay_1 + by_2 + cy_3}{a + b + c}$$

where, a, b and c are the lengths of the sides of the triangle.

Find also the coordinates of the centres of the escribed circles.

Let ABC be the triangle and let AD and CE be the bisectors of the angles A and C and let them meet in O'.

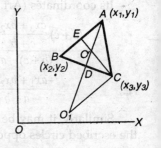

Then O' is the required point.

Since, AD bisects the angle BAC we have, by geometry,

$$\frac{BD}{BA} = \frac{DC}{AC} = \frac{BD + DC}{BA + AC} = \frac{a}{b + c},$$

So that,
$$DC = \frac{ba}{b + c}$$

Also, since CO' bisects the angle ACD, we have

$$\frac{AO'}{O'D} = \frac{AC}{CD} = \frac{b}{\dfrac{ba}{b + c}} = \frac{b + c}{a}$$

The point D therefore, divides BC in the ratio

$$BA : AC, \quad \text{*i.e.*,} \quad c : b$$

Also, O' divides AD in the ratio $b + c ; a$

Hence, by Art. 22, the coordinates of D are

$$\frac{cx_3 + bx_2}{c + b} \quad \text{and} \quad \frac{cy_3 + by_2}{c + b}$$

Also, by the same article, the coordinates of O' are

$$\frac{(b+c)\times\dfrac{cx_3+bx_2}{c+b}+ax_1}{(b+c)+a} \quad\text{and}\quad \frac{(b+c)\times\dfrac{cy_3+by_2}{c+b}+ay_1}{(b+c)+a}$$

i.e., $\quad \dfrac{ax_1+bx_2+cx_3}{a+b+c} \quad\text{and}\quad \dfrac{ay_1+by_2+cy_3}{a+b+c}$

Again, if O_1 be the centre of the escribed circle opposite to the angle A, the line CO_1 bisects the exterior angle of ACB.

Hence, by geometry, we have

$$\frac{AO_1}{O_1D}=\frac{AC}{CD}=\frac{b+c}{a}$$

Therefore, O_1 is the point which divides AD *externally* in the ratio $b+c:a$.

Its coordinates (Art. 22) are therefore

$$\frac{(b+c)\dfrac{cx_3+bx_2}{c+b}-ax_1}{(b+c)-a} \quad\text{and}\quad \frac{(b+c)\dfrac{cy_3+by_2}{c+b}-ay_1}{(b+c)-a}$$

i.e., $\quad \dfrac{-ax_1+bx_2+cx_3}{-a+b+c} \quad\text{and}\quad \dfrac{-ay_1+by_2+cy_3}{-a+b+c}$

Similarly, it may be shewn that the coordinates of the centres of the escribed circles opposite to B and C are respectively.

$$\left(\frac{ax_1-bx_2+cx_3}{a-b+c},\ \frac{ay_1-by_2+cy_3}{a-b+c}\right)$$

and

$$\left(\frac{ax_1+bx_2-cx_3}{a+b-c},\ \frac{ay_1+by_2-cy_3}{a+b-c}\right)$$

➤ **99.** As a numerical example consider the case of the triangle formed by the straight lines

$$3x+4y-7=0,\quad 12x+5y-17=0$$

and $\qquad\qquad 5x+12y-34=0$

These three straight lines being BC, CA and AB respectively we easily obtain, by solving, that the points A, B and C are

$$\left(\frac{2}{7},\frac{19}{7}\right),\ \left(\frac{-52}{16},\frac{67}{16}\right)\text{ and }(1,1)$$

Hence, $\quad a=\sqrt{\left(\dfrac{-52}{16}-1\right)^2+\left(\dfrac{67}{16}-1\right)^2}=\sqrt{\dfrac{68^2}{16^2}+\dfrac{51^2}{16^2}}$

$$= \frac{17}{16} \sqrt{4^2 + 3^2} = \frac{85}{16}$$

$$b = \sqrt{\left(1 - \frac{2}{7}\right)^2 + \left(1 - \frac{19}{7}\right)^2} = \sqrt{\frac{5^2}{7^2} + \frac{12^2}{7^2}} = \frac{13}{7}$$

and

$$c = \sqrt{\left(\frac{2}{7} + \frac{52}{16}\right)^2 + \left(\frac{19}{7} - \frac{67}{16}\right)^2} = \sqrt{\frac{396^2 + 165^2}{112^2}}$$

$$= \frac{33}{112} \sqrt{169} = \frac{429}{112}$$

Hence, $ax_1 = \frac{85}{16} \times \frac{2}{7} = \frac{170}{112}$; $ay_1 = \frac{85}{16} \times \frac{19}{7} = \frac{1615}{112}$

$$bx_2 = \frac{13}{7} \times \frac{-52}{16} = -\frac{676}{112} ; \quad by_2 = \frac{13}{7} \times \frac{67}{16} = \frac{871}{112}$$

$$cx_3 = \frac{429}{112}, \quad \text{and} \quad cy_3 = \frac{429}{112}$$

The coordinates of the centre of the incircle are therefore

$$\frac{\frac{170}{112} - \frac{676}{112} + \frac{429}{112}}{\frac{85}{16} + \frac{13}{7} + \frac{429}{112}} \quad \text{and} \quad \frac{\frac{1615}{112} + \frac{871}{112} + \frac{429}{112}}{\frac{85}{16} + \frac{13}{7} + \frac{429}{112}}$$

i.e., $\dfrac{-1}{16}$ and $\dfrac{265}{112}$

The length of the radius of the incircle is the perpendicular from $\left(-\dfrac{1}{16}, \dfrac{265}{112}\right)$ upon the straight line

$$3x + 4y - 7 = 0$$

and therefore, $\dfrac{\left(3 \times -\dfrac{1}{16}\right) + \left(4 \times \dfrac{265}{112}\right) - 7}{\sqrt{3^2 + 4^2}} = \dfrac{-21 + 1060 - 784}{5 \times 112}$

$$= \frac{255}{5 \times 112} = \frac{51}{112}$$

The coordinates of the centre of the escribed circle which touches the side BC externally are

$$\frac{-\dfrac{170}{112}-\dfrac{676}{112}+\dfrac{429}{112}}{-\dfrac{85}{16}+\dfrac{13}{7}+\dfrac{429}{112}} \quad \text{and} \quad \frac{-\dfrac{1615}{112}+\dfrac{871}{112}+\dfrac{429}{112}}{-\dfrac{85}{16}+\dfrac{13}{7}+\dfrac{429}{112}}$$

i.e., $\qquad\qquad\qquad \dfrac{-417}{42} \quad \text{and} \quad \dfrac{-315}{42}$

Similarly, the coordinates of the centres of the other escribed circles can be written down.

➤ **100.**

EXAMPLE *Find the radius, and the coordinates of the centre, of the circle circumscribing the triangle formed by the points.*

$$(0,1), (2, 3) \text{ and } (3, 5)$$

Let (x_1, y_1) be the required centre and R the radius.

Since, the distance of the centre from each of the three points is the same, we have

$$x_1^2 + (y_1 - 1)^2 = (x_1 - 2)^2 + (y_1 - 3)^2$$
$$= (x_1 - 3)^2 + (y_1 - 5^2) = R^2 \qquad \qquad \text{...(1)}$$

From the first two we have, on reduction

$$x_1 + y_1 = 3$$

From the first and third equations we obtain

$$6x_1 + 8y_1 = 33$$

Solving, we have $\quad x_1 = -\dfrac{9}{2}$ and $y_1 = \dfrac{15}{2}$

Substituting these values in (1), we get

$$R = \frac{5}{2}\sqrt{10}$$

➤ **101**

EXAMPLE *Prove that the middle points of the diagonals of a complete quadrilateral lie on the same straight line.*

Complete quadrilateral. Def.: Let
$OACB$ be any quadrilateral. Let AC and
OB be produced to meet in E, and BC and
OA to meet in F. Join AB, OC and EF. The
resulting figure is called a complete quadrilateral; the lines AB, OC and EF are
called its diagonals, and the points E, F
and D(the intersection of AB and OC) are
called its vertices.]

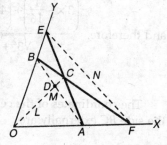

Take the lines OAF and OBE as the
axes of x and y.

Let $OA = 2a$ and $OB = 2b$, so that A is the point $(2a, 0)$ and B is the point $(0, 2b)$; also let C be the point $(2h, 2k)$.

Then I, the middle point of OC, is the point (h, k) and M, the middle point of AB, is (a, b).

The equation to LM is therefore

$$y - b = \frac{k - b}{h - a}(x - a)$$

i.e., $(h - a)y - (k - b)x = bh - ak$ ...(1)

Again, the equation to BC is $y - 2b = \dfrac{k - b}{h}x$

Putting $y = 0$, we have $x = \dfrac{-2bh}{k - b}$, so that F is the point

$$\left(\frac{-2bh}{k - b}, 0\right)$$

Similarly, E is the point $\left(0, -\dfrac{2ak}{h - a}\right)$

Hence, N the middle point of EF, is $\left(\dfrac{-bh}{k - b}, \dfrac{-ak}{h - a}\right)$

These coordinates clearly satisfy (1), *i.e.*, N lies on the straight line LM.

EXAMPLES X

1. A straight line is such that the algebraic sum of the perpendicular let fall upon it from any number of fixed points is zero; shew that it always passes through a fixed point.

2. Two fixed straight line OX and OY are cut by a variable line in the points A and B respectively and P and Q are the feet of the perpendiculars drawn from A and B upon the lines OBY and OAX. Show that, if AB pass through a fixed point, then PQ will also pass through a fixed point.

3. If the equal sides AB and AC of an isosceles triangle be produced to E and F so that $BE. CF = AB^2$, shew that the line EF will always pass through a fixed point.

4. If a straight line move so that the sum of the perpendiculars let fall on it from the two fixed points $(3, 4)$ and $(7, 2)$ is equal to three times the perpendicular on it from a third fixed point $(1, 3)$ prove that there is another fixed point through which this line always passes and find its coordinates.

   Find the centre and radius of the circle which is inscribed in the triangle formed by the straight lines whose equations are

5. $3x + 4y + 2 = 0$, $3x - 4y + 12 = 0$ and $4x - 3y = 0$

6. $2x + 4y + 3 = 0$, $4x + 3y + 3 = 0$ and $x + 1 = 0$

7. $y = 0$, $12x - 5y = 0$ and $3x + 4y - 7 = 0$

8. Prove that the coordinates of the centre of the circle inscribed in the triangle whose angular points are (1, 2) (2, 3) and (3, 1) are
$$\frac{8 + \sqrt{10}}{6} \text{ and } \frac{16 - \sqrt{10}}{6}.$$
Find also the coordinates of the centres of the escribed circles.

9. Find the coordinates of the centres, and the radii, of the four circles which touch the sides of the triangle the coordinates of whose angular points are the points (6, 0), (0, 6) and (7, 7).

10. Find the position of the centre of the circle circumscribing the triangle whose vertices are the points (2, 3), (3, 4) and (6, 8).

Find the area of the triangle formed by the straight lines whose equations are

11. $y = x$, $y = 2x$ and $y = 3x + 4$

12. $y + x = 0$, $y = x + 6$ and $y = 7x + 5$

13. $2y + x - 5 = 0$, $y + 2x - 7 = 0$ and $x - y + 1 = 0$

14. $3x - 4y + 4a = 0$, $2x - 3y + 4a = 0$, and $5x - y + a = 0$, proving also that the feet of the perpendiculars from the origin upon them are collinear.

15. $y = ax - bc$, $y = bx - ca$, and $y = cx - ab$

16. $y = m_1 x + \dfrac{a}{m_1}$, $y = m_2 x + \dfrac{a}{m_2}$, and $y = m_3 x + \dfrac{a}{m_3}$

17. $y = m_1 x + c_1$, $y = m_2 x + c_2$, and the axis of y.

18. $y = m_1 x + c_1$, $y = m_2 x + c_2$ and $y = m_3 x + c_3$.

19. Prove that the area of the triangle formed by the three straight lines $a_1 x + b_1 y + c_1 = 0$, $a_2 x + b_2 y + c_2 = 0$ and $a_3 x + b_3 y + c_3 = 0$ is

$$\frac{1}{2} \left\{ \begin{vmatrix} a_1, & b_1, & c_1 \\ a_2, & b_2, & c_2 \\ a_3, & b_3, & c_3 \end{vmatrix} \right\}^2 \div (a_1 b_2 - a_2 b_1)(a_2 b_3 - a_3 b_2)(a_3 b_1 - a_1 b_3)$$

20. Prove that the area of the triangle formed by the three straight lines
$$x \cos \alpha + y \sin \alpha - p_1 = 0, \quad x \cos \beta + y \sin \beta - p_2 = 0$$
and
$$x \cos \gamma + y \sin \gamma - p_3 = 0$$
is
$$\frac{1}{2} \frac{\{p_1 \sin (\gamma - \beta) + p_2 \sin (\alpha - \gamma) + p_3 \sin (\beta - \alpha)\}^2}{\sin (\gamma - \beta) \sin (\alpha - \gamma) \sin (\beta - \alpha)}$$

21. Prove that the area of the parallelogram contained by the lines
$$4y - 3x - a = 0, \quad 3y - 4x + a = 0, \quad 4y - 3x - 3a = 0$$
and
$$3y - 4x + 2a = 0 \text{ is } \frac{2}{7}a^2$$

22. Prove that the area of the parallelogram whose sides are the straight lines
$$a_1 x + b_1 y + c_1 = 0, \quad a_1 x + b_1 y + d_1 = 0, \quad a_2 x + b_2 y + c_2 = 0$$

and
$$a_2x + b_2y + d_2 = 0$$

is
$$\frac{(d_1 - c_1)(d_2 - c_2)}{a_1b_2 - a_2b_1}$$

23. The vertices of a quadrilateral, taken in order, are the points (0, 0), (4, 0), (6, 7) and (0, 3); find the coordinates of the point of intersection of the two lines joining the middle points of opposite sides.

24. The lines $x + y + 1 = 0$, $x - y + 2 = 0$, $4x + 2y + 3 = 0$
and
$$x + 2y - 4 = 0$$
are the equations to the sides of a quadrilateral taken in order; find the equations to its three diagonals and the equation to the line on which their middle points lie.

25. Shew that the orthocentre of the triangle formed by the three straight lines

$$y = m_1x + \frac{a}{m_1}, \quad y = m_2x + \frac{a}{m_2}, \text{ and } y = m_3x + \frac{a}{m_3}$$

is the point

$$\left\{ -a, \ a\left(\frac{1}{m_1} + \frac{1}{m_2} + \frac{1}{m_3} + \frac{1}{m_1m_2m_3}\right) \right\}.$$

26. A and B are two fixed points whose coordinates are (3, 2) and (5, 1) respectively; ABP is an equilateral triangle on the side of AB remote from the origin. Find the coordinates of P and the orthocentre of the triangle ABP.

▶ **102.**

EXAMPLE *The base of a triangle is fixed; find the locus of the vertex when one base angle is double of the other.*

Let AB be the fixed base of the triangle; take its middle point O as origin, the direction of OB as the axis of x and a perpendicular line as the axis of y.

Let $\qquad AO = OB = a$

If P be one position of the vertex, the condition of the problem then gives

$$\angle PBA = 2 \angle PAB$$

i.e.,
$$\pi - \phi = 2\theta$$

i.e.,
$$-\tan \phi = \tan 2\theta \qquad \qquad ...(1)$$

Let P be the point (h, k).
We then have

$$\frac{k}{h + a} = \tan \theta \text{ and } \frac{k}{h - a} = \tan \phi$$

Substituting these values in (1), we have

$$-\frac{k}{h-a} = \frac{2\dfrac{k}{h+a}}{1-\left(\dfrac{k}{h+a}\right)^2} = \frac{2(h+a)k}{(h+a)^2-k^2}$$

i.e., $\qquad -(h+a)^2 + k^2 = 2(h^2-a^2)$

i.e., $\qquad k^2 - 3h^2 - 2ah + a^2 = 0$

But this is the condition that the point (h, k) should lie on the curve

$$y^2 - 3x^2 - 2ax + a^2 = 0$$

This is therefore the equation to the required locus.

➤ **103.**

EXAMPLE *From a point P perpendiculars PM and PN are drawn upon two fixed lines which are inclined at an angle ω and meet in a fixed point O; if P move on a fixed straight line, find the locus of the middle point of MN.*

Let the two fixed lines be taken as the axes. Let the coordinates of P, any position of the moving point, be (h, k).

Let the equation of the straight line on which P lies be

$$Ax + By + C = 0$$

so that we have

$$Ah + Bk + C = 0 \qquad ...(1)$$

Draw PL and PL′ parallel to the axes.

We then have

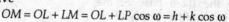

$$OM = OL + LM = OL + LP\cos\omega = h + k\cos\omega$$

and $\qquad ON = OL' + L'N = LP + L'P\cos\omega = k + h\cos\omega$

M is therefore the point $(h + k\cos\omega, 0)$ and N is the point $(0, k + h\cos\omega)$.

Hence, if (x', y') be the coordinates of the middle point of MN, we have

$$2x' = h + k\cos\omega \qquad ...(2)$$

and $\qquad 2y' = k + h\cos\omega \qquad ...(3)$

Equations (1), (2) and (3) express analytically all the relations which hold between x', y', h and k.

Also h and k are the quantities which by their variation cause Q to take up different positions. If therefore between (1,) (2) and (3) we eliminate h and k we shall obtain a relation between x' and y' which is true for all values of h and k, i.e., a relation which is true whatever be the position that P takes on the given straight line.

From (2) and (3), by solving, we have

$$h = \frac{2(x' - y'\cos\omega)}{\sin^2\omega} \quad \text{and} \quad k = \frac{2(y' - x'\cos\omega)}{\sin^2\omega}$$

Substituting these values in(1), we obtain

$$2A (x' - y' \cos \omega) + 2B (y' - x' \cos \omega) + C \sin^2 \omega = 0$$

But this is the condition that the point (x', y') shall always lie on the straight line

$$2A (x - y \cos \omega) + 2B (y - x \cos \omega) + C \sin^2 \omega = 0$$

i.e., on the straight line

$$x (A - B \cos \omega) + y (B - A \cos \omega) + \frac{1}{2} C \sin^2 \omega = 0$$

which is therefore the equation to the locus of Q.

➤ **104.**

EXAMPLE *A straight line is drawn parallel to the base of a given triangle and its extremities are joined transversely to those of the base; find the locus of the point of intersection of the joining lines.*

Let the triangle be OAB and take O as the origin and the directions of OA and OB as the axes of x and y.

Let $OA = a$ and $OB = b$, so that a and b are given quantities.

Let $A'B'$ be the straight line which is parallel to the base AB, so that

$$\frac{OA'}{OA} = \frac{OB'}{OB} = \lambda \text{ (say)},$$

and hence, $\qquad OA' = \lambda a$ and $OB' = \lambda b$

For different values of λ we therefore have different positions of $A'B'$.

The equation to AB' is

$$\frac{x}{a} + \frac{y}{\lambda b} = 1 \qquad \qquad ...(1)$$

and that to $A'B$ is

$$\frac{x}{\lambda a} + \frac{y}{b} = 1 \qquad \qquad ...(2)$$

Since, P is the intersection of AB' and $A'B$ its coordinates satisfy both (1) and (2). Whatever equation we derive from them must therefore denote a locus going through P. Also if we derive from (1) and (2) an equation which does not contain λ, it must represent a locus which passes through P whatever be the value of λ; in other words it must go through all the different positions of the point P.

Subtracting (2) from(1), we have

$$\frac{x}{a} \left(1 - \frac{1}{\lambda} \right) + \frac{y}{b} \left(\frac{1}{\lambda} - 1 \right) = 0$$

$$\frac{x}{a} = \frac{y}{b}$$

This then is the equation to the locus of P. Hence, P always lies o
the straight line

$$y = \frac{b}{a}x,$$

which is the straight line OQ where $OAQB$ is a parallelogram.

Aliter. By solving the equations (1) and (2), we have easily see tha
they meet at the point

$$\left(\frac{\lambda}{\lambda+1}a, \ \frac{\lambda}{\lambda+1}b \right)$$

Hence, if P be the point (h, k), we have

$$h = \frac{\lambda}{\lambda+1}a \quad \text{and} \quad k = \frac{\lambda}{\lambda+1}b$$

Hence, for all values of λ, i.e., for all positions of the straight lin
$A'B'$, we have

$$\frac{h}{a} = \frac{k}{b}$$

But this is the condition that the point (h, k), i.e., P, should lie on th
straight line

$$\frac{x}{a} = \frac{y}{b}$$

The straight line is therefore the required locus.

➤ **105.**

EXAMPLE *A variable straight line is drawn through a given point O to cut two
fixed straight lines in R and S; on it is taken a point P such that*

$$\frac{2}{OP} = \frac{1}{OR} + \frac{1}{OS}$$

shew that the locus of P is a third fixed straight line.

Take any two fixed straight lines, at right angles and passing through
O, as the axes and let the equation to the two given fixed straight lines
be

$$Ax + By + C = 0 \quad \text{and} \quad A'x + B'y + C' = 0$$

Transforming to polar coordinates these equations are

$$\frac{1}{r} = -\frac{A\cos\theta + B\sin\theta}{C} \quad \text{and} \quad \frac{1}{r} = -\frac{A'\cos\theta + B'\sin\theta}{C'}$$

If the angle XOR be θ the values of $\dfrac{1}{OR}$ and $\dfrac{1}{OS}$ are therefore

$$-\frac{A\cos\theta + B\sin\theta}{C} \quad \text{and} \quad -\frac{A'\cos\theta + B'\sin\theta}{C'}$$

We therefore have

$$\frac{2}{OP} = -\frac{A\cos\theta + B\sin\theta}{C} - \frac{A'\cos\theta + B'\sin\theta}{C'}$$

$$= -\left(\frac{A}{C} + \frac{A'}{C'}\right)\cos\theta - \left(\frac{B}{C} + \frac{B'}{C'}\right)\sin\theta$$

The equation to the locus of P is therefore, on again transforming to Cartesian coordinates,

$$2 = -x\left(\frac{A}{C} + \frac{A'}{C'}\right) - y\left(\frac{B}{C} + \frac{B'}{C'}\right)$$

and this is a fixed straight line.

EXAMPLES XI

The base BC ($= 2a$) of a triangle ABC is fixed.; the axes being BC and a perpendicular to it through its middle point, find the locus of the vertex A, when

1. the difference of the base angles is given ($= \alpha$)
2. the product of the tangents of the base angles is given ($= \lambda$).
3. the tangent of one base angle is m times the tangent of the other.
4. m times the square of one side added to n times the square of the other side is equal to a constant quantity c^2.

From a point P perpendiculars PM and PN are drawn upon two fixed lines which are inclined at an angle ω, and which are taken as the axes of coordinates and meet in O; find the locus of P.

5. if $OM + ON$ be equal to $2c$.
6. if $OM - ON$ be equal to $2d$.
7. if $PM + PN$ be equal to $2c$.
8. if $PM - PN$ be equal to $2c$.
9. if MN be equal to $2c$.
10. if MN pass through the fixed point (a, b).
11. if MN be parallel to the given line $y = mx$.
12. Two fixed points A and B are taken on the axes such that $OA = a$ and $OB = b$; two variable points A' and B' are taken on the same axes; find the locus of the intersection of AB' and $A'B$
    (i) when $OA' + OB' = OA + OB$

and (ii) when $\dfrac{1}{OA'} - \dfrac{1}{OB'} = \dfrac{1}{OA} - \dfrac{1}{OB}$

13. Through a fixed point P are drawn any two straight lines to cut one fixed straight line OX in A and B and another fixed straight line OY in C and D; prove that the locus of the intersection of the straight lines AC and BD is a straight line passing through O.
14. OX and OY are two straight lines at right angles to one another; on OY is taken a fixed point A and on OX any point B; on AB an equilateral triangle is described, its vertex C being on the side of AB away from O. Shew that the locus of C is a straight line.
15. If a straight line pass through a fixed point, find the locus of the middle point of the portion of it which is intercepted between two given straight lines.
16. A and B are two fixed points; if PA and PB intersect a constant distance $2c$ from a given straight line, find the locus of P.

17. Through a fixed point O are drawn two straight lines at right angles to meet two fixed straight lines, which are also at right angles, in the points P and Q. Shew that the locus of the foot of the perpendicular from O on PQ is a straight line.

18. Find the locus of a point at which two given portions of the same straight line subtend equal angles.

19. Find the locus of a point which moves so that the difference of its distances from two fixed straight lines at right angles is equal to its distance from a fixed straight line.

20. A straight line AB, whose length is c, slides between two given oblique axes which meet at O; find the locus of the orthocentre of the triangle OAB.

21. Having given the bases and the sum of the area of a number of triangles which have a common vertex, shew that the locus of this vertex is a straight line.

22. Through a given point O a straight line is drawn to cut two given straight lines in R and S; find the locus of a point P on this variable straight line, which is such that

(i) $2OP = OR + OS$ and (ii) $OP^2 = OR \cdot OS$

23. Given n straight lines and a fixed point O; through O is drawn a straight line meeting these lines in the points $R_1, R_2, R_3, \dots R_n$ and on it is taken a point R such that

$$\frac{n}{OR} = \frac{1}{OR_1} + \frac{1}{OR_2} + \frac{1}{OR_3} + \dots + \frac{1}{OR_n} \, ;$$

shew that the locus of R is a straight line.

24. A variable straight line cuts off from n given concurrent straight line intercepts the sum of the reciprocals of which is constant. Shew that it always passes through a fixed point.

25. If a triangle ABC remain always similar to a given triangle, and if the point A be fixed and the point B always move along a given straight line, find the locus of the point C.

26. A right-angled triangle ABC, having C a right angle, is of given magnitude, and the angular points A and B slide along two given perpendicular axes; shew that the locus of C is the pair of straight lines whose equations are $y = \pm \dfrac{b}{a} x$.

27. Two given straight lines meet in O, and through a given point P is drawn a straight line to meet them in Q and R; if the parallelogram $OQSR$ be completed find the equation to the locus of S.

28. Through a given point O is drawn a straight line to meet two given parallel straight lines in P and Q; through P and Q are drawn straight lines in given directions to meet in R; prove that the locus of R is a straight line.

6

ON EQUATIONS REPRESENTING TWO OR MORE STRAIGHT LINES

➤ **106.** Suppose we have to trace the locus represented by the equation,

$$y^2 - 3xy + 2x^2 = 0 \qquad \ldots(1)$$

This equation is equivalent to,

$$(y - x)(y - 2x) = 0 \qquad \ldots(2)$$

It is satisfied by the coordinates of all points which make the first of these brackets equal to zero and also by the coordinates of all points which make the second bracket zero, *i.e.*, by all the points which satisfy the equation,

$$y - x = 0 \qquad \ldots(3)$$

and also by the points which satisfy,

$$y - 2x = 0 \qquad \ldots(4)$$

But, by Art. 47, the (3), represents a straight line passing through the origin and so also does equation (4).

Hence, equation (1), represents the two straight lines which pass through the origin, and are inclined at angles of 45° and $\tan^{-1} 2$ respectively to the axis of x.

➤ **107.**

EXAMPLE 1 Trace the locus $xy = 0$. This equation is satisfied by all the points which satisfy the equation, $x = 0$ and by all the points which satisfy $y = 0$, *i.e.*, by all the points which lie either on the axis of y or on the axis of x.

The required locus is therefore, the two axes of coordinates.

EXAMPLE 2 *Trace the locus* $x^2 - 5x + 6 = 0$. This equation is equivalent to $(x - 2)(x - 3) = 0$. It is therefore, satisfied by all points which satisfy the equation, $x - 2 = 0$ and also by all the points which satisfy the equation, $x - 3 = 0$.

But these equations represent two straight lines which are parallel to the axis of y and are at distances 2 and 3 respectively from the origin (Art. 46).

EXAMPLE 3 *Trace the locus* $xy - 4x - 5y + 20 = 0$. This equation is equivalent to $(x - 5)(y - 4) = 0$, and therefore, represents a straight line parallel to the axis of y at a distance 5 and also a straight line parallel to the axis of x at a distance 4.

➤ **108.** Let us consider the general equation,

$$ax^2 + 2hxy + by^2 = 0 \qquad \qquad \text{...(1)}$$

On multiplying it by a it may be written in the form

$$(a^2x^2 + 2ahxy + h^2y^2) - (h^2 - ab)y^2 = 0$$

$$i.e., \{(ax + hy) + y\sqrt{h^2 - ab}\}\{(ax + hy) - y\sqrt{h^2 - ab}\} = 0$$

As in the last article the equation (1), therefore, represents the two straight lines whose equations are:

$$ax + hy + y\sqrt{h^2 - ab} = 0 \qquad \qquad \text{...(2)}$$

and

$$ax + hy - y\sqrt{h^2 - ab} = 0 \qquad \qquad \text{...(3)}$$

each of which passes through the origin.

For (1), is satisfied by *all* the points which satisfy (2), and also by *all* the points which satisfy (3).

These two straight lines are real and different if $h^2 > ab$, real and coincident if $h^2 = ab$, and imaginary if $h^2 < ab$.

[For in the latter case the coefficient of y in each of the equations (2) and (3), is partly real and partly imaginary.]

In the case when $h^2 < ab$, the straight lines, though themselves imaginary, intersect in a real point. For the origin lies on the locus given by (1), since the equation (1), is always satisfied by the values $x = 0$ and $y = 0$.

➤ **109.** An equation such as equation (1) of the previous article, which is such that in each term the sum of the indices of x and y is the same, is called a homogeneous equation. This equation (1), is of the second degree; for in the first term the index of x is 2; in the second term the index of both x and y is 1 and hence, their sum is 2; whilst in the third term the index of y is 2. Similarly, the expression,

$$3x^3 + 4x^2y - 5xy^2 + 9y^3$$

is a homogeneous expression of the third degree.

The expression,

$$3x^3 + 4x^2y - 5xy^2 - 9y^3 - 7xy$$

is not however, homogeneous; for in the first four terms the sum of the indices is 3 in each case, whilst in the last term this sum is 2.

From Art. 108 it follows that a homogeneous equation of the second degree represents two straight lines, real and different, coincident, or imaginary.

▶ **110.** *The axes being rectangular, to find the angle between the straight lines given by the equation,*

$$ax^2 + 2hxy + by^2 = 0 \qquad \text{...(1)}$$

Let the separate equations to the two lines be

$$y - m_1 x = 0 \quad \text{and} \quad y - m_2 x = 0 \qquad \text{...(2)}$$

So that, (1), must be equivalent to

$$b(y - m_1 x)(y - m_2 x) = 0 \qquad \text{...(3)}$$

Equating the coefficients of xy and x^2 in (1) and (3), we have

$$-b(m_1 + m_2) = 2h \quad \text{and} \quad bm_1 m_2 = a,$$

So that, $\qquad m_1 + m_2 = -\dfrac{2h}{b} \quad \text{and} \quad m_1 m_2 = \dfrac{a}{b}$

If θ be the angle between the straight lines (2), we have by Art 66.

$$\tan \theta = \frac{m_1 - m_2}{1 + m_1 m_2} = \frac{\sqrt{(m_1 + m_2)^2 - 4m_1 m_2}}{1 + m_1 m_2}$$

$$= \frac{\sqrt{\dfrac{4h^2}{b^2} - \dfrac{4a}{b}}}{1 + \dfrac{a}{b}} = \frac{2\sqrt{h^2 - ab}}{a + b} \qquad \text{...(4}$$

Hence, the required angle is found.

▶ **111.** *Condition that the straight lines of the previous article may b-* (1) *perpendicular, and* (2), *coincident.*

(1) If $a + b = 0$ the value of $\tan \theta$ is ∞ and hence, θ is $90°$; t. straight lines are therefore, perpendicular.

Hence, two straight lines, represented by one equation, are at righ angles if the algebraic sum of the coefficients of x^2 and y^2 be zero.

For example, the equations,

$$x^2 - y^2 = 0 \quad \text{and} \quad 6x^2 + 11xy - 6y^2 = 0$$

both represent pairs of straight lines at right angles.

Similarly, whatever, be the value of h, the equation,

$$x^2 + 2hxy - y^2 = 0$$

represents a pair of straight lines at right angles.

(2) If $h^2 = ab$, the value of tan θ is zero and hence, θ is zero. The angle between the straight lines is therefore, zero and since they both pass through the origin, they are therefore, coincident.

This may be seen directly from the original equation. For if $h^2 = ab$, i.e., $h = \sqrt{ab}$, it may be written,

$$ax^2 + 2\sqrt{ab}\,xy + by^2 = 0$$

i.e., $(\sqrt{ax} + \sqrt{by})^2 = 0$

which is two coincident straight lines.

➤ **112.** *To find the equation to the straight lines bisecting the angle between the straight lines given by,*

$$ax^2 + 2hxy + by^2 = 0 \qquad \qquad ...(1)$$

Let the equation (1), represent the two straight lines L_1OM_1 and L_2OM_2 inclined at angles θ_1 and θ_2 to the axis of x, so that equation (1), is equivalent to,

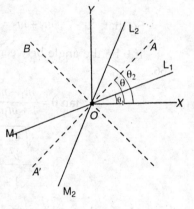

$$b(y - x \tan \theta_1)(y - x \tan \theta_2) = 0$$

Hence, $\tan \theta_1 + \tan \theta_2 = -\dfrac{2h}{b}$

and $\tan \theta_1 \tan \theta_2 = \dfrac{a}{b}$ ...(2)

Let OA and OB be the required bisectors.

Since, $\angle AOL_1 = \angle L_2OA$

∴ $\angle AOX - \theta_1 = \theta_2 - \angle AOX$

∴ $2\angle AOX = \theta_1 + \theta_2$

Also, $\angle BOX = 90° + \angle AOX$

∴ $2\angle BOX = 180° + \theta_1 + \theta_2$

Hence, if θ stand for *either* of the angles AOX or BOX, we have

$$\tan 2\theta = \tan (\theta_1 + \theta_2) = \frac{\tan \theta_1 + \tan \theta_2}{1 - \tan \theta_1 \tan \theta_2} = -\frac{2h}{b - a}$$

by equations (2).

But, if (x, y) be the coordinates of any point on either of the lines OA or OB, we have

$$\tan \theta = \frac{y}{x}$$

$$\therefore \qquad -\frac{2h}{b-a} = \tan 2\theta = \frac{2\tan\theta}{1-\tan^2\theta}$$

$$= \frac{2\dfrac{y}{x}}{1-\dfrac{y^2}{x^2}} = \frac{2xy}{x^2-y^2}$$

i.e.,
$$\frac{x^2-y^2}{a-b} = \frac{xy}{h}$$

This being a relation holding between the coordinates of *any* point on *either* of the bisectors, is, by Art. 42, the equation to the bisectors.

➤ **113.** The foregoing equation may also be obtained in the following manner:

Let the given equation represent the straight lines,

$$y - m_1 x = 0 \quad \text{and} \quad y - m_2 x = 0 \qquad \qquad \dots(1)$$

So that,
$$m_1 + m_2 = -\frac{2h}{b} \quad \text{and} \quad m_1 m_2 = \frac{a}{b} \qquad \qquad \dots(2)$$

The equations to the bisectors of the angles between the straight lines (1) are, by Art. 84.

$$\frac{y - m_1 x}{\sqrt{1+m_1^2}} = \frac{y - m_2 x}{\sqrt{1+m_2^2}} \quad \text{and} \quad \frac{y - m_1 x}{\sqrt{1+m_1^2}} = -\frac{y - m_2 x}{\sqrt{1+m_2^2}}$$

or expressed in one equation,

$$\left\{ \frac{y - m_1 x}{\sqrt{1+m_1^2}} - \frac{y - m_2 x}{\sqrt{1+m_2^2}} \right\} \left\{ \frac{y - m_1 x}{\sqrt{1+m_1^2}} + \frac{y - m_2 x}{\sqrt{1+m_2^2}} \right\} = 0$$

i.e.,
$$\frac{(y - m_1 x)^2}{1+m_1^2} - \frac{(y - m_2 x)^2}{1+m_2^2} = 0$$

i.e., $\quad (1+m_2^2)(y^2 - 2m_1 xy + m_1^2 x^2) - (1+m_1^2)(y^2 - 2m_2 xy + m_2^2 x^2) = 0$

i.e., $\quad (m_1^2 - m_2^2)(x^2 - y^2) + 2(m_1 m_2 - 1)(m_1 - m_2)xy = 0$

i.e., $\quad (m_1 + m_2)(x^2 - y^2) + 2(m_1 m_2 - 1)xy = 0$

Hence, by (2), the required equation is,

$$-\frac{2h}{b}(x^2 - y^2) + 2\left(\frac{a}{b} - 1\right)xy = 0,$$

i.e.,
$$\frac{x^2 - y^2}{a-b} = \frac{xy}{b}$$

═══ EXAMPLES XII ═══

Find what straight lines are represented by the following equations and determine the angles between them.

1. $x^2 - 7xy + 12y^2 = 0$ 2. $4x^2 - 24xy + 11y^2 = 0$
3. $33x^2 - 71xy - 14y^2 = 0$ 4. $x^3 - 6x^2 + 11x - 6 = 0$
5. $y^2 - 16 = 0$ 6. $y^3 - xy^2 - 14x^2y + 24x^3 = 0$
7. $x^2 + 2xy \sec \theta + y^2 = 0$ 8. $x^2 + 2xy \cot \theta + y^2 = 0$

9. Find the equations of the straight lines bisecting the angles between the pairs of straight lines given in examples 2, 3, 7 and 8.

10. Shew that the two straight lines,
$$x^2(\tan^2 \theta + \cos^2 \theta) - 2xy \tan \theta + y^2 \sin^2 \theta = 0$$
make with the axis of x angles such that the difference of their tangents is 2.

11. Prove that the two straight lines
$$(x^2 + y^2)(\cos^2 \theta \sin^2 \alpha + \sin^2 \theta) = (x \tan \alpha - y \sin \theta)^2$$
include an angle 2α.

12. Prove that the two straight lines,
$$x^2 \sin^2 \alpha \cos^2 \theta + 4xy \sin \alpha \sin \theta + y^2[4 \cos \alpha - (1 + \cos \alpha)^2 \cos^2\theta] = 0$$
meet at an angle α.

GENERAL EQUATION OF THE SECOND DEGREE

114. The most general expression, which contains terms involving x and y in a degree not higher than the second, must contain terms involving x^2, xy, y^2, x, y and a constant.

The notation which is in general use for this expression is:
$$ax^2 + 2hxy + by^2 + 2gx + 2fy + c \qquad \qquad ...(1)$$

The quantity (1) is known as the general expression of the second degree, and when equated to zero is called the **general equation of the second degree**.

The student may better remember the seemingly arbitrary coefficients of the terms in the expression (1) if the reason for their use be given.

The most general expression involving terms only of the second degree in x, y and z is:
$$ax^2 + by^2 + cz^2 + 2fyz + 2gzx + 2hxy \qquad \qquad ...(2)$$

where the coefficients occur in the order of the alphabet.

If in this expression we put z equal to unity, we get
$$ax^2 + by^2 + c + 2fy + 2gx + 2hxy$$

which, after rearrangement, is the same as (1).

Now, in Solid Geometry we use three coordinates x, y and z. Also many formulae in Plane Geometry and derived from those of Solid Geometry by putting z equal to unity.

We therefore, in Plane Geometry, use that notation corresponding to which we have the standard notation in Solid Geometry.

➤ **115.** In general, as will be shewn in Chapter 15, the general equation represents a Curve-Locus.

If a certain condition holds between the coefficients of its terms it will, however, represent a pair of straight lines.

This condition we shall determine in the following article.

➤ **116.** *To find the condition that the general equation of the second degree,*

$$ax^2 + 2hxy + by^2 + 2gx + 2fy + c = 0 \qquad \text{...(1)}$$

may represent two straight lines.

If we can break the left-hand members of (1) into two factors, each of the first degree, then, as in Art. 108, it will represent two straight lines.

If a be not zero, multiply equation (1), by a and arrange in powers of x; it then becomes

$$a^2x^2 + 2ax(hy + g) = -aby^2 - 2afy - ac$$

On completing the square on the left hand we have

$$a^2x^2 + 2ax(hy + g) + (hy + g)^2 = y^2(h^2 - ab)$$
$$+ 2y(gh - af) + g^2 - ac$$

i.e., $\quad (ax + hy + g) = \pm \sqrt{y^2(h^2 - ab) + 2y(gh - af) + g^2 - ac} \qquad \text{...(2)}$

From (2) we cannot obtain x in terms of y, involving only terms of the *first* degree, unless the quantity under the radical sign be a perfect square.

The condition for this is,

$$(gh - af)^2 = (h^2 - ab)(g^2 - ac)$$

i.e., $\quad g^2h^2 - 2afgh + a^2f^2 = g^2h^2 - abg^2 - ach^2 + a^2bc$

Cancelling and dividing by a, we have the required condition, *viz.*

$$abc + 2fgh - af^2 - bg^2 - ch^2 = 0 \qquad \text{...(3)}$$

➤ **117.** The foregoing condition may be otherwise obtained thus:

The given equation, multiplied by (a), is

$$a^2x^2 + 2ahxy + aby^2 + 2agx + 2afy + ac = 0 \qquad \text{...(4)}$$

The terms of the second degree in this equation break up, as in Art. 108, into the factors.

$$ax + hy - y\sqrt{h^2 - ab} \quad \text{and} \quad ax + hy + y\sqrt{h^2 - ab}$$

If then (4) break into factors it must be equivalent to,

$$\{ax + (h - \sqrt{h^2 - ab})y + A\}\{ax + (h + \sqrt{h^2 - ab})y + B\} = 0$$

where A and B are given by the relations,

$$a(A + B) = 2ga \qquad \qquad \ldots(5)$$

$$A(h + \sqrt{h^2 - ab}) + B(h - \sqrt{h^2 - ab}) = 2fa \qquad \ldots(6)$$

and
$$AB = ac \qquad \qquad \ldots(7)$$

The equations (5) and (6), give

$$A + B = 2g \quad \text{and} \quad A - B = \frac{2fa - 2gh}{\sqrt{h^2 - ab}}$$

The relation (7), then gives

$$4ac = 4AB = (A + B)^2 - (A - B)^2$$

$$= 4g^2 - 4\frac{(fa - gh)^2}{h^2 - ab}$$

i.e.
$$(fa - gh)^2 = (g^2 - ac)(h^2 - ab)$$

which, as before, reduces to

$$abc + 2fgh - af^2 - bg^2 - ch^2 = 0$$

EXAMPLE If a be zero, prove that the general equation will represent two straight lines if,

$$2fgh - bg^2 - ch^2 = 0$$

If both a and b be zero, prove that the condition is $2fg - ch = 0$.

▶ **118.** The relation (3) of Art. 116 is equivalent to the expression

$$\begin{vmatrix} a, & h, & g \\ h, & b, & f \\ g, & f, & c \end{vmatrix} = 0$$

This may be easily verified by writing down the value of the determinant by the rule of Art. 5.

A geometrical meaning to this form of the relation (3) will be given in a later chapter. [Art. 355]

The quantity on the left-hand side of equation (3) is called the **Discriminant** of the General Equation.

The general equation therefore, represents two straight lines if its discriminant be zero.

➤ **119.**

EXAMPLE 1 *Prove that the equation,*

$$12x^2 + 7xy - 10y^2 + 13x + 45y - 35 = 0$$

represents two straight lines, and find the angle between them.

Here, $a = 12$, $h = \dfrac{7}{2}$, $b = -10$, $g = \dfrac{13}{2}$, $f = \dfrac{45}{2}$ and $c = -35$

Hence, $abc + 2fgh - af^2 - bg^2 - ch^2$

$$= 12 \times (-10) \times (-35) + 2 \times \frac{45}{2} \times \frac{13}{2} \times \frac{7}{2} - 12 \times \left(\frac{45}{2}\right)^2$$

$$- (-10) \times \left(\frac{13}{2}\right)^2 - (-35)\left(\frac{7}{2}\right)^2$$

$$= 4200 + \frac{4095}{4} - 6075 + \frac{1690}{4} + \frac{1715}{4}$$

$$= -1875 + \frac{7500}{4} = 0$$

The equation therefore, represents two straight lines.
Solving it for x, we have

$$x^2 + x\frac{7y+13}{12} + \left(\frac{7y+13}{24}\right)^2 = \frac{10y^2 - 45y + 35}{12} + \left(\frac{7y+13}{24}\right)^2$$

$$= \left(\frac{23y - 43}{24}\right)^2$$

$$\therefore \qquad x + \frac{7y+13}{24} = \pm\frac{23y-43}{24}$$

i.e., $$x = \frac{2y-7}{3} \quad \text{or} \quad \frac{-5y+5}{4}$$

The given equation therefore, represents the two straight lines,
$$3x = 2y - 7 \quad \text{and} \quad 4x = -5y + 5$$

The "m's" of these two lines are therefore, $\dfrac{3}{2}$ and $-\dfrac{4}{5}$ and the angle between them, by Art. 66,

$$= \tan^{-1}\frac{\dfrac{3}{2} - \left(-\dfrac{4}{5}\right)}{1 + \dfrac{3}{2}\left(-\dfrac{4}{5}\right)} = \tan^{-1}\left(-\frac{23}{2}\right)$$

EXAMPLE 2 *Find the value of h so that the equation,*

$$6x^2 + 2hxy + 12y^2 + 22x + 31y + 20 = 0$$

may represent two straight lines.

Here, $a = 6$, $b = 12$, $g = 11$, $f = \dfrac{31}{2}$, and $c = 20$

The condition (3) of Art. 116 then gives

$$20h^2 - 341h + \frac{2907}{2} = 0$$

i.e.,

$$\left(h - \frac{17}{2}\right)(20h - 171) = 0$$

Hence,

$$h = \frac{17}{2} \quad \text{or} \quad \frac{171}{20}$$

Taking the first of these values, the given equation becomes,

$$6x^2 + 17xy + 12y^2 + 22x + 31y + 20 = 0$$

i.e.,

$$(2x + 3y + 4)(3x + 4y + 5) = 0$$

Taking the second value, the equation is,

$$20x^2 + 57xy + 40y^2 + \frac{220}{3}x + \frac{310}{3}y + \frac{200}{3} = 0$$

i.e.,

$$\left(4x + 5y + \frac{20}{3}\right)(5x + 8y + 10) = 0$$

EXAMPLES XIII

Prove that the following equations represent two straight lines; find also their point of intersection and the angle between them.

1. $6y^2 - xy - x^2 + 30y + 36 = 0$
2. $x^2 - 5xy + 4y^2 + x + 2y - 2 = 0$
3. $3y^2 - 8xy - 3x^2 - 29x + 3y - 18 = 0$
4. $y^2 + xy - 2x^2 - 5x - y - 2 = 0$
5. Prove that the equation,

$$x^2 + 6xy + 9y^2 + 4x + 12y - 5 = 0$$

represents two parallel lines.

Find the value of k so that the following equations may represent pairs of straight lines:

6. $6x^2 + 11xy - 10y^2 + x + 31y + k = 0$
7. $12x^2 - 10xy + 2y^2 + 11x - 5y + k = 0$
8. $12x^2 + kxy + 2y^2 + 11x - 5y + 2 = 0$
9. $6x^2 + xy + ky^2 - 11x + 43y - 35 = 0$
10. $kxy - 8x + 9y - 12 = 0$
11. $x^2 + \dfrac{10}{3}xy + y^2 - 5x - 7y + k = 0$
12. $12x^2 + xy - 6y^2 - 29x + 8y + k = 0$

13. $2x^2 + xy - y^2 + kx + 6y - 9 = 0$
14. $x^2 + kxy + y^2 - 5x - 7y + 6 = 0$
15. Prove that the equations to the straight lines passing through the origin which make an angle α with the straight line $y + x = 0$ are given by the equation,

$$x^2 + 2xy \sec 2\alpha + y^2 = 0$$

16. What relations must hold between the coefficients of the equations,

(i) $ax^2 + by^2 + cx + cy = 0$

and   (ii) $ay^2 + bxy + dy + ex = 0$

so that each of them may represent a pair of straight lines?

17. The equations to a pair of opposite sides of a parallelogram are:

$$x^2 - 7x + 6 = 0 \text{ and } y^2 - 14y + 40 = 0$$

find the equations to its diagonals.

➤ **120.** *To prove that a homogeneous equation of the nth degree represents n straight lines, real or imaginary, which all pass through the origin.*
Let the equation be,

$$y^n + A_1 xy^{n-1} + A_2 x^2 y^{n-2} + A_3 x^3 y^{n-3} + \ldots + A_n x^n = 0$$

On division by x^n, it may be written,

$$\left(\frac{y}{x}\right)^n + A_1 \left(\frac{y}{x}\right)^{n-1} + A_2 \left(\frac{y}{x}\right)^{n-2} + \ldots + A_n = 0 \qquad \ldots(1)$$

This is an equation of the nth degree in $\frac{y}{x}$, and hence must have n roots.

Let these roots be $m_1, m_2, m_3, \ldots, m_n$. Then (C. Smith's Algebra, Art. 89) the equation (1) must be equivalent to the equation,

$$\left(\frac{y}{x} - m_1\right)\left(\frac{y}{x} - m_2\right)\left(\frac{y}{x} - m_3\right) \ldots \left(\frac{y}{x} - m_n\right) = 0 \qquad \ldots(2)$$

The equation (2) is satisfied by *all* the points which satisfy the separate equations

$$\frac{y}{x} - m_1 = 0, \ \frac{y}{x} - m_2 = 0, \ \ldots \frac{y}{x} - m_n = 0$$

i.e., by all the points which lie on the n straight lines

$$y - m_1 x = 0, \ y - m_2 x = 0, \ \ldots \ y - m_n x = 0$$

all of which pass through the origin. Conversely, the coordinates of all the points which satisfy these n equations satisfy equation (1). Hence, the proposition.

➤ **121.**

EXAMPLE 1 The equation,

$$y^3 - 6xy^2 + 11x^2y - 6x^3 = 0$$

which is equivalent to,

$$(y - x)(y - 2x)(y - 3x) = 0$$

represents the three straight lines

$$y - x = 0, \quad y - 2x = 0 \quad \text{and} \quad y - 3x = 0$$

all of which pass through the origin.

EXAMPLE 2 The equation, $y^3 - 5y^2 + 6y = 0$

i.e.,

$$y(y - 2)(y - 3) = 0$$

Similarly, represents the three straight lines

$$y = 0, \ y = 2 \text{ and } y = 3$$

all of which are parallel to the axis of x.

➤ **122.** To *find the equation to the two straight lines joining the origin to the points in which the straight line,*

$$lx + my = n \qquad \qquad \dots(1)$$

meets the locus whose equation is,

$$ax^2 + 2hxy + by^2 + 2gx + 2fy + c = 0 \qquad \dots(2)$$

The equation (1), may be written

$$\frac{lx + my}{n} = 1 \qquad \qquad \dots(3)$$

The coordinates of the points in which the straight line meets the locus satisfy both equation (2) and equation (3), and hence satisfy the equation

$$ax^2 + 2hxy + by^2 + 2(gx + fy)\frac{lx + my}{n} + c\left(\frac{lx + my}{n}\right)^2 = 0$$

[For at the points where (3) and (4) are true it is clear that (2), is true.]

Hence, (4), represents *some locus* which passes through the intersections of (2) and (3).

But, since the equation (4), is homogeneous and of the second degree, it represents two straight lines passing through the origin (Art. 108).

It therefore, must represent the two straight lines joining the origin to the intersections of equation (2) and (3).

➤ **123.** The preceding article may be illustrated geometrically if we assume that the equation (2), represents some such curve as *PQRS* in the given figure.

Let the given straight line cut the curve in the points P and Q.

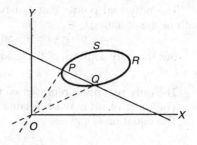

The equation (2) holds for all points on the curve $PQRS$.

The equation (3) holds for all points on the line PQ.

Both equations are therefore, true at the points of intersection P and Q.

The equation (4), which is derived from (2) and (3), holds therefore, at P and Q.

But the equation (4), represents two straight lines, each of which passes through the point O.

It must therefore, represent the two straight lines OP and OQ.

➤ **124.**

EXAMPLE *Prove that the straight lines joining the origin to the points of intersection of the straight line $x - y = 2$ and the curve,*

$$5x^2 + 12xy - 8y^2 + 8x - 4y + 12 = 0$$

make equal angles with the axes.

As in Art. 122 the equation to the required straight lines is,

$$5x^2 + 12xy - 8y^2 + (8x - 4y)\frac{x - y}{2} + 12\left(\frac{x - y}{2}\right)^2 = 0 \qquad ...(1)$$

For this equation is homogeneous and therefore represents two straight lines through the origin; also it is satisfied at the points where the two given equations are satisfied.

Now, (1) is, on reduction,

$$y^2 = 4x^2$$

so that the equations to the two lines are

$$y = 2x \quad \text{and} \quad y = -2x$$

These lines are equally inclined to the axes.

➤ **125.** It was stated in Art. 115 that, *in general*, an equation of the second degree represents a curve-line, including (Art. 116) as a particular case two straight lines.

In some cases however it will be found that such equations only represent isolated points. Some examples are appended.

EXAMPLE 1 *What is represented by the locus*

$$(x - y + c)^2 + (x + y - c)^2 = 0 \qquad ...(1)$$

We know that the sum of the squares of two real quantities cannot be zero unless each of the squares is separately zero.

The only real points that satisfy the equation (1), therefore, satisfy both of the equations

$$x - y + c = 0 \quad \text{and} \quad x + y - c = 0$$

But the only solution of these two equations is,

$$x = 0 \quad \text{and} \quad y = c$$

The only real point represented by equation (1) is therefore, $(0, c)$. The same result may be obtained in a different manner.

The equation (1), gives

$$(x - y + c)^2 = -(x + y - c)^2$$

i.e., $x - y + c = \pm \sqrt{-1}(x + y - c)$

It therefore, represents the two imaginary straight lines

$$x(1 - \sqrt{-1}) - y(1 + \sqrt{-1}) + c(1 + \sqrt{-1}) = 0$$

and $x(1 + \sqrt{-1}) - y(1 - \sqrt{-1}) + c(1 - \sqrt{-1}) = 0$

Each of these two straight lines passes through the real point $(0, c)$. We may therefore, say that (1) represents two imaginary straight lines passing through the point $(0, c)$.

EXAMPLE 2 *What is represented by the equation,*

$$(x^2 - a^2)^2 + (y^2 - b^2)^2 = 0$$

As in the last example, the only real points on the locus are those that satisfy *both* of the equations,

$$x^2 - a^2 = 0 \quad \text{and} \quad y^2 - b^2 = 0$$

i.e., $x = \pm a \quad \text{and} \quad y = \pm b$

The points represented are therefore,

$$(a, b), (a, -b), (-a, b) \text{ and } (-a, -b)$$

EXAMPLE 3 *What is represented by the equation,*

$$x^2 + y^2 + a^2 = 0$$

The only real points on the locus are those that satisfy all three of the equations,

$$x = 0, \ y = 0 \text{ and } a = 0$$

Hence, unless a vanishes, there are no such points, and the given equation represents nothing real.

The equation may be written,

$$x^2 + y^2 = -a^2$$

so that it represents points whose distance from the origin is $a\sqrt{-1}$. It therefore, represents the *imaginary* circle whose radius is $a\sqrt{-1}$ and whose centre is the origin.

➤ **126.**

EXAMPLE 1 *Obtain the condition that one of the straight lines given by the equation*

$$ax^2 + 2hxy + by^2 = 0 \qquad \qquad \qquad \ldots (1)$$

may coincide with one of those given by the equation,

$$a'x^2 + 2h'xy + b'y^2 = 0 \qquad \ldots(2)$$

Let the equation to the common straight line be

$$\bar{y} - m_1 x = 0 \qquad \ldots(3)$$

The quantity $y - m_1 x$ must therefore be a factor of the left-hand of both (1) and (2), and therefore, the value $y = m_1 x$ must satisfy both (1) and (2).

We therefore, have

$$bm_1{}^2 + 2hm_1 + a = 0 \qquad \ldots(4)$$

and

$$b'm_1{}^2 + 2h'm_1 + a' = 0 \qquad \ldots(5)$$

Solving (4) and (5), we have

$$\frac{m_1{}^2}{2(ha' - h'a)} = \frac{m_1}{ab' - a'b} = \frac{1}{2(bh' - b'h)}$$

$$\therefore \qquad \frac{ha' - h'a}{bh' - b'h} = m_1{}^2 = \left\{ \frac{ab' - a'b}{2(bh' - b'h)} \right\}^2$$

so that, we must have

$$(ab' - a'b)^2 = 4(ha' - h'a)(bh' - b'h)$$

EXAMPLE 2 *Prove that the equation,*

$$m(x^3 - 3xy^2) + y^3 - 3x^2 y = 0$$

represents three straight lines equally inclined to one another.

Transforming to polar coordinates (Art. 35) the equation gives

$$m (\cos^3 \theta - 3 \cos \theta \sin^2 \theta) + \sin^3 \theta - 3 \cos^2 \theta \sin \theta = 0$$

i.e., $$m (1 - 3 \tan^2 \theta) + \tan^3 \theta - 3 \tan \theta = 0$$

i.e., $$m = \frac{3 \tan \theta - \tan^3 \theta}{1 - 3 \tan^2 \theta} = \tan 3\theta$$

If $m = \tan \alpha$, this equation gives

$$\tan 3\theta = \tan \alpha$$

the solutions of which are

$$3\theta = \alpha \quad \text{or} \quad 180° + \alpha \quad \text{or} \quad 360° + \alpha$$

i.e., $$\theta = \frac{\alpha}{3} \quad \text{or} \quad 60° + \frac{\alpha}{3} \quad \text{or} \quad 120° + \frac{\alpha}{3}$$

The locus is therefore, three straight lines through the origin inclined at angles

$$\frac{\alpha}{3}, \ 60° + \frac{\alpha}{3} \ \text{and} \ 120° + \frac{\alpha}{3}$$

to the axis of x.

They are therefore, equally inclined to one another.

EXAMPLE 3 *Prove that two of the straight lines represented by the equation,*

$$ax^3 + bx^2y + cxy^2 + dy^3 = 0 \qquad \ldots(1)$$

will be at right angles if,

$$a^2 + ac + bd + d^2 = 0$$

Let the separate equations to the three lines be

$$y - m_1x = 0, \quad y - m_2x = 0 \text{ and } y - m_3x = 0$$

so that the equation (1) must be equivalent to

$$d(y - m_1x)(y - m_2x)(y - m_3x) = 0$$

and therefore,

$$m_1 + m_2 + m_3 = -\frac{c}{d} \qquad \ldots(2)$$

$$m_2m_3 + m_3m_1 + m_1m_2 = \frac{b}{d} \qquad \ldots(3)$$

and

$$m_1m_2m_3 = -\frac{a}{d} \qquad \ldots(4)$$

If the first two of these straight lines be at right angles we have, in addition,

$$m_1m_2 = -1 \qquad \ldots(5)$$

From (4) and (5), we have

$$m_3 = \frac{a}{d}$$

and therefore, from (2),

$$m_1 + m_2 = -\frac{c}{d} - \frac{a}{d} = -\frac{c+a}{d}$$

The equation (3), then becomes,

$$\frac{a}{d}\left(-\frac{c+a}{d}\right) - 1 = \frac{b}{d}$$

i.e.,

$$a^2 + ac + bd + d^2 = 0$$

EXAMPLES XIV

1. Prove that the equation,

$$y^3 - x^3 + 3xy(y - x) = 0$$

represents three straight lines equally inclined to one another.

2. Prove that the equation,

$$y^2 (\cos \alpha + \sqrt{3} \sin \alpha) \cos \alpha - xy (\sin 2\alpha - \sqrt{3} \cos 2\alpha)$$

$$+ x^2 (\sin \alpha - \sqrt{3} \cos \alpha) \sin \alpha = 0$$

represents two straight lines inclined at 60° to each other.

Prove also that the area of the triangle formed with them by the straight lines,

$$(\cos \alpha - \sqrt{3} \sin \alpha)y - (\sin \alpha + \sqrt{3} \cos \alpha)x + \alpha = 0 \text{ is } \frac{a^2}{4\sqrt{3}}$$

and that this triangle is equilateral.

3. Shew that the straight lines,

$$(A^2 - 3B^2)x^2 + 8ABxy + (B^2 - 3A^2)y^2 = 0$$

form with the line $Ax + By + C = 0$ an equilateral triangle whose area

is $\dfrac{C^2}{\sqrt{3}\,(A^2 + B^2)}$.

4. Find the equation to the pair of straight lines joining the origin to the intersections of the straight line $y = mx + c$ and the curve,

$$x^2 + y^2 = a^2$$

Prove that they are at right angles if,

$$2c^2 = a^2(1 + m^2)$$

5. Prove that the straight lines joining the origin to the points of intersection of the straight line,

$$kx + hy = 2hk$$

with the curve, $(x - h)^2 + (y - k)^2 = c^2$
are at right angles if, $h^2 + k^2 = c^2$

6. Prove that the angle between the straight lines joining the origin to the intersection of the straight line $y = 3x + 2$ with the curve,

$$x^2 + 2xy + 3y^2 + 4x + 8y - 11 = 0 \text{ is } \tan^{-1} \frac{2\sqrt{2}}{3}.$$

7. Shew that the straight lines joining the origin to the other two points of intersection of the curves whose equations are:

$$ax^2 + 2hxy + by^2 + 2gx = 0$$

and $\qquad a'x^2 + 2h'xy + b'y^2 + 2g'x = 0$

will be at right angles if,

$$g(a' + b') - g'(a + b) = 0$$

What loci are represented by the equations:

8. $x^2 - y^2 = 0$ 9. $x^2 - xy = 0$ 10. $xy - ay = 0$
11. $x^3 - x^2 - x + 1 = 0$ 12. $x^3 - xy^2 = 0$ 13. $x^3 + y^3 = 0$
14. $x^2 + y^2 = 0$ 15. $x^2y = 0$ 16. $(x^2 - 1)(y^2 - 4) = 0$
17. $(x^2 - 1)^2 + (y^2 - 4)^2 = 0$ 18. $(y - mx - c)^2 + (y - m'x - c')^2 = 0$
19. $(x^2 - a^2)^2(x^2 - b^2)^2 + c^4(y^2 - a^2)^2 = 0$ 20. $(x - a)^2 - y^2 = 0$
21. $(x + y)^2 - c^2 = 0$ 22. $r = a \sec(\theta - \alpha)$
23. Shew that the equation,

$$bx^2 - 2hxy + ay^2 = 0$$

represents a pair of straight lines which are at right angles to the pair given by the equation,

$$ax^2 + 2hxy + by^2 = 0$$

24. If pairs of straight lines,

$$x^2 - 2pxy - y^2 = 0 \quad \text{and} \quad x^2 - 2qxy - y^2 = 0$$

be such that each pair bisects the angles between the other pair, prove that $pq = -1$.

25. Prove that the pair of lines

$$a^2x^2 + 2h(a + b)xy + b^2y^2 = 0$$

is equally inclined to the pair

$$ax^2 + 2hxy + by^2 = 0$$

26. Shew also that the pair

$$ax^2 + 2hxy + by^2 + \lambda(x^2 + y^2) = 0$$

is equally inclined to the same pair.

27. If one of the straight lines given by the equation,

$$ax^2 + 2hxy + by^2 = 0$$

coincide with one of those given by,

$$a'x^2 + 2h'xy + b'y^2 = 0$$

and the other lines represented by them be perpendicular, prove that

$$\frac{ha'b'}{b' - a'} = \frac{h'ab}{b - a} = \frac{1}{2}\sqrt{-aa'bb'}$$

28. Prove that the equation to the bisectors of the angle between the straight lines $ax^2 + 2hxy + by^2 = 0$ is,

$$h(x^2 - y^2) + (b - a)xy = (ax^2 - by^2)\cos \omega$$

the axes being inclined at an angle ω.

29. Prove that the straight lines,

$$ax^2 + 2hxy + by^2 = 0$$

make equal angles with the axis of x if $h = a \cos \omega$, the axes being inclined at an angle ω.

30. If the axes be inclined at an angle ω, shew that the equation,

$$x^2 + 2xy \cos \omega + y^2 \cos 2\omega = 0$$

represents a pair of perpendicular straight lines.

31. Shew that the equation,

$$\cos 3\alpha(x^3 - 3xy^2) + \sin 3\alpha(y^3 - 3x^2y) + 3a(x^2 + y^2) - 4a^3 = 0$$

represents three straight lines forming an equilateral triangle. Prove also that its area is $3\sqrt{3}a^2$.

32. Prove that the general equation,
$$ax^2 + 2hxy + by^2 + 2gx + 2fy + c = 0$$
represents two parallel straight lines if
$$h^2 = ab \quad \text{and} \quad bg^2 = af^2$$
Prove also that the distance between them is,
$$2\sqrt{\frac{g^2 - ac}{a(a + b)}}$$

33. If the equation, $ax^2 + 2hxy + by^2 + 2gx + 2fy + c = 0$
represent a pair of straight lines, prove that the equation to the third pair of straight lines passing through the points where these meet the axes is,
$$ax^2 - 2hxy + by^2 + 2gx + 2fy + c + \frac{4fg}{c}xy = 0$$

34. If the equation, $ax^2 + 2hxy + by^2 + 2gx + 2fy + c = 0$
represent two straight lines, prove that the square of the distance of their point of intersection from the origin is,
$$\frac{c(a + b) - f^2 - g^2}{ab - h^2}$$

35. Shew that the orthocentre of the triangle formed by the straight lines,
$$ax^2 + 2hxy + by^2 = 0 \quad \text{and} \quad lx + my = 1$$
is a point (x', y') such that,
$$\frac{x'}{l} = \frac{y'}{m} = \frac{a + b}{am^2 - 2hlm + bl^2}$$

36. Hence, find the locus of the orthocentre of a triangle of which two sides are given in position and whose third side goes through a fixed point.

37. Shew that the distance between the points of intersection of the straight line,
$$x \cos \alpha + y \sin \alpha - p = 0$$
with the straight lines
$$ax^2 + 2hxy + by^2 = 0$$
is $\dfrac{2p\sqrt{h^2 - ab}}{b \cos^2 \alpha - 2h \cos \alpha \sin \alpha + a \sin^2 \alpha}$
Deduce the area of the triangle formed by them.

38. Prove that the product of the perpendiculars let fall from the point (x', y') upon the pair of straight lines,
$$ax^2 + 2hxy + by^2 = 0$$

is $\dfrac{ax'^2 + 2hx'y' + by'^2}{\sqrt{(a-b)^2 + 4h^2}}$

39. Shew that two of the straight lines represented by the equation,

$$ay^4 + bxy^3 + cx^2y^2 + dx^3y + ex^4 = 0$$

will be at right angles if,

$$(b+d)(ad+be) + (e-a)^2(a+c+e) = 0$$

40. Prove that two of the lines represented by the equation,

$$ax^4 + bx^3y + cx^2y^2 + dxy^3 + ay^4 = 0$$

will bisect the angles between the other two if

$$c + 6a = 0 \quad \text{and} \quad b + d = 0$$

41. Prove that one of the lines represented by the equation,

$$ax^3 + bx^2y + cxy^2 + dy^3 = 0$$

will bisect the angle between the other two if

$$(3a+c)^2(bc + 2cd - 3ad) = (b+3d)^2(bc + 2ab - 3ad)$$

∎

7

TRANSFORMATION OF COORDINATES

➤ **127.** It is sometimes found desirable in the discussion of problems to alter the origin and axes of coordinates, either by altering the origin without alteration of the direction of the axes, or by altering the directions of the axes and keeping the origin unchanged, or by altering the origin and also the directions of the axes. The latter case is merely a combination of the first two. Either of these processes is called a transformation of coordinates.

We proceed to establish the fundamental formulae for such transformation of coordinates.

➤ **128.** *To alter the origin of coordinates without altering the directions of the axes.*

Let OX and OY be the original axes and let the new axes, parallel to the original, be

$$O'X' \quad \text{and} \quad O'Y'$$

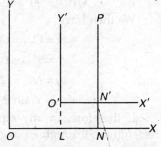

Let the coordinates of the new origin O', referred to the original axes be h and k, so that, if $O'L$ be perpendicular to OX, we have

$$OL = h \quad \text{and} \quad LO' = k$$

Let P be any point in the plane of the paper, and let its coordinates, referred to the original axes, be x and y and referred to the new axes let them be x' and y'.

Draw PN perpendicular to OX to meet $O'X'$ in N'.

then, $ON = x, NP = y, O'N' = x'$ and $N'P = y'$

We therefore, have

$$x = ON = OL + O'N' = h + x'$$

and $$y = NP = LO' + N'P = k + y'$$

The origin is therefore, transferred to the point (h, k) when we substitute for the coordinates x and y the quantities.

$$x' + h \text{ and } y' + k$$

The above article is true whether the axes be oblique or rectangular.

➤ **129.** *To change the direction of the axes of coordinates, without changing the origin, both systems of coordinates being rectangular.*

Let OX and OY be the original system of axes and OX' and OY' the new system, and let the angle, XOX', through which the axes are turned be called θ.

Take any point P in the plane of the paper.

Draw PN and PN' perpendicular to OX and OX', and also $N'L$ and $N'M$ perpendicular to OX and PN.

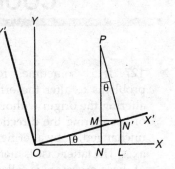

If the coordinates of P, referred to the original axes, be x and y, and, referred to the new axes, be x' and y', we have

$$ON = x, \ NP = y, \ ON' = x' \text{ and } N'P = y'$$

The angle,

$$MPN' = 90° - \angle MN'P = \angle MN'O = \angle XOX' = \theta$$

We then have

$$x = ON = OL - MN' = ON' \cos \theta - N'P \sin \theta$$
$$= x' \cos \theta - y' \sin \theta \qquad \qquad \text{...(1)}$$

and

$$y = NP = LN' + MP = ON' \sin \theta + N'P \cos \theta$$
$$= x' \sin \theta + y' \cos \theta \qquad \qquad \text{...(2)}$$

If therefore, in any equation we wish to turn the axes, being rectangular, through an angle θ we must substitute

$$x' \cos \theta - y' \sin \theta \ \text{ and } \ x' \sin \theta + y' \cos \theta$$

for x and y.

When we have both to change the origin, and also the direction of the axes, the transformation is clearly obtained by combining the results of the previous articles.

If the origin is to be transformed to the point (h, k) and the axes to be turned through an angle θ, we have to substitute

$$h + x' \cos \theta - y' \sin \theta \ \text{ and } \ k + x' \sin \theta + y' \cos \theta$$

for x and y respectively.

The student, who is acquainted with the theory of projection of straight lines, will see that equations (1) and (2), express the fact that the projections of OP on OX and OY are respectively equal to the sum of the projections of ON' and $N'P$ on the same two lines.

➤ **130.**

EXAMPLE 1 *Transform to parallel axes through the point* $(-2, 3)$ *the equation,*
$$2x^2 + 4xy + 5y^2 - 4x - 22y + 7 = 0$$

We substitute $x = x' - 2$ and $y = y' + 3$, and the equation becomes,

$$2(x' - 2)^2 + 4(x' - 2)(y' + 3) + 5(y' + 3)^2 - 4(x' - 2) - 22(y' + 3) + 7 = 0$$

i.e., $\qquad\qquad\qquad\qquad\qquad\qquad 2x'^2 + 4x'y' + 5y'^2 - 22 = 0$

EXAMPLE 2 *Transform to axes inclined at* 30° *to the original axes the equation,*
$$x^2 + 2\sqrt{3}\,xy - y^2 = 2a^2.$$

For x and y we have to substitute

$$x'\cos 30° - y'\sin 30° \quad \text{and} \quad x'\sin 30° + y'\cos 30°$$

i.e., $\qquad\qquad \dfrac{x'\sqrt{3} - y'}{2} \quad \text{and} \quad \dfrac{x' + y'\sqrt{3}}{2}$

The equation then becomes

$$(x'\sqrt{3} - y')^2 + 2\sqrt{3}(x'\sqrt{3} - y')(x' + y'\sqrt{3}) - (x' + y'\sqrt{3})^2 = 8a^2$$

i.e., $\qquad\qquad\qquad\qquad\qquad\qquad x'^2 - y'^2 = a^2$

EXAMPLES XV

1. Transform to parallel axes through the point $(1, -2)$ the equations,
   (i) $y^2 - 4x + 4y + 8 = 0$ and (ii) $2x^2 + y^2 - 4x + 4y = 0$
2. What does the equation,
$$(x - a)^2 + (y - b)^2 = c^2$$
   become when it is transferred to parallel axes through
   (i) the point $(a - c, b)$ (ii) the point $(a, b - c)$?
3. What does the equation,
$$(a - b)(x^2 + y^2) - 2abx = 0$$
   become if the origin be moved to the point $\left(\dfrac{ab}{a - b}, 0\right)$?

4. Transform to axes inclined at 45° to the original axes the equations,
   (i) $x^2 - y^2 = a^2$ $\qquad\qquad$ (ii) $17x^2 - 16xy + 17y^2 = 225$
   (iii) $y^4 + x^4 + 6x^2y^2 = 2$
5. Transform to axes inclined at an angle α to the original axes the equations,
   (i) $x^2 + y^2 = r^2$ and (ii) $x^2 + 2xy\tan 2\alpha - y^2 = a$

6. If the axes be turned through an angle $\tan^{-1} 2$, what does the equation, $4xy - 3x^2 = a^2$ become?

7. By transforming to parallel axes through a properly chosen point (h, k), prove that the equation,

$$12x^2 - 10xy + 2y^2 + 11x - 5y + 2 = 0$$

can be reduced to one containing only terms of the second degree.

8. Find the angle through which the axes may be turned so that the equation,

$$Ax + By + C = 0$$

may be reduced to the form $x =$ constant, and determine the value of this constant.

➤ **131.** The general proposition, which is given in the next article, on the transformation from one set of oblique axes to any other set of oblique axes is of very little importance and is hardly ever required.

➤ ***132.** *To change from one set of axes, inclined at an angle ω, to another set, inclined at an angle ω', the origin remaining unaltered.*

Let OX and OY be the original axes, OX' and OY' the new axes, and let the angle XOX' be θ.

Take any point P in the plane of the paper.

Draw PN and PN' parallel to OY and OY' to meet OX and OX' respectively in N and N', PL perpendicular to OX, and $N'M$ and $N'M'$ perpendicular to OL and LP.

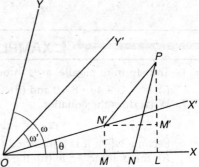

Now, $\angle PNL = \angle YOX = \omega$

and $PN'M' = Y'OX = \omega' + \theta$

Hence, if $ON = x$, $NP = y$, $ON' = x'$ and $N'P = y'$

We have $y \sin \omega = NP \sin \omega = LP = MN' + M'P$

$$= ON' \sin \theta + N'P \sin (\omega' + \theta)$$

So that, $y \sin \omega = x' \sin \theta + y' \sin (\omega' + \theta)$ ...(1)

Also, $x + y \cos \omega = ON + NL = OL = OM + N'M'$

$$= x' \cos \theta + y' \cos (\omega' + \theta)$$ ...(2)

Multiplying (2), by $\sin \omega$, (1) by $\cos \omega$, and subtracting, we have

$$x \sin \omega = x' \sin (\omega - \theta) + y' \sin (\omega - \omega' - \theta)$$ ...(3)

[This equation (3), may also be obtained by drawing a perpendicular from P upon OY and proceeding as for equation (1).]

The equations (1) and (3), give the proper substitutions for the change of axes in the general case.

As in Art. 130 the equations (1) and (2), may be obtained by equating the projections of OP and of ON' and $N'P$ on OX and a straight line perpendicular to OX.

➤ ***133.** *Particular cases of the preceding article.*

1. Suppose we wish to transfer our axes from a rectangular pair to one inclined at an angle ω'. In this case ω is $90°$, and the formulae of the preceding article become,

$$x = x' \cos \theta + y' \cos (\omega' + \theta)$$

and $$y = x' \sin \theta + y' \sin (\omega' + \theta)$$

2. Suppose the transference is to be from oblique axes, inclined at ω, to rectangular axes. In this case ω' is $90°$, and our formulae become,

$$x \sin \omega = x' \sin (\omega - \theta) - y' \cos (\omega - \theta)$$

and $$y \sin \omega = x' \sin \theta + y' \cos \theta$$

These particular formulae may easily be proved independently, by drawing the corresponding figures.

EXAMPLE *Transform the equation,* $\dfrac{x^2}{a^2} - \dfrac{y^2}{b^2} = 1$, *from rectangular axes to axes inclined at an angle* 2α, *the new axis of x being inclined at an angle* $-\alpha$ *to the old axes and sin* α *being equal to* $-\dfrac{b}{\sqrt{a^2 + b^2}}$

Here, $\theta = -\alpha$ and $\omega' = 2\alpha$, so that the formulae of transformation (1), become,

$$x = (x' + y') \cos \alpha \quad \text{and} \quad y = (y' - x') \sin \alpha$$

Since, $\sin \alpha = \dfrac{b}{\sqrt{a^2 + b^2}}$, we have $\cos \alpha = \dfrac{a}{\sqrt{a^2 + b^2}}$ and hence, the given equation becomes,

$$\frac{(x' + y')^2}{a^2 + b^2} - \frac{(y' - x')^2}{a^2 + b^2} = 1$$

i.e., $$x'y' = \frac{1}{4} (a^2 + b^2)$$

➤ ***134.** *The degree of an equation is unchanged by any transformation of coordinates.*

For the most general form of transformation is found by combining together Arts. 128 and 132. Hence, the most general formulae of transformation are:

$$x = h + x' \frac{\sin(\omega - \theta)}{\sin \omega} + y' \frac{\sin(\omega - \omega' - \theta)}{\sin \omega}$$

and

$$y = k + x' \frac{\sin \theta}{\sin \omega} + y' \frac{\sin(\omega' + \theta)}{\sin \omega}$$

For x and y we have therefore, to substitute expressions in x' and y' of the first degree, so that by this substitution the degree of the equation cannot be raised.

Neither can, by this substitution, the degree be lowered. For, if it could, then, by transforming back again, the degree would be raised and this we have just shown to be impossible.

➤ *135. *If by any change of axes, without change of origin, the quantity $ax^2 + 2hxy + by^2$ become,*

$$a'x'^2 + 2h'x'y' + b'y'^2$$

the axes in each case being rectangular, to prove that

$$a + b = a' + b' \quad \text{and} \quad ab - h^2 = a'b' - h'^2$$

By Art. 129, the new axis of x being inclined at an angle θ to the old axis, we have to substitute.

$$x' \cos \theta - y' \sin \theta \quad \text{and} \quad x' \sin \theta + y' \cos \theta$$

for x and y respectively.

Hence, $ax^2 + 2hxy + by^2$

$$= a(x' \cos \theta - y' \sin \theta)^2 + 2h (x' \cos \theta - y' \sin \theta)(x' \sin \theta + y' \cos \theta)$$
$$+ b(x' \sin \theta + y' \cos \theta)^2$$

$$= x'^2[a \cos^2 \theta + 2h \cos \theta \sin \theta + b \sin^2 \theta]$$
$$+ 2x'y'[-a \cos \theta \sin \theta + h(\cos^2 \theta - \sin^2 \theta) + b \cos \theta \sin \theta]$$
$$+ y'^2 [a \sin^2 \theta - 2h \cos \theta \sin \theta + b \cos^2 \theta]$$

We then have

$$a' = a \cos^2 \theta + 2h \cos \theta \sin \theta + b \sin^2 \theta$$

$$= \frac{1}{2} [(a + b) + (a - b) \cos 2\theta + 2h \sin 2\theta] \qquad \dots(1)$$

$$b' = a \sin^2 \theta - 2h \cos \theta \sin \theta + b \cos^2 \theta$$

$$= \frac{1}{2} [(a + b) - (a - b) \cos 2\theta - 2h \sin 2\theta] \qquad \dots(2)$$

and $\quad h' = -a \cos\theta \sin\theta + h(\cos^2\theta - \sin^2\theta) + b \cos\theta \sin\theta$

$$= \frac{1}{2}[2h \cos 2\theta - (a-b)\sin 2\theta] \qquad \ldots(3)$$

By adding (1) and (2), we have $a' + b' = a + b$

Also, by multiplying them, we have

$$4a'b' = (a+b)^2 - \{(a-b)\cos 2\theta + 2h \sin 2\theta\}^2$$

Hence, $\quad 4a'b' - 4h'^2 = (a+b)^2 - [\{2h \sin 2\theta + (a-b)\cos 2\theta\}^2$

$$+ \{2h \cos 2\theta - (a-b)\sin 2\theta\}^2]$$

$$= (a+b)^2 - [(a-b)^2 + 4h^2] = 4ab - 4h^2$$

So that, $\qquad\qquad a'b' - h'^2 = ab - h^2$

➤ **136.** *To find the angle through which the axes must be turned so that the expression $ax^2 + 2hxy + by^2$ may become an expression in which there is no term involving $x'y'$.*

Assuming the work of the previous article the coefficient of $x'y'$ vanishes if h' be zero, or from equation (3), if

$$2h \cos 2\theta = (a-b)\sin 2\theta$$

i.e., if $\qquad\qquad \tan 2\theta = \dfrac{2h}{a-b}$

The required angle is therefore,

$$\frac{1}{2}\tan^{-1}\left(\frac{2h}{a-b}\right)$$

➤ ***137.** The proposition of Art. 135 is a particular case, when the axes are rectangular, of the following more general proposition.*

If by any change of axes, without change of origin, the quantity $ax^2 + 2hxy + by^2$ becomes $a'x^2 + 2h'xy + b'y^2$, then

$$\frac{a+b-2h \cos\omega}{\sin^2\omega} = \frac{a'+b'-2h' \cos\omega'}{\sin^2\omega'}$$

and $\qquad\qquad \dfrac{ab-h^2}{\sin^2\omega} = \dfrac{a'b'-h'^2}{\sin^2\omega'}$

ω *and* ω' *being the angles between the original and final pairs of axes.*

Let the coordinates of any point P, referred to the original axes, be x and y and, referred to the final axes, let them be x' and y'.

By Art. 20 the square of the distance between P and the origin is $x^2 + 2xy \cos\omega + y^2$, referred to the original axes, and $x'^2 + 2x'y' \cos\omega' + y'^2$, referred to the final axes.

We therefore, always have

$$x^2 + 2xy \cos \omega + y^2 = x'^2 + 2x'y' \cos \omega' + y'^2 \qquad \ldots(1)$$

Also, by supposition, we have

$$ax^2 + 2hxy + by^2 = a'x'^2 + 2h'x'y' + b'y'^2 \qquad \ldots(2)$$

Multiplying (1) by λ and adding it to (2), we therefore, have

$$x^2(a + \lambda) + 2xy(h + \lambda \cos \omega) + y^2(b + \lambda)$$

$$= x'^2 (a' + \lambda) + 2x'y'(h' + \lambda \cos \omega') + y'^2(b' + \lambda) \qquad \ldots(3)$$

If then any value of λ makes the left-hand side of (3), a perfect square, the same value must make the right-hand side also a perfect square.

But the values of λ which make the left-hand a perfect square are given by the condition,

$$(h + \lambda \cos \omega)^2 = (a + \lambda)(b + \lambda)$$

i.e., by $\lambda^2(1 - \cos^2 \omega) + \lambda(a + b - 2h \cos \omega) + ab - h^2 = 0$

i.e., by $$\lambda^2 + \lambda \frac{a + b - 2h \cos \omega}{\sin^2 \omega} + \frac{ab - h^2}{\sin^2 \omega} = 0 \qquad \ldots(4)$$

In a similar manner the values of λ which make the right-hand side of (3), a perfect square are given by the equation,

$$\lambda^2 + \lambda \frac{a' + b' - 2h' \cos \omega'}{\sin^2 \omega'} + \frac{a'b' - h'^2}{\sin^2 \omega'} = 0 \qquad \ldots(5)$$

Since, the values of λ given by equation (4), are the same as the values of λ given by (5), the two equations (4) and (5), must be the same.

Hence, we have

$$\frac{a + b - 2h \cos \omega}{\sin^2 \omega} = \frac{a' + b' - 2h' \cos \omega'}{\sin^2 \omega'}$$

and

$$\frac{ab - h^2}{\sin^2 \omega} = \frac{a'b' - h'^2}{\sin^2 \omega'}$$

EXAMPLES XVI

1. The equation to a straight line referred to axes inclined at 30° to one another is $y = 2x + 1$. Find its equation referred to axes inclined at 45°, the origin and axis of x being unchanged.

2. Transform the equation $2x^2 + 3\sqrt{3}\, xy + 3y^2 = 2$ from axes inclined at 30° to rectangular axes, the axis of x remaining unchanged.

3. Transform the equation, $x^2 + xy + y^2 = 8$ from axes inclined at 60° to axes bisecting the angles between the original axes.

4. Transform the equation, $y^2 + 4y \cot \alpha - 4x = 0$ from rectangular axes to oblique axes meeting at an angle α, the axis of x being kept the same.

5. It x and y be the coordinates of a point referred to a system of oblique axes, and x' and y' be its coordinates referred to another system of oblique axes with the same origin, and if the formulae of transformation be,

$$x = mx' + ny' \quad \text{and} \quad y = m'x' + n'y',$$

prove that, $\dfrac{m^2 + m'^2 - 1}{n^2 + n'^2 - 1} = \dfrac{mm'}{nn'}.$

8

THE CIRCLE

➤ **138. Def.:** A circle is the locus of a point which moves so that its distance from a fixed point, called the centre, is equal to a given distance. The given distance is called the radius of the circle.

➤ **139.** *To find the equation to a circle, the axes of coordinates being two straight lines through its centre at right angles.*

Let O be the centre of the circle and let a be its radius.

Let OX and OY be the axes of coordinates.

Let P be any point on the circumference of the circle, and let its coordinates be x and y.

Draw PM perpendicular to OX and join OP.

Then (Euc. I. 47)

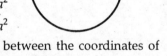

$$OM^2 + MP^2 = a^2$$

i.e.,
$$x^2 + y^2 = a^2$$

This being the relation which holds between the coordinates of any point on the circumference is, by Art. 42, the required equation.

➤ **140.** *To find the equation to a circle referred to any rectangle axes.*

Let OX and OY be the two rectangular axes.

Let C be the centre of the circle and a its radius.

Take any point P on the circumference and draw perpendiculars CM and PN upon OX; let P be the point (x, y).

Draw CL perpendicular to NP.

Let the coordinates of C be h and k; these are supposed to be known.

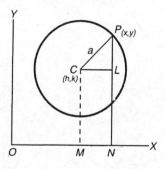

We have $\qquad CL = MN = ON - OM = x - h$

and
$$LP = NP - NL = NP - MC = y - k$$

Hence, since
$$CL^2 + LP^2 = CP^2$$

We have
$$(x - h)^2 + (y - k)^2 = a^2 \qquad \text{...(1)}$$

This is the required equation.

EXAMPLE The equation to the circle, whose centre is the point $(-3, 4)$ and whose radius is 7, is

$$(x + 3)^2 + (y - 4)^2 = 7^2$$

i.e.,
$$x^2 + y^2 + 6x - 8y = 24$$

➤ **141.** Some particular cases of the preceding article may be noticed:

(a) Let the origin O be on the circle so that, in this case,

$$OM^2 + MC^2 = a^2$$

i.e.,
$$h^2 + k^2 = a^2$$

The equation (1), then becomes

$$(x - h)^2 + (y - k)^2 = h^2 + k^2$$

i.e.,
$$x^2 + y^2 - 2hx - 2ky = 0$$

(b) Let the origin be not on the curve, but let the centre lie on the axis of x. In this case $k = 0$, and the equation becomes,

$$(x - h)^2 + y^2 = a^2$$

(c) Let the origin be on the curve and let the axis of x be a diameter. We now have $k = 0$ and $a = h$, so that the equation becomes,

$$x^2 + y^2 - 2hx = 0$$

(d) By taking O at C, and thus making both h and k zero, we have the case of Art. 139.

(e) The circle will touch the axis of x if MC be equal to the radius, i.e., if $k = a$.

The equation to a circle touching the axis of x is therefore,

$$x^2 + y^2 - 2hx - 2ky + h^2 = 0$$

Similarly, one touching the axis of y is

$$x^2 + y^2 - 2hx - 2ky + k^2 = 0$$

➤ **142.** *To prove that the equation,*

$$x^2 + y^2 + 2gx + 2fy + c = 0 \qquad \text{...(1)}$$

always represents a circle for all values of g, f, and c, and to find its centre and radius. [The axes are assumed to be rectangular.]

This equation may be written,

$$(x^2 + 2gx + g^2) + (y^2 + 2fy + f^2) = g^2 + f^2 - c$$

i.e., $(x + g)^2 + (y + f)^2 = \left\{\sqrt{g^2 + f^2 - c}\right\}^2$

Comparing this with the equation (1) of Art. 140, we see that the equations are the same if,

$$h = -g, \quad k = -f \text{ and } a = \sqrt{g^2 + f^2 - c}$$

Hence, (1), represents a circle whose centre is the point $(-g, -f)$, and whose radius is $\sqrt{g^2 + f^2 - c}$.

If $g^2 + f^2 > c$, the radius of this circle is real.

If $g^2 + f^2 = c$, the radius vanishes, *i.e.*, the circle becomes a point coinciding with the point $(-g, -f)$. Such a circle is called a point-circle.

If $g^2 + f^2 < c$, the radius of the circle is imaginary. In this case the equation does not represent any real geometrical locus. It is better not to say that the circle does not exist, but to say that it is a circle with a real centre and an imaginary radius.

EXAMPLE 1   The equation, $x^2 + y^2 + 4x - 6y = 0$ can be written in the form,

$$(x + 2)^2 + (y - 3)^2 = 13 = (\sqrt{13})^2,$$

and therefore, represents a circle whose centre is the point $(-2, 3)$ and whose radius is $\sqrt{13}$.

EXAMPLE 2   The equation, $45x^2 + 45y^2 - 60x + 36y + 19 = 0$ is equivalent to,

$$x^2 + y^2 - \frac{4}{3} x + \frac{4}{5} y = -\frac{19}{45}$$

i.e., $\left(x - \dfrac{2}{3}\right)^2 + \left(y + \dfrac{2}{5}\right)^2 = \dfrac{4}{9} + \dfrac{4}{25} - \dfrac{19}{45} = \dfrac{41}{225},$

and therefore, represents a circle whose centre is the point $\left(\dfrac{2}{3}, -\dfrac{2}{5}\right)$ and whose radius is $\dfrac{\sqrt{41}}{15}$.

➤ **143.** *Condition that the general equation of the second degree may represent a circle.*

The equation (1) of the preceding article, multiplied by any arbitrary constant, is a particular case of the general equation of the second degree (Art. 114) in which there is no term containing xy and in which the coefficients of x^2 and y^2 are equal.

The general equation of the second degree in rectangular coordinates therefore, represents a circle **if the coefficients of x^2 and y^2 be the same and if the coefficient of xy be zero.**

➤ **144.** The equation (1) of Art. 142 is called the **general equation of a circle,** since it can, by a proper choice of g, f and c, be made to represent *any* circle.

The three constants g, f and c in the general equation correspond to the geometrical fact that a circle can be found to satisfy three independent geometrical conditions and no more. Thus, a circle is determined when three points on it are given, or when it is required to touch three straight lines.

➤ **145.** *To find the equation to the circle which is described on the line joining the points (x_1, y_1) and (x_2, y_2) as diameter.*

Let A be the point (x_1, y_1) and B be the point (x_2, y_2), and let the coordinates of any point P on the circle be h and k.

The equation to AP is (Art. 62)

$$y - y_1 = \frac{k - y_1}{h - x_1} (x - x_1) \qquad \ldots(1)$$

and the equation to BP is

$$y - y_2 = \frac{k - y_2}{h - x_2} (x - x_2) \qquad \ldots(2)$$

But, since APB is a semicircle, the angle APB is a right angle, and hence the straight lines (1) and (2) are at right angles.

Hence, by Art. 69, we have

$$\frac{k - y_1}{h - x_1} \cdot \frac{k - y_2}{h - x_2} = -1$$

i.e., $\qquad (h - x_1)(h - x_2) + (k - y_1)(k - y_2) = 0$

But this is the condition that the point (h, k) may lie on the curve whose equation is,

$$(x - x_1)(x - x_2) + (y - y_1)(y - y_2) = 0$$

This therefore, is the required equation.

➤ **146.** *Intercepts made on the axes by the circle whose equation is,*

$$ax^2 + ay^2 + 2gx + 2fy + c = 0 \qquad \ldots(1)$$

The abscissae of the points where the circle (1) meets the axis of x, *i.e.*, $y = 0$, are given by the equation,

$$ax^2 + 2gx + c = 0 \qquad \ldots(2)$$

The roots of this equation being x_1 and x_2, we have

$$x_1 + x_2 = -\frac{2g}{a}$$

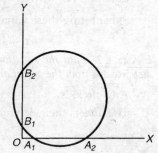

and
$$x_1 x_2 = \frac{c}{a}$$
(Art. 2)

Hence, $A_1 A_2 = x_2 - x_1 = \sqrt{(x_1 + x_2)^2 - 4x_1 x_2}$

$$= \sqrt{\frac{4g^2}{a^2} - \frac{4c}{a}} = 2\frac{\sqrt{g^2 - ac}}{a}$$

Again, the roots of the equation (2) are both imaginary if $g^2 < ac$. In this case the circle does not meet the axis of x in real points, *i.e.*, geometrically it does not meet the axis of x at all.

The circle will touch the axis of x if the intercept $A_1 A_2$ be just zero *i.e.*, if $g^2 = ac$.

It will meet the axis of x in two points lying on opposite sides of the origin O if the two roots of the equation (2) are of opposite signs, *i.e.*, if c be negative.

➤ **147.**

EXAMPLE 1 *Find the equation to the circle which passes through the points* (1, 0), (0, –6) *and* (3, 4).

Let the equation to the circle be,
$$x^2 + y^2 + 2gx + 2fy + c = 0 \qquad \ldots(1)$$

Since, the three points, whose coordinates are given, satisfy this equation, we have

$$1 + 2g + c = 0 \qquad \ldots(2)$$
$$36 - 12f + c = 0 \qquad \ldots(3)$$

and
$$25 + 6g + 8f + c = 0 \qquad \ldots(4)$$

Subtracting (2) from (3) and (3) from (4), we have

$$2g + 12f = 35$$

and
$$6g + 20f = 11$$

Hence, $f = \dfrac{47}{8}$ and $g = -\dfrac{71}{4}$

Equation (2), then gives $c = \dfrac{69}{2}$.

Substituting these values in (1) the required equation is,
$$4x^2 + 4y^2 - 142x + 47y + 138 = 0$$

EXAMPLE 2 *Find the equation to the circle which touches the axis of y at a distance +4 from the origin and cuts off an intercept 6 from the axis of x.*

Any circle is, $x^2 + y^2 + 2gx + 2fy + c = 0$

This meets the axis of y in points given by
$$y^2 + 2fy + c = 0$$

The roots of this equation must be equal and each equal to 4, so that it must be equivalent to $(y - 4)^2 = 0$.

Hence, $2f = -8$ and $c = 16$

The equation to the circle is then

$$x^2 + y^2 + 2gx - 8y + 16 = 0$$

This meets the axis of x in points given by,

$$x^2 + 2gx + 16 = 0$$

i.e., at points distant

$$-g + \sqrt{g^2 - 16} \quad \text{and} \quad -g - \sqrt{g^2 - 16}$$

Hence, $6 = 2\sqrt{g^2 - 16}$

Therefore, $g = \pm 5$, and the required equation is,

$$x^2 + y^2 \pm 10x - 8y + 16 = 0$$

There are therefore, two circles satisfying the given conditions. This is geometrically obvious.

EXAMPLES XVII

Find the equation to the circle:

1. Whose radius is 3 and whose centre is $(-1, 2)$.
2. Whose radius is 10 and whose centre is $(-5, -6)$.
3. Whose radius is $a + b$ and whose centre is $(a, -b)$.
4. Whose radius is $\sqrt{a^2 - b^2}$ and whose centre is $(-a, -b)$.

Find the coordinates of the centres and the radii of the circles whose equations are:

5. $x^2 + y^2 - 4x - 8y = 41$
6. $3x^2 + 3y^2 - 5x - 6y + 4 = 0$
7. $x^2 + y^2 = k(x + k)$
8. $x^2 + y^2 = 2gx - 2fy$
9. $\sqrt{1 + m^2}(x^2 + y^2) - 2cx - 2mcy = 0$

Draw the circles whose equations are:

10. $x^2 + y^2 = 2ay$
11. $3x^2 + 3y^2 = 4x$
12. $5x^2 + 5y^2 = 2x + 3y$
13. Find the equation to the circle which passes through the points $(1, -2)$ and $(4, -3)$ and which has its centre on the straight line $3x + 4y = 7$.
14. Find the equation to the circle passing through the points $(0, a)$ and (b, h), and having its centre on the axis of x.

Find the equations to the circles which pass through the points:

15. $(0, 0)$, $(a, 0)$ and $(0, b)$

16. $(1, 2)$, $(3, -4)$ and $(5, -6)$

17. $(1, 1)$, $(2, -1)$ and $(3, 2)$

18. $(5, 7)$, $(8, 1)$ and $(1, 3)$

19. (a, b), $(a, -b)$ and $(a + b, a - b)$

20. $ABCD$ is a square whose side is a; taking AB and AD as axes, prove that the equation to the circle circumscribing the square is,

$$x^2 + y^2 = a(x + y).$$

21. Find the equation to the circle which passes through the origin and cuts off intercepts equal to 3 and 4 from the axes.

22. Find the equation to the circle passing through the origin and the points (a, b) and (b, a). Find the lengths of the chords that it cuts off from the axes.

23. Find the equation to the circle which goes through the origin and cuts off intercepts equal to h and k from the positive parts of the axes.

24. Find the equation to the circle, of radius a, which passes through the two points on the axis of x which are at a distance b from the origin.

Find the equation to the circle which:

25. touches each axis at a distance 5 from the origin.

26. touches each axis and is of radius a.

27. touches both axes and passes through the point $(-2, -3)$.

28. touches the axis of x and passes through the two points $(1, -2)$ and $(3, -4)$

29. touches the axis of y at the origin and passes through the point (b, c).

30. touches the axis of x at a distance 3 from the origin and intercepts a distance 6 on the axis of y.

31. points $(1, 0)$ and $(2, 0)$ are taken on the axis of x, the axes being rectangular. On the line joining these points an equilateral triangle is described, its vertex being in the positive quadrant. Find the equations to the circles described on its sides as diameters.

32. If $y = mx$ be the equation of a chord of a circle whose radius is a, the origin of coordinates being one extremity of the chord and the axis of x being a diameter of the circle, prove that the equation of a circle of which this chord is the diameter is,

$$(1 + m^2)(x^2 + y^2) - 2a(x + my) = 0.$$

33. Find the equation to the circle passing through the points $(12, 43)$, $(18, 39)$, and $(42, 3)$ and prove that it also passes through the points $(-54, -69)$ and $(-81, -38)$.

34. Find the equation to the circle circumscribing the quadrilateral formed by the straight lines,

$$2x + 3y = 2, \; 3x - 2y = 4, \; x + 2y = 3 \text{ and } 2x - y = 3.$$

35. Prove that the equation to the circle of which the points (x_1, y_1) and (x_2, y_2) are the ends of a chord of a segment containing an angle θ is,

$$(x - x_1)(x - x_2) + (y - y_1)(y - y_2)$$
$$\pm \cot \theta \left[(x - x_1)(y - y_2) - (x - x_2)(y - y_1) \right] = 0.$$

36. Find the equations to the circles in which the line joining the points (a, b) and $(b, -a)$ is a chord subtending an angle of $45°$ at any point on its circumference.

➤ **148. Tangent :** In Geometry the tangent at any point of a circle is defined to be a straight line which meets the circle there, but, being produced, does not cut it; this tangent is shown to be always perpendicular to the radius drawn from the centre to the point of contact.

From this property, may be deduced the equation to the tangent at any point (x', y') of the circle $x^2 + y^2 = a^2$.

For let the point P (Fig. Art. 139) be the point (x', y').

The equation to any straight line passing through P is, by Art. 62,

$$y - y' = m(x - x') \qquad \qquad \text{...(1)}$$

Also, the equation to OP is,

$$y = \frac{y'}{x'} x \qquad \qquad \text{...(2)}$$

The straight lines (1) and (2) are at **right angles**, i.e., the line (1) is a tangent, if

$$m \times \frac{y'}{x'} = -1 \qquad \qquad \text{(Art. 69)}$$

i.e., if

$$m = -\frac{x'}{y'}$$

Substituting this value of m in (1), the equation of the tangent at (x', y') is,

$$y - y' = -\frac{x'}{y'} (x - x')$$

i.e.,

$$xx' + yy' = x'^2 + y'^2 \qquad \qquad \text{...(3)}$$

But, since (x', y') lies on the circle, we have $x'^2 + y'^2 = a^2$, and the required equation is then,

$$xx' + yy' = a^2.$$

➤ **149.** In the case of most curves it is impossible to give a simple construction for the tangent as in the case of the circle. It is therefore, necessary, in general to give a different definition.

Tangent Def.: Let P and Q be any two points, near to one another, on any curve.

Join PQ; then PQ is called a secant.

The position of the line PQ when the point Q is taken indefinitely close to, and ultimately coincident with, the point P is called the tangent at P.

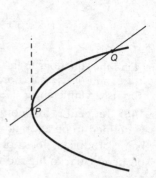

The student may better appreciate this definition, if he conceive the curve to be made up of a succession of very small points (much smaller than could be made by the finest conceivable drawing pen) packed close to one another along the curve. The tangent at P is then the straight line joining P and the next of these small points.

➤ **150.** *To find the equation of the tangent at the point (x', y') of the circle* $x^2 + y^2 = a^2$.

Let P be the given point and Q a point (x'', y'') lying on the curve and close to P.

The equation to PQ is then

$$y - y' = \frac{y'' - y'}{x'' - x'}(x - x') \qquad \text{...(1)}$$

Since, both (x', y') and (x'', y'') lie on the circle, we have

$$x'^2 + y'^2 = a^2$$

and

$$x''^2 + y''^2 = a^2$$

By subtraction, we have

$$x''^2 - x'^2 + y''^2 - y'^2 = 0$$

i.e., $(x'' - x')(x'' + x') + (y'' - y')(y'' + y') = 0$

i.e.,

$$\frac{y'' - y'}{x'' - x'} = -\frac{x'' + x'}{y'' + y'}$$

Substituting this value in (1), the equation to PQ is

$$y - y' = -\frac{x'' + x'}{y'' + y'}(x - x') \qquad \text{...(2)}$$

Now, let Q be taken very close to P, so that it ultimately coincides with P, i.e., put $x'' = x'$ and $y'' = y'$.

Then, (2) becomes

$$y - y' = -\frac{2x'}{2y'}(x - x')$$

i.e.,

$$yy' + xx' = x'^2 + y'^2 = a^2$$

The required equation is therefore,

$$xx' + yy' = a^2 \qquad \qquad ...(3)$$

It will be noted that the equation to the tangent found in this article coincides with the equation found from the geometrical definition in Art. 148.

Our definition of a tangent and the geometrical definition therefore, give the same straight line in the case of a circle.

➤ **151.** *To obtain the equation of the tangent at any point* (x', y') *lying on the circle:*

$$x^2 + y^2 + 2gx + 2fy + c = 0$$

Let P be the given point and Q a point (x'', y'') lying on the curve close to P.

The equation to PQ is therefore,

$$y - y' = \frac{y'' - y'}{x'' - x'}(x - x') \qquad \qquad ...(1)$$

Since, both (x', y') and (x'', y'') lie on the circle, we have

$$x'^2 + y'^2 + 2gx' + 2fy' + c = 0 \qquad \qquad ...(2)$$

and

$$x''^2 + y''^2 + 2gx'' + 2fy'' + c = 0 \qquad \qquad ...(3)$$

By subtraction, we have

$$x''^2 - x'^2 + y''^2 - y'^2 + 2g(x'' - x') + 2f(y'' - y') = 0$$

i.e., $(x'' - x')(x'' + x' + 2g) + (y'' - y')(y'' + y' + 2f) = 0$

i.e.,

$$\frac{y'' - y'}{x'' - x'} = -\frac{x'' + x' + 2g}{y'' + y' + 2f}$$

Substituting this value in (1), the equation to PQ becomes,

$$y - y' = -\frac{x'' + x' + 2g}{y'' + y' + 2f}(x - x') \qquad \qquad ...(4)$$

Now, let Q be taken very close to P, so that it ultimately coincides with P, *i.e.*, put $x'' = x'$ and $y'' = y'$.

The equation (4), then becomes

$$y - y' = -\frac{x' + g}{y' + f}(x - x')$$

i.e., $y(y' + f) + x(x' + g) = y'(y' + f) + x'(x' + g)$

$$= x'^2 + y'^2 + gx' + fy'$$

$$= -gx' - fy' - c \qquad \qquad \text{by (2),}$$

This may be written,

$$xx' + yy' + g(x + x') + f(y + y') + c = 0$$

which is the required equation.

➤ **152.** The equation to the tangent at (x', y') is therefore, obtained from that of the circle itself by substituting xx' for x^2, yy' for y^2, $x + x'$ for $2x$, and $y + y'$ for $2y$.

This is a particular case of a general rule which will be found to enable us to write down at sight the equation to the tangent at (x', y') to any of the curves with which we shall deal in this book.

➤ **153.** *Points of intersection, in general, of the straight line,*

$$y = mx + c \qquad \qquad \text{...(1)}$$

with the circle, $\qquad x^2 + y^2 = a^2 \qquad \qquad \text{...(2)}$

The coordinates of the points in which the straight line (1) meets (2) satisfy both equations (1) and (2).

If therefore, we solve them as simultaneous equations we shall obtain the coordinates of the common point or points.

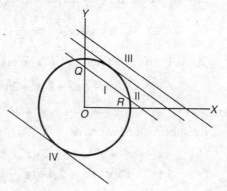

Substituting for y from (1) in (2), the abscissae of the required points are given by the equation,

$$x^2 + (mx + c)^2 = a^2$$

i.e., $\qquad x^2(1 + m^2) + 2mcx + c^2 - a^2 = 0 \qquad \qquad \text{...(3)}$

The roots of this equation are, by Art. 1, real, coincident, or imaginary, according as,

$(2mc)^2 - 4(1 + m^2)(c^2 - a^2)$ is positive, zero, or negative, *i.e.,* according as,

$a^2(1 + m^2) - c^2$ is positive, zero, or negative,

i.e., according as,

$$c^2 \text{ is } < = \text{ or } > a^2(1 + m^2).$$

In the figure the lines marked I, II and III are all parallel, *i.e.,* their equations all have the same "m".

The straight line I corresponds to a value of c^2 which is $< a^2(1 + m^2)$ and it meets the circle in two real points.

The straight line III which corresponds to a value of c^2, $> a^2(1 + m^2)$, does not meet the circle at all, or rather, as in Art. 108, this is better expressed by saying that it meets the circle in imaginary points.

The straight line II corresponds to a value of c^2, which is equal to $a^2(1 + m^2)$, and meets the curve in two coincident points, *i.e.*, is a tangent.

➤ **154.** We can now obtain the length of the chord intercepted by the circle on the straight line (1). For, if x_1 and x_2 be the roots of the equation (3), we have

$$x_1 + x_2 = -\frac{2mc}{1 + m^2} \quad \text{and} \quad x_1 x_2 = \frac{c^2 - a^2}{1 + m^2}$$

Hence,

$$x_1 - x_2 = \sqrt{(x_1 + x_2)^2 - 4x_1 x_2} = \frac{2}{1 + m^2}\sqrt{m^2 c^2 - (c^2 - a^2)(1 + m^2)}$$

$$= \frac{2}{1 + m^2}\sqrt{a^2(1 + m^2) - c^2}$$

If y_1 and y_2 be the ordinates of Q and R we have, since these points are on, (1),

$$y_1 - y_2 = (mx_1 + c) - (mx_2 + c) = m(x_1 - x_2)$$

Hence, $QR = \sqrt{(y_1 - y_2)^2 + (x_1 - x_2)^2} = \sqrt{1 + m^2}\,(x_1 - x_2)$

$$= 2\sqrt{\frac{a^2(1 + m^2) - c^2}{1 + m^2}}$$

In a similar manner we can consider the points of intersection of the straight line $y = mx + k$ with the circle

$$x^2 + y^2 + 2gx + 2fy + c = 0$$

➤ **155.** *The straight line,*

$$y = mx + a\sqrt{1 + m^2}$$

is always a tangent to the circle,

$$x^2 + y^2 = a^2$$

As in Art. 153 the straight line

$$y = mx + c$$

meets the circle in two points which are coincident if

$$c = a\sqrt{1 + m^2}$$

But if a straight line meets the circle in two points which are indefinitely close to one another then, by Art. 149, it is a tangent to the circle.

The straight line $y = mx + c$ is therefore, a tangent to the circle if

$$c = a\sqrt{1 + m^2}$$

i.e., the equation to any tangent to the circle is,

$$y = mx + a\sqrt{1 + m^2} \qquad \qquad \text{...(1)}$$

Since, the radical on the right hand may have the + or − sign prefixed we see that corresponding to any value of m there are two tangents. They are makred II and IV in the figure of Art. 153.

➤ **156.** The above result may also be deduced from the equation (3) of Art. 150, which may be written,

$$y = -\frac{x'}{y'} x + \frac{a^2}{y'} \qquad \qquad \text{...(1)}$$

Put $-\dfrac{x'}{y'} = m$, so that $x' = -my'$ and the relation $x'^2 + y'^2 = a^2$ gives

$$y'^2(m^2 + 1) = a^2, \quad i.e., \quad \frac{a}{y'} = \sqrt{1 + m^2}$$

The equation (1), then becomes,

$$y = mx + a\sqrt{1 + m^2}$$

This is therefore, the tangent at the point whose coordinates are,

$$\frac{-ma}{\sqrt{1 + m^2}} \quad \text{and} \quad \frac{a}{\sqrt{1 + m^2}}$$

➤ **157.** If we assume that a tangent to a circle is always perpendicular to the radius vector to the point of contact, the result of Art. 155 may be obtained in another manner.

For a tangent is a line whose perpendicular distance from the centre is equal to the radius.

The straight line $y = mx + c$ will therefore, touch the circle if the perpendicular on it from the origin be equal to a, i.e., if

$$\frac{c}{\sqrt{1 + m^2}} = a$$

i.e., if

$$c = a\sqrt{1 + m^2}$$

This method is not however applicable to any other curve besides the circle.

➤ **158.**

EXAMPLE *Find the equations to the tangents to the circle,*

$$x^2 + y^2 - 6x + 4y = 12$$

which are parallel to the straight line

$$4x + 3y + 5 = 0$$

Any straight line parallel to the given one is,

$$4x + 3y + C = 0. \qquad \qquad ...(1)$$

The equation to the circle is,

$$(x - 3)^2 + (y + 2)^2 = 5^2$$

The straight line (1), if it be a tangent, must be therefore, such that its distance from the point (3, –2) is equal to ±5.

Hence, $\qquad \dfrac{12 - 6 + C}{\sqrt{4^2 + 3^2}} = \pm 5 \qquad \qquad$ (Art. 75)

So, that $\qquad \qquad C = -6 \pm 25 = 19 \ \ \text{or} \ -31$

The required tangents are therefore,

$$4x + 3y + 19 = 0 \quad \text{and} \quad 4x + 3y - 31 = 0$$

➤ **159. Normal Def.:** The normal at any point P of a curve is the straight line which passes through P and is perpendicular to the tangent at P.

To find the equation to the normal at the point (x', y') of (1), the circle,

$$x^2 + y^2 = a^2$$

and (2), the circle

$$x^2 + y^2 + 2gx + 2fy + c = 0$$

(1) The tangent at (x', y') is,

$$xx' + yy' = a^2$$

i.e., $\qquad \qquad y = -\dfrac{x'}{y'} x + \dfrac{a^2}{y'}$

The equation to the straight line passing through (x', y') perpendicular to this tangent is,

$$y - y' = m (x - x'),$$

Where $\qquad \qquad m \times \left(-\dfrac{x'}{y'} \right) = -1, \qquad \qquad$ (Art. 69),

i.e., $\qquad \qquad m = \dfrac{y'}{x'}.$

The required equation is therefore

$$y - y' = \dfrac{y'}{x'} (x - x'),$$

i.e., $\qquad \qquad x'y - xy' = 0.$

This straight line passes through the centre of the circle which is the point (0, 0).

If we assume the ordinary geometrical propositions the equation is at once written down, since the normal is the straight line joining (0, 0) to (x', y').

(2) The equation to the tangent at (x', y') to the circle

$$x^2 + y^2 + 2gx + 2fy + c = 0$$

is

$$y = -\frac{x' + g}{y' + f} x - \frac{gx' + fy' + c}{y' + f}. \qquad \text{(Art. 151.)}$$

The equation to the straight line, passing through the point (x', y') and perpendicular to this tangent, is

$$y - y' = m(x - x'),$$

where

$$m \times \left(-\frac{x' + g}{y' + f}\right) = -1 \qquad \text{(Art. 69)}$$

i.e.,

$$m = \frac{y' + f}{x' + g}$$

The equation to the normal is therefore,

$$y - y' = \frac{y' + f}{x' + g}(x - x')$$

i.e.,

$$y(x' + g) - x(y' + f) + fx' - gy' = 0$$

EXAMPLES XVIII

Write down the equation of the tangent to the circle

1. $x^2 + y^2 - 3x + 10y = 15$ at the point (4, –11).

2. $4x^2 + 4y^2 - 10x + 24y = 117$ at the point $\left(-4, -\dfrac{11}{2}\right)$

Find the equations to the tangents to the circle

3. $x^2 + y^2 = 4$ which are parallel to the line $x + 2y + 3 = 0$

4. $x^2 + y^2 + 2gx + 2fy + c = 0$ which are parallel to the lines

$$x + 2y - 6 = 0$$

5. Prove that the straight line $y = x + c\sqrt{2}$ touches the circle $x^2 + y^2 = c^2$ and find its point of contact.

6. Find the condition that the straight line $cx - by + b^2 = 0$ may touch the circle $x^2 + y^2 = ax + by$ and find the point of contact.

7. Find whether the straight line $x + y = 2 + \sqrt{2}$ touches the circle

$$x^2 + y^2 - 2x - 2y + 1 = 0$$

8. Find the condition that the straight line $3x + 4y = k$ may touch the circle $x^2 + y^2 = 10x$.

9. Find the value of p so that the straight line,

$$x \cos \alpha + y \sin \alpha - p = 0$$

may touch the circle

$$x^2 + y^2 - 2ax \cos \alpha - 2by \sin \alpha - a^2 \sin^2 \alpha = 0.$$

10. Find the condition that the straight line $Ax + By + C = 0$ may touch the circle $(x - a)^2 + (y - b)^2 = c^2$

11. Find the equation to the tangent to the circle $x^2 + y^2 = a^2$ which,
    (i) is parallel to the straight line $y = mx + c$,
    (ii) is perpendicular to the straight line $y = mx + c$,
    (iii) passes through the point $(b, 0)$,

and (iv) makes with the axes a triangle whose area is a^2.

12. Find the length of the chord joining the points in which the straight line,

$$\frac{x}{a} + \frac{y}{b} = 1$$

meets the circle, $x^2 + y^2 = r^2$

13. Find the quation to the circles which pass through the origin and cut off equal chords a from the straight lines $y = x$ and $y = -x$.

14. Find the equation to the straight lines joining the origin to the points in which the straight line $y = mx + c$ cuts the circle,

$$x^2 + y^2 = 2ax + 2by$$

Hence, find the condition that these points may subtend a right angle at the origin.

Find also the condition that the straight line may touch the circle.

Find the equation to the circle which:

15. has its centre at the point (3, 4) and touches the straight line,

$$5x + 12y = 1$$

16. touches the axes of coordinates and also the line

$$\frac{x}{a} + \frac{y}{b} = 1$$

the centre being in the positive quadrant.

17. has its centre at the point (1, –3) and touches the straight line,

$$2x - y - 4 = 0$$

18. Find the general equation of a circle referred to two perpendicular tangents as axes.

19. Find the equation to a circle of radius r which touches the axis of y at a point distant h from the origin, the centre of the circle being in the positive quadrant.

Prove also that the equation to the other tangent which passes through the origin is,

$$(r^2 - h^2)x + 2rhy = 0$$

20. Find the equation to the circle whose centre is at the point (α, β) and which passes through the origin, and prove that the equation of the tangent at the origin is,

$$\alpha x + \beta y = 0$$

21. Two circles are drawn through the points $(a, 5a)$ and $(4a, a)$ to touch the axis of y. Prove that they intersect at an angle $\tan^{-1}\left(\dfrac{40}{9}\right)$

22. A circle passes through the points $(-1, 1)$, $(0, 6)$ and $(5, 5)$. Find the points on this circle the tangents at which are parallel to the straight line joining the origin to its centre.

➤ **160.** *To shew that from any point there can be drawn two tangents, real or imaginary, to a circle.*

Let the equation to the circle be $x^2 + y^2 = a^2$, and let given point be (x_1, y_1). [Fig. Art. 161]

The equation to any tangents is, by Art. 155,

$$y = mx + a\sqrt{1 + m^2}$$

If this pass through the given point (x_1, y_1) we have

$$y_1 = mx_1 + a\sqrt{1 + m^2} \qquad \qquad \text{...(1)}$$

This is the equation which gives the values of m corresponding to the tangents which pass through (x_1, y_1).

Now (1), gives

$$y_1 - mx_1 = a\sqrt{1 + m^2}$$

i.e., $$y_1{}^2 - 2mx_1y_1 + m^2x_1{}^2 = a^2 + a^2m^2$$

i.e., $$m^2(x_1{}^2 - a^2) - 2mx_1y_1 + y_1{}^2 - a^2 = 0 \qquad \text{...(2)}$$

The equation (2) is a quadratic equation and gives therefore, two values of m (real, coincident, or imaginary) corresponding to any given values of x_1 and y_1. For each of these values of m we have a corresponding tangent.

The roots of equation (2) are, by Art. 1, real, coincident or imaginary according as,

$$(2x_1y_1)^2 \div 4(x_1{}^2 - a^2)(y_1{}^2 - a^2)$$ is positive, zero, or negative, i.e., according as,

$$a^2(-a^2 + x_1{}^2 + y_1{}^2)$$ is positive, zero, or negative, i.e., according as,

$$x_1{}^2 + y_1{}^2 \gtreqless a^2$$

If $x_1^2 + y_1^2 > a^2$, the distance of the point (x_1, y_1) from the centre is greater than the radius and hence it lies outside the circle.

If $x_1^2 + y_1^2 = a^2$, the point (x_1, y_1) lies on the circle and the two coincident tangents become the tangent at (x_1, y_1).

If $x_1^2 + y_1^2 < a^2$, the point (x_1, y_1) lies within the circle, and no tangents can then be geometrically drawn to the circle. It is however, better to say that the tangents are imaginary.

➤ **161. Chord of Contact. Def.:** If from any point T without a circle two tangents TP and TQ be drawn to the circle, the straight line PQ joining the points of contact is called the chord of contact of tangents from T.

To find the equation of the chord of contact of tangents drawn to the circle $x^2 + y^2 = a^2$ from the external point (x_1, y_1).

Let T be the point (x_1, y_1) and P and Q the points (x', y') and (x'', y'') respectively.

The tangent at P is

$$xx' + yy' = a^2 \qquad \ldots(1)$$

and that at Q is,

$$xx'' + yy'' = a^2 \qquad \ldots(2)$$

Since, these tangents pass through T, its coordinates (x_1, y_1) must satisfy both (1) and (2).

Hence, $\qquad\qquad x_1 x' + y_1 y' = a^2 \qquad \ldots(3)$

and $\qquad\qquad x_1 x'' + y_1 y'' = a^2 \qquad \ldots(4)$

The equation to PQ is then,

$$xx_1 + yy_1 = a^2 \qquad \ldots(5)$$

For, since (3) is true, it follows that the point (x', y'), i.e., P, lies on (5).

Also, since (4) is true, it follows that the point (x'', y''), i.e., Q, lies on (5).

Hence, both P and Q lie on the straight line (5), i.e., (5), is the equation to the required chord of contact.

If the point (x_1, y_1) lie within the circle the argument of the preceding article will show that the line joining the (imaginary) points of contact of the two (imaginary) tangents drawn from (x_1, y_1) is $xx_1 + yy_1 = a^2$.

We thus see, since this line is always real, that we may have a real straight line joining the imaginary points of contact of two imaginary tangents.

➤ **162. Pole and Polar. Def.:** If through a point P (within or without a circle) there be drawn any straight line to meet the circle in Q and R, the locus of the point of intersection of the tangents at Q and R is called the polar of P; also P is called the pole of the polar.

In the next article the locus will be proved to be a straight line.

➤ **163.** *To find the equation to the polar of the point* (x_1, y_1) *with respect to the circle* $x^2 + y^2 = a^2$.

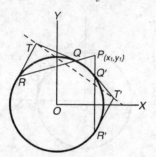   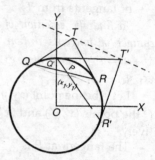

Let QR be any chord drawn through P and let the tangents at Q and R meet in the point T whose coordinates are (h, k).

Hence, QR is the chord of contact of tangents drawn from the point (h, k) and therefore, by Art. 161, its equation is $xh + yk = a^2$.

Since, this line passes through the point (x_1, y_1) we have

$$x_1 h + y_1 k = a^2 \qquad \ldots(1)$$

Since, the relation (1) is true it follows that the variable point (h, k) always lies on the straight line whose equation is,

$$xx_1 + yy_1 = a^2 \qquad \ldots(2)$$

Hence, Eq. (2) is the polar of the point (x_1, y_1).

In a similar manner it may be proved that the polar of (x_1, y_1) with respect to the circle.

$$x^2 + y^2 + 2gx + 2fy + c = 0$$

is $\qquad xx_1 + yy_1 + g(x + x_1) + f(y + y_1) + c = 0$

➤ **164.** The equation (2) of the preceding article is the same as equation (5) of Art. 161. If, therefore, the point (x_1, y_1) be without the circle, as in the right-hand figure, the polar is the same as the chord of contact of the real tangents drawn through (x_1, y_1).

If the point (x_1, y_1) be on the circle, the polar coincides with the tangent at it. (Art. 150).

If the point (x_1, y_1) be within the circle, then, as in Art. 161, the equation (2) is the line joining the (imaginary) points of contact of the two (imaginary) tangents that can be drawn from (x_1, y_1).

We see therefore, that the polar might have been defined as follows:

The polar of a given point is the straight line which passes through the (real or imaginary) points of contact of tangents drawn from the given point; also the pole of any straight line is the point of intersection of tangents at the points (real or imaginary) in which this straight line meets the circle.

➤ **165.** *Geometrical construction for the polar of a point.*

The equation to OP, which is the line joining $(0, 0)$ to (x_1, y_1) is

$$y = \frac{y_1}{x_1} x$$

i.e., $$xy_1 - x_1 y = 0 \qquad \qquad \text{...(1)}$$

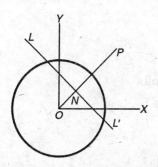

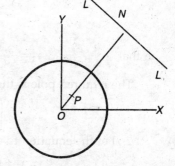

Also, the polar of P is

$$xx_1 + yy_1 = a^2 \qquad \qquad \text{...(2)}$$

By Art. 69, the lines (1) and (2) are perpendicular to one another. Hence, OP is perpendicular to the polar of P.

Also, the length $OP = \sqrt{x_1{}^2 + y_1{}^2}$,

and the perpendicular, ON from O upon (2)

$$= \frac{a^2}{\sqrt{x_1{}^2 + y_1{}^2}}$$

Hence, the product $ON \cdot OP = a^2$

The polar of any point P is therefore, constructed thus:

Join OP and on it (produced if necessary) take a point N such that the rectangle $ON. OP$ is equal to the square of the radius of the circle.

Through N draw the straight line LL' perpendicular to OP; this is the polar required.

[It will be noted that the middle point N of any chord LL' lies on the line joining the centre to the pole of the chord.]

➤ **166.** *To find the pole of a given line with respect to any circle.*

Let the equation to the given line be

$$Ax + By + C = 0 \qquad \qquad \text{...(1)}$$

1. Let the equation to the circle be,

$$x^2 + y^2 = a^2$$

and let the required pole be (x_1, y_1).

Then, (1) must be the equation to the polar of (x_1, y_1), *i.e.*, it is the same as the equation,

$$xx_1 + yy_1 - a^2 = 0 \qquad \qquad \text{...(2)}$$

Comparing equations (1) and (2), we have

$$\frac{x_1}{A} = \frac{y_1}{B} = \frac{-a^2}{C}$$

so that $\qquad x_1 = -\frac{A}{C} a^2 \quad$ and $\quad y_1 = -\frac{B}{C} a^2$

The required pole is therefore, the point

$$\left(-\frac{A}{C} a^2, \ -\frac{B}{C} a^2 \right)$$

2. Let the equation to the circle be

$$x^2 + y^2 + 2gx + 2fy + c = 0$$

If (x_1, y_1) be the required pole, then (1) must be equivalent to the equation,

$$xx_1 + yy_1 + g(x + x_1) + f(y + y_1) + c = 0 \qquad \text{(Art. 163)}$$

i.e., $\qquad x(x_1 + g) + y(y_1 + f) + gx_1 + fy_1 + c = 0 \qquad \text{...(3)}$

Comparing (1) with (3), we therefore, have

$$\frac{x_1 + g}{A} = \frac{y_1 + f}{B} = \frac{gx_1 + fy_1 + c}{C}$$

By solving these equations we have the values of x_1 and y_1.

EXAMPLE *Find the pole of the straight line:*
$$9x + y - 28 = 0 \qquad \ldots(1)$$
with respect to the circle,
$$2x^2 + 2y^2 - 3x + 5y - 7 = 0 \qquad \ldots(2)$$

If (x_1, y_1) be the required point the line (1) must coincide with the polar of (x_1, y_1), whose equation is,

$$2xx_1 + 2yy_1 - \frac{3}{2}(x + x_1) + \frac{5}{2}(y + y_1) - 7 = 0$$

i.e., $\qquad x(4x_1 - 3) + y(4y_1 + 5) - 3x_1 + 5y_1 - 14 = 0 \qquad \ldots(3)$

Since, (1) and (3), are the same, we have

$$\frac{4x_1 - 3}{9} = \frac{4y_1 + 5}{1} = \frac{-3x_1 + 5y_1 - 14}{-28}$$

Hence, $\qquad\qquad\qquad x_1 = 9y_1 + 12$

and $\qquad\qquad\qquad 3x_1 - 117y_1 = 126$

Solving these equations, we have $x_1 = 3$ and $y_1 = -1$, so that the required point is $(3, -1)$.

➤ **167.** *If the polar of a point P pass through a point T, then the polar of T passes through P.*

Let P and T be the points (x_1, y_1) and (x_2, y_2) respectively. (Fig. Art. 163).

The polar of (x_1, y_1) with respect to the circle $x^2 + y^2 = a^2$ is,

$$xx_1 + yy_1 = a^2$$

This straight line passes through the point T if,

$$x_2x_1 + y_2y_1 = a^2 \qquad \ldots(1)$$

Since, the relation (1) is true, it follows that the point (x_1, y_1), *i.e.,* P, lies on the straight line $xx_2 + yy_2 = a^2$, which is the polar of (x_2, y_2), *i.e., T*, with respect to the circle.

Hence, the proposition.

Cor. : The intersection T, of the polars of two points, P and Q, is the pole of the line PQ.

➤ **168.** *To find the length of the tangent that can be drawn from the point (x_1, y_1) to the circles.*

(1) $x^2 + y^2 = a^2$ and

(2) $x^2 + y^2 + 2gx + 2fy + c = 0$

If T be an external point (Fig. Art. 163), TQ a tangent and O the centre of the circle, then TQO is a right angle and hence,

$$TQ^2 = OT^2 - OQ^2$$

1. If the equation, to the circle be $x^2 + y^2 = a^2$, O is the origin,

$$OT^2 = x_1^2 + y_1^2 \quad \text{and} \quad OQ^2 = a^2$$

Hence, $TQ^2 = x_1^2 + y_1^2 - a^2$

2. Let the equation to the circle be,

$$x^2 + y^2 + 2gx + 2fy + c = 0$$

i.e., $(x + g)^2 + (y + f)^2 = g^2 + f^2 - c$

In   this   case O is   the   point $(-g, -f)$ and
$OQ^2 = (\text{radius})^2 = g^2 + f^2 - c$.

Hence, $OT^2 = [x_1 - (-g)]^2 + [y_1 - (-f)]^2$ (Art. 20)

$$= (x_1 + g)^2 + (y_1 + f)^2$$

Therefore, $TQ^2 = (x_1 + g)^2 + (y_1 + f)^2 - (g^2 + f^2 - c)$

$$= x_1^2 + y_1^2 + 2gx_1 + 2fy_1 + c$$

In each case we see that (the equation to the circle being written so that the coefficients of x^2 and y^2 are each unity, and the right-hand member zero), the square of the length of the tangent drawn to the circle from the point (x_1, y_1) is obtained by substituting x_1 and y_1 for x and y in the left-hand member of the equation.

➤ **169.** *To find the equation to the pair of tangents that can be drawn from the point (x_1, y_1) to the circle $x^2 + y^2 = a^2$.*

Let (h, k) be any point on either of the tangents from (x_1, y_1).

Since, any straight line touches a circle if the perpendicular on it from the centre is equal to the radius, the perpendicular from the origin upon the line joining (x_1, y_1) to (h, k) must be equal to a.

The equation to the straight line joining these two points is,

$$y - y_1 = \frac{k - y_1}{h - x_1}(x - x_1)$$

i.e., $y(h - x_1) - x(k - y_1) + kx_1 - hy_1 = 0$

Hence, $\dfrac{kx_1 - hy_1}{\sqrt{(h - x_1)^2 + (k - y_1)^2}} = a$

So that, $(kx_1 - hy_1)^2 = a^2[(h - x_1)^2 + (k - y_1)^2]$

Therefore, the point (h, k) always lies on the locus

$$(x_1y - xy_1)^2 = a^2[(x - x_1)^2 + (y - y_1)^2] \qquad \text{...(1)}$$

This therefore, is the required equation.

The equation (1), may be written in the form

$$x^2(y_1{}^2 - a^2) + y^2(x_1{}^2 - a^2) - a^2(x_1{}^2 + y_1{}^2)$$
$$= 2xyx_1y_1 - 2a^2xx_1 - 2a^2yy_1$$

i.e., $(x^2 + y^2 - a^2)(x_1{}^2 + y_1{}^2 - a^2) = x^2x_1{}^2 + y^2y_1{}^2 + a^4 + 2xyx_1y_1$
$$- 2a^2xx_1 - 2a^2yy_1 = (xx_1 + yy_1 - a^2)^2 \qquad \dots(2)$$

➤ ***170.** In a later chapter we shall obtain the equation to the pair of tangents to any curve of the second degree in a form analogous to that of equation (2) of the previous article.

Similarly, the equation to the pair of tangents that can be drawn from (x_1, y_1) to the circle

$$(x - f)^2 + (y - g)^2 = a^2$$

is $\{(x - f)^2 + (y - g)^2 - a^2\}\{(x_1 - f)^2 + (y_1 - g)^2 - a^2\}$
$$= \{(x - f)(x_1 - f) + (y - g)(y_1 - g) - a^2\}^2 \qquad \dots(1)$$

If the equation to the circle be given in the form

$$x^2 + y^2 + 2gx + 2fy + c = 0$$

the equation to the tangents is, similarly,

$$(x^2 + y^2 + 2gx + 2fy + c)(x_1{}^2 + y_1{}^2 + 2gx_1 + 2fy_1 + c)$$
$$= [xx_1 + yy_1 + g(x + x_1) + f(y + y_1) + c]^2 \qquad \dots(2)$$

EXAMPLES XIX

Find the polar of the point:

1. $(1, 2)$ with respect to the circle $x^2 + y^2 = 7$.

2. $(4, -1)$ with respect to the circle $2x^2 + 2y^2 = 11$.

3. $(-2, 3)$ with respect to the circle $x^2 + y^2 - 4x - 6y + 5 = 0$.

4. $\left(5, -\dfrac{1}{2}\right)$ with respect to the circle $3x^2 + 3y^2 - 7x + 8y - 9 = 0$.

5. $(a, -b)$ with respect to the circle $x^2 + y^2 + 2ax - 2by + a^2 - b^2 = 0$.
   Find the pole of the straight line:

6. $x + 2y = 1$ with respect to the circle $x^2 + y^2 = 5$.

7. $2x - y = 6$ with respect to the circle $5x^2 + 5y^2 = 9$.

8. $2x + y + 12 = 0$ with respect to the circle $x^2 + y^2 - 4x + 3y - 1 = 0$.

9. $48x - 54y + 53 = 0$ with respect to the circle
$$3x^2 + 3y^2 + 5x - 7y + 2 = 0.$$

10. $ax + by + 3a^2 + 3b^2 = 0$ with respect to the circle,
$$x^2 + y^2 + 2ax + 2by = a^2 + b^2$$

11. Tangents are drawn to the circle $x^2 + y^2 = 12$ at the points where it is met by the circle $x^2 + y^2 - 5x + 3y - 2 = 0$; find the point of intersection of these tangents.

12. Find the equation to that chord of the circle $x^2 + y^2 = 81$ which is bisected at the point $(-2, 3)$ and its pole with respect to the circle.

13. Prove that the polars of the point $(1, -2)$ with respect to the circles whose equations are:

$$x^2 + y^2 + 6y + 5 = 0 \quad \text{and} \quad x^2 + y^2 + 2x + 8y + 5 = 0$$

coincide; prove also that there is another point the polars of which with respect to these circles are the same and find its coordinates.

14. Find the condition that the chord of contact of tangents from the point (x', y') to the circle $x^2 + y^2 = a^2$ should subtend a right angle at the centre.

15. Prove that the distance of two points, P and Q each from the polar of the other with respect to a circle, are to one another as the distances of the points from the centre of the circle.

16. Prove that the polar of a given point with respect to any one of the circles $x^2 + y^2 - 2kx + c^2 = 0$, where k is variable, always passes through a fixed point, whatever be the value of k.

17. Tangents are drawn from the point (h, k) to the circle $x^2 + y^2 = a^2$; prove that the area of the triangle formed by them and the straight line joining their points of contact is,

$$\frac{a(h^2 + k^2 - a^2)^{3/2}}{h^2 + k^2}$$

Find the lengths of the tangents drawn:

18. to the circle $2x^2 + 2y^2 = 3$ from the point $(-2, 3)$.

19. to the circle $3x^2 + 3y^2 - 7x - 6y = 12$ from the point $(6, -7)$.

20. to the circle $x^2 + y^2 + 2bx - 3b^2 = 0$ from the point $(a + b, a - b)$

21. Given the three circles,

$$x^2 + y^2 - 16x + 60 = 0,$$
$$3x^2 + 3y^2 - 36x + 81 = 0,$$
and $$x^2 + y^2 - 16x - 12y + 84 = 0$$

Find (1) the point from which the tangents to them are equal in length and (2) this length.

22. The distances from the origin of the centres of three circles $x^2 + y^2 - 2\lambda x = c^2$ (where c is a constant and λ a variable) are in geometrical progression; prove that the lengths of the tangents drawn to them from any point on the circle, $x^2 + y^2 = c^2$ are also in geometrical progression.

23. Find the equation to the pair of tangents drawn,

(i) from the point (11, 3) to the circle $x^2 + y^2 = 65$,

(ii) from the point (4, 5) to the circle

$$2x^2 + 2y^2 - 8x + 12y + 21 = 0.$$

➤ **171.** *To find the general equation of a circle referred to polar coordinates.*

Let O be the origin, or pole OX the initial line, C the centre and a the radius of the circle.

Let the polar coordinates of C be R and α, so that $OC = R$ and $\angle XOC = \alpha$.

Let a radius vector through O at an angle θ with the initial line cut the circle in P and Q. Let OP or OQ be r.

Then, (*Trig.* Art. 164) we have

$$CP^2 = OC^2 + OP^2 - 2OC \cdot OP \cos COP,$$

i.e., $a^2 = R^2 + r^2 - 2Rr \cos(\theta - \alpha)$

i.e., $\qquad r^2 - 2Rr \cos(\theta - \alpha) + R^2 - a^2 = 0$ ...(1)

This is the required polar equation.

➤ **172.** *Particular cases of the general equation in polar coordinates.*

(1) Let the initial line be taken to go through the centre C. Then $\alpha = 0$ and the equation becomes,

$$r^2 - 2Rr \cos \theta + R^2 - a^2 = 0$$

(2) Let the pole O be taken on the circle, so that

$$R = OC = a$$

The general equation then becomes

$$r^2 - 2ar \cos(\theta - \alpha) = 0$$

i.e., $\qquad r = 2a \cos(\theta - \alpha)$

(3) Let the pole be on the circle and also let the initial line pass through the centre of the circle. In this case,

$$\alpha = 0 \quad \text{and} \quad R = a$$

The general equation reduces then to the simple form $r = 2a \cos \theta$.

This is at once evident from the figure.

For, if OCA be a diameter, we have

$$OP = OA \cos \theta$$

i.e., $\qquad r = 2a \cos \theta$

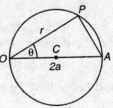

➤ **173.** The equation (1) of Art. 171 is a quadratic equation which, for any given value of θ, gives two values of r. These two values in the figure are OP and OQ.

If these two values be called r_1 and r_2, we have from equation (1),

$$r_1 r_2 = \text{product of the roots} = R^2 - a^2$$

i.e., $OP \cdot OQ = R^2 - a^2$

The value of the rectangle $OP \cdot OQ$ is therefore, the same for all values of θ. It follows that if we drew any other line through O to cut the circle in P_1 and Q_1 we should have $OP \cdot OQ = OP_1 \cdot OQ_1$.

This is the well-known geometrical proposition.

➤ **174.** *Find the equation to the chord joining the points on the circle $r = 2a \cos\theta$ whose vectorial angles are θ_1 and θ_2, and deduce the equation to the tangent at the point θ_1.*

The equation to any straight line in polar coordinates is (Art. 88).

$$p = r \cos(\theta - \alpha) \qquad \ldots(1)$$

If this pass through the points $(2a \cos\theta_1, \theta_1)$ and $(2a \cos\theta_2, \theta_2)$, we have

$$2a \cos\theta_1 \cos(\theta_1 - \alpha) = p = 2a \cos\theta_2 \cos(\theta_2 - \alpha) \qquad \ldots(2)$$

Hence, $\cos(2\theta_1 - \alpha) + \cos\alpha = \cos(2\theta_2 - \alpha) + \cos\alpha,$

i.e., $2\theta_1 - \alpha = -(2\theta_2 - \alpha)$

Since, θ_1 and θ_2 are not, in general, equal.

Hence, $\alpha = \theta_1 + \theta_2$

and then, from (2), $p = 2a \cos\theta_1 \cos\theta_2$.

On substitution in (1), the equation to the required chord is,

$$r \cos(\theta - \theta_1 - \theta_2) = 2a \cos\theta_1 \cos\theta_2 \qquad \ldots(3)$$

The equation to the tangent at the point θ_1 is found, as in Art. 150, by putting $\theta_2 = \theta_1$ in equation (3).

We thus obtain as the equation to the tangent,

$$r \cos(\theta - 2\theta_1) = 2a \cos^2\theta_1$$

As in the foregoing article it could be shewn that the equation to the chord joining the points θ_1 and θ_2 on the circle $r = 2a \cos(\theta - \gamma)$ is

$$r \cos[\theta - \theta_1 - \theta_2 + \gamma] = 2a \cos(\theta_1 - \gamma) \cos(\theta_2 - \gamma)$$

and hence that the equation to the tangent at the point θ_1 is

$$r \cos(\theta - 2\theta_1 + \gamma) = 2a \cos^2(\theta_1 - \gamma)$$

EXAMPLES XX

1. Find the coordinates of the centre of the circle,
$$r = A \cos \theta + B \sin \theta$$

2. Find the polar equation of a circle, the initial line being a tangent. What does it become if the origin be on the circumference?

3. Draw the loci:
   (i) $r = a$;   (ii) $r = a \sin \theta$;   (iii) $r = a \cos \theta$;   (iv) $r = a \sec \theta$;
   (v) $r = a \cos (\theta - \alpha)$;   (vi) $r = a \sec (\theta - \alpha)$.

4. Prove that the equations $r = a \cos (\theta - \alpha)$ and $r = b \sin (\theta - \alpha)$ represent two circles which cut at right angles.

5. Prove that the equation $r^2 \cos \theta - ar \cos 2\theta - 2a^2 \cos \theta = 0$ represents a straight line and a circle.

6. Find the polar equation to the circle described on the straight line joining the points (a, α), and (b, β) as diameter.

7. Prove that the equation to the circle described on the straight line joining the points $(1, 60°)$ and $(2, 30°)$ as diameter is,
$$r^2 - r [\cos (\theta - 60°) + 2 \cos (\theta - 30°)] + \sqrt{3} = 0$$

8. Find the condition that the straight line,
$$\frac{1}{r} = a \cos \theta + b \sin \theta$$
   may touch the circle, $r = 2c \cos \theta$

➤ **175.** *To find the general equation to a circle referred to oblique axes which meet at an angle* ω.

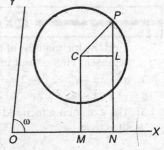

Let C be the centre and a the radius of the circle. Let the coordinates of C be (h, k) so that if CM, drawn parallel to the axis of y, meets OX in M, then,
$$OM = h \quad \text{and} \quad MC = k$$

Let P be any point on the circle whose coordinates are x and y. Draw PN, the ordinate of P, and CL parallel to OX to meet PN in L.

Then, $CL = MN = ON - OM = x - h,$

and $LP = NP - NL = NP - MC = y - k$

Also, $\angle CLP = \angle ONP = 180° - \angle PNX = 180° - \omega$

Hence, since $CL^2 + LP^2 - 2CL \cdot LP \cos CLP = a^2$

we have $(x - h)^2 + (y - k)^2 + 2(x - h)(y - k) \cos \omega = a^2$

i.e., $x^2 + y^2 + 2xy \cos \omega - 2x(h + k \cos \omega) - 2y(k + h \cos \omega)$
$$+ h^2 + k^2 + 2hk \cos \omega = a^2$$

The required equation is therefore, found.

➤ **176.** As in Art. 142 it may be shewn that the equation,
$$x^2 + 2xy \cos \omega + y^2 + 2gx + 2fy + c = 0$$

represents a circle and its radius and centre found.

EXAMPLE *If the axes be inclined at 60°, prove that the equation,*
$$x^2 + xy + y^2 - 4x - 5y - 2 = 0 \qquad \qquad \ldots(1)$$

represents a circle and find its centre and radius.

If ω be equal to 60°, so that $\cos \omega = \dfrac{1}{2}$, the equation of Art. 175 becomes

$$x^2 + xy + y^2 - x(2h + k) - y(2k + h) + h^2 + k^2 + hk = a^2$$

This equation agrees with (1), if

$$2h + k = 4 \qquad \qquad \ldots(2)$$
$$2k + h = 5 \qquad \qquad \ldots(3)$$

and $\qquad \qquad h^2 + k^2 + hk - a^2 = -2 \qquad \qquad \ldots(4)$

Solving (2) and (3), we have $h = 1$ and $k = 2$. Equation (4) then gives
$$a^2 = h^2 + k^2 + hk + 2 = 9$$

so that $\qquad \qquad a = 3$

The equation (1) therefore, represents a circle whose centre is the point (1, 2) and whose radius is 3, the axes being inclined at 60°.

EXAMPLES XXI

Find the inclinations of the axes so that the following equations may represent circles, and in each case find the radius and centre:

1. $x^2 - xy + y^2 - 2gx - 2fy = 0$
2. $x^2 + \sqrt{3} xy + y^2 - 4x - 6y + 5 = 0$
3. The axes being inclined at an angle ω, find the centre and radius of the circle,
$$x^2 + 2xy \cos \omega + y^2 - 2gx - 2fy = 0$$
4. The axes being inclined at 45°, find the equation to the circle whose centre is the point (2, 3) and whose radius is 4.
5. The axes being inclined at 60°, find the equation to the circle whose centre is the point (–3, –5) and whose radius is 6.
6. Prove that the equation to a circle whose radius is a and which touches the axes of coordinates, which are inclined at an angle ω, is
$$x^2 + 2xy \cos \omega + y^2 - 2a (x + y) \cot \frac{\omega}{2} + a^2 \cot^2 \frac{\omega}{2} = 0$$

7. Prove that the straight line $y = mx$ will touch the circle

$$x^2 + 2xy \cos \omega + y^2 + 2gx + 2fy + c = 0$$

if $\qquad (g + fm)^2 = c(1 + 2m \cos \omega + m^2)$

8. The axes being inclined at an angle ω, find the equation to the circle whose diameter is the straight line joining the points,

$$(x', y') \text{ and } (x'', y'')$$

Coordinates of a point on a circle expressed in terms of one single variable.

➤ **177.** If, in the figure of Art. 139, we put the angle MOP equal to α, the coordinates of the point P are easily seen to be $a \cos \alpha$ and $a \sin \alpha$.

These equations clearly satisfy equation (1) of that article.

The position of the point P is therefore, known when the value of α is given, and it may be, for brevity, called "the point α."

With the ordinary Cartesian coordinates we have to give the values of *two* separate quantities x' and y' (which are however, connected by the relation $x' = \sqrt{a^2 - y'^2}$) to express the position of a point P on the circle. The above substitution therefore, often simplifies solutions of problems.

➤ **178.** *To find the equation to the straight line joining two points α and β, on the circle $x^2 + y^2 = a^2$.*

Let the points be P and Q, and let ON be the perpendicular from the origin on the straight line PQ; then ON bisects the angle POQ, and hence,

$$\angle XON = \frac{1}{2}(\angle XOP + \angle XOQ) = \frac{1}{2}(\alpha + \beta)$$

Also, $\qquad ON = OP \cos NOP = a \cos \dfrac{\alpha - \beta}{2}$

The equation to PQ is therefore, (Art. 53),

$$x \cos \frac{\alpha + \beta}{2} + y \sin \frac{\alpha + \beta}{2} = a \cos \frac{\alpha - \beta}{2}$$

If we put $\beta = \alpha$ we have, as the equation to the tangent at the point a,

$$x \cos \alpha + y \sin \alpha = a$$

This may also be deduced from the equation of Art. 150 by putting $x' = a \cos \alpha$ and $y' = a \sin \alpha$.

➤ **179.** If the equation to the circle be in the more general form

$$(x - h)^2 + (y - k)^2 = a^2 \qquad \text{(Art. 140)}$$

we may express the coordinates of P in the form

$$(h + a \cos \alpha, k + a \sin \alpha)$$

For these values satisfy the above equation.

Here, α is the angle LCP [Fig. Art. 140]

The equation to the straight line joining the points α and β can be easily shewn to be

$$(x - h) \cos \frac{\alpha + \beta}{2} + (y - k) \sin \frac{\alpha + \beta}{2} = a \cos \frac{\alpha - \beta}{2}$$

and so the tangent at the point α is

$$(x - h) \cos \alpha + (y - k) \sin \alpha = a$$

➤ ***180. Common tangents to two circles:** If O_1 and O_2 be the centres of two circles whose radii are r_1 and r_2, and if one pair of common tangents meet O_1O_2 in T_1 and the other pair meet it in T_2, then, by similar triangles, we have $\dfrac{O_1T_2}{T_2O_2} = \dfrac{r_1}{r_2} = \dfrac{O_1T_1}{O_2T_1}$. The points T_1 and T_2 therefore, divide O_1O_2 in the ratio of the radii.

The coordinates of T_1 having been found, the corresponding tangents are straight lines passing through it, such that the perpendiculars on them from O_1 are each equal to r_1. So for the other pair which pass through T_2.

EXAMPLE   *Find the four common tangents to the circles*

$$x^2 + y^2 - 22x + 4y + 100 = 0 \quad \text{and} \quad x^2 + y^2 + 22x - 4y - 100 = 0$$

The equations may be written.

$$(x - 11)^2 + (y + 2)^2 = 5^2 \text{ and } (x + 11)^2 + (y - 2)^2 = 15^2$$

The centre of the first is the point $(11, -2)$ and its radius is 5.

The centre of the second is the point $(-11, 2)$ and its radius is 15.

Then, T_2 is the point dividing internally the line joining the centres in the ratio $5 : 15$ and hence, (Art. 22) its coordinates are

$$\frac{15 \times 11 + 5 \times (-11)}{15 + 5} \quad \text{and} \quad \frac{15 \times (-2) + 5 \times 2}{15 + 5}$$

that is, T_2 is the point $\left(\dfrac{11}{2}, -1 \right)$

Similarly, T_1 is the point dividing this line externally in the ratio $5 : 15$, and hence its coordinates are:

$$\frac{15 \times 11 - 5 \times (-11)}{15 - 5} \quad \text{and} \quad \frac{15 \times (-2) - 5 \times 2}{15 - 5}$$

that is T_1 is the point $(22, -4)$.

Let the equation to either of the tangents passing through T_2 be

$$y + 1 = m\left(x - \frac{11}{2}\right) \qquad \text{...(1)}$$

Then, the perpendicular from the point $(11, -2)$ on it is equal to ± 5, and hence,

$$\frac{m\left(11 - \frac{11}{2}\right) - (-2 + 1)}{\sqrt{1 + m^2}} = \pm 5$$

On solving, we have $m = -\dfrac{24}{7}$ or $\dfrac{4}{3}$

The required tangents through T_2 are therefore,

$$24x + 7y = 125 \quad \text{and} \quad 4x - 3y = 25$$

Similarly, the equations to the tangents through T_1 are

$$y + 4 = m(x - 22) \qquad \text{...(2)}$$

where

$$\frac{m(11 - 22) - (-2 + 4)}{\sqrt{1 + m^2}} = \pm 5$$

On solving, we have $\quad m = \dfrac{7}{24} \quad$ or $\quad -\dfrac{3}{4}$

On substitution in (2), the required equations are therefore,

$$7x - 24y = 250 \quad \text{and} \quad 3x + 4y = 50$$

The four common tangents are therefore, found.

➤ **181.** We shall conclude this chapter with some miscellaneous examples on loci.

EXAMPLE 1 *Find the locus of a point P which moves so that its distance from a given point O is always in a given ratio (n : 1) to its distance from another given point A.*

Take O as origin and the direction of OA as the axis of x. Let the distance OA be a, so that A is the point $(a, 0)$.

If (x, y) be the coordinates of any position of P, we have

$$OP^2 = n^2 \cdot AP^2$$

i.e., $$x^2 + y^2 = n^2[(x - a)^2 + y^2]$$

i.e., $$(x^2 + y^2)(n^2 - 1) - 2an^2 x + n^2 a^2 = 0 \qquad \text{...(1)}$$

Hence, by Art. 143, the locus of P is a circle.

Let this circle meet the axis of x in the points C and D. Then OC and OD are the roots of the equation obtained by putting y equal to zero in (1).

Hence, $$OC = \frac{na}{n + 1} \quad \text{and} \quad OD = \frac{na}{n - 1}$$

We therefore, have

$$CA = \frac{a}{n+1} \quad \text{and} \quad AD = \frac{a}{n-1}$$

Hence,
$$\frac{OC}{CA} = \frac{OD}{AD} = n$$

The points C and D therefore, divide the line OA in the given ratio, and the required circle is on CD as diameter.

EXAMPLE 2 *From any point on one given circle tangents are drawn to another given circle; prove that the locus of the middle point of the chord of contact is a third circle.*

Take the centre of the first circle as origin and let the axis of x pass through the centre of the second circle. Their equations are then

$$x^2 + y^2 = a^2 \qquad \qquad \text{...(1)}$$

and
$$(x - c)^2 + y^2 = b^2 \qquad \qquad \text{...(2)}$$

where a and b are the radii, and c the distance between the centres of the circles.

Any point on (1) is $(a \cos \theta, a \sin \theta)$ where θ is vairable. Its chord of contact with respect to (2) is,

$$(x - c)(a \cos \theta - c) + ya \sin \theta = b^2 \qquad \qquad \text{...(3)}$$

The middle point of this chord of contact is the point where it is met by the perpendicular from the centre, *viz.*, the point $(c, 0)$.

The equation to this perpendicular is (Art. 70).

$$- (x - c) a \sin \theta + (a \cos \theta - c)y = 0 \qquad \qquad \text{...(4)}$$

Any equation deduced from (3) and (4) is satisfied by the coordinates of the point under consideration. If we eliminate θ from them, we shall have an equation always satisfied by the coordinates of the point, whatever be the value of θ. The result will thus be the equation to the required locus.

Solving (3) and (4), we have

$$a \sin \theta = \frac{b^2 y}{y^2 + (x - c)^2}$$

and
$$a \cos \theta - c = \frac{b^2 (x - c)}{y^2 + (x - c)^2}$$

so that,
$$a \cos \theta = c + \frac{b^2 (x - c)}{y^2 + (x - c)^2}$$

Hence,
$$a^2 = a^2 \cos^2 \theta + a^2 \sin^2 \theta$$

$$= c^2 + 2cb^2 \frac{x - c}{y^2 + (x - c)^2} + \frac{b^4}{y^2 + (x - c)^2}$$

The required locus is therefore,

$$(a^2 - c^2)\,[y^2 + (x - c)^2] = 2cb^2(x - c) + b^4$$

This is a circle and its centre and radius are easily found.

EXAMPLE 3 *Find the locus of a point P which is such that its polar with respect to one circle touches a second circle.*

Taking the notation of the last article, the equations to the two circles are

$$x^2 + y^2 = a^2 \qquad \qquad \ldots(1)$$

and

$$(x - c)^2 + y^2 = b^2 \qquad \qquad \ldots(2)$$

Let (h, k) be the coordinates of any position of P. Its polar with respect to (1) is

$$xh + yk = a^2 \qquad \qquad \ldots(3)$$

Also any tangent to (2) has its equation of the form (Art. 179)

$$(x - c) \cos \theta + y \sin \theta = b \qquad \qquad \ldots(4)$$

If then (3) be a tangent to (2) it must be of the form (4)

Therefore, $\qquad \dfrac{\cos \theta}{h} = \dfrac{\sin \theta}{k} = \dfrac{c \cos \theta + b}{a^2}$

These equations give,

$$\cos \theta\,(a^2 - ch) = bh \quad \text{and} \quad \sin \theta\,(a^2 - ch) = bk$$

Squaring and adding, we have

$$(a^2 - ch)^2 = b^2(h^2 + k^2) \qquad \qquad \ldots(5)$$

The locus of the point (h, k) is therefore, the curve

$$b^2(x^2 + y^2) = (a^2 - cx)^2$$

Aliter: The condition that (3) may touch (2) may be otherwise found.

For, as in Art. 153, the straight line (3) meets the circle (2) in the points whose abscissae are given by the equation,

$$k^2(x - c)^2 + (a^2 - hx)^2 = b^2 k^2$$

i.e., $\qquad x^2(h^2 + k^2) - 2x(ck^2 + a^2 h) + (k^2 c^2 + a^4 - b^2 k^2) = 0$

The line (3), will therefore, touch (2) if

$$(ck^2 + a^2 h)^2 = (h^2 + k^2)(k^2 c^2 + a^4 - b^2 k^2)$$

i.e., if $\qquad b^2(h^2 + k^2) = (ch - a^2)^2$

which is equation (5).

EXAMPLE 4 *O is a fixed point and P any point on a given circle; OP is joined and on it a point Q is taken so that OP. OQ = a constant quantity k^2; prove that the locus of Q is a circle which becomes a straight line when O lies on the original circle.*

Let O be taken as pole and the line through the centre C as the initial line. Let $OC = d$, and let the radius of the circle be a.

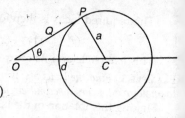

The equation to the circle is then,

$$a^2 = r^2 + d^2 - 2rd \cos \theta \text{ (Art. 171)}$$

where $OP = r$ and $\angle POC = \theta$.

Let OQ be ρ, so that, by the given condition, we have $r\rho = k^2$ and hence, $$r = \frac{k^2}{\rho}.$$

Substituting this value in the equation to the circle, we have

$$a^2 = \frac{k^4}{\rho^2} + d^2 - 2\frac{k^2 d}{\rho} \cos \theta \qquad \ldots(1)$$

so that the equation to the locus of Q is

$$r^2 - 2\frac{k^2 d}{d^2 - a^2} r \cos \theta = -\frac{k^4}{d^2 - a^2} \qquad \ldots(2)$$

But the equation to a circle, whose radius is a' and whose centre is on the initial line at a distance d', is

$$r^2 - 2rd' \cos \theta = a'^2 - d'^2 \qquad \ldots(3)$$

Comparing (1) and (2), we see that the required locus is a circle, such that

$$d' = \frac{k^2 d}{d^2 - a^2} \quad \text{and} \quad a'^2 - d'^2 = -\frac{k^4}{d^2 - a^2}$$

Hence, $$a'^2 = \frac{k^4}{d^2 - a^2}\left[\frac{d^2}{d^2 - a^2} - 1\right] = \frac{k^4 a^2}{(d^2 - a^2)^2}$$

The required locus is therefore, a circle, of radius $\dfrac{k^2 a}{d^2 - a^2}$, whose centre is on the same line as the original centre at a distance $\dfrac{k^2 d}{d^2 - a^2}$ from the fixed point.

When O lies on the original circle the distance d is equal to a, and the equation (1) becomes $k^2 = 2dr \cos \theta$, i.e., in Cartesian coordinates,

$$x = \frac{k^2}{2d}$$

In this case the required locus is a straight line perpendicular to OC.

When a second curve is obtained from a given curve by the above geometrical process, the second curve is said to be the **inverse** of the first curve and the fixed point O is called the centre of inversion.

The inverse of a circle is therefore a circle or a straight line according as the centre of inversion is not, or is, on the circumference of the original circle.

EXAMPLE 5 *PQ is a straight line drawn through O, one of the common points of two circles, and meets them again in P and Q; find the locus of the point S which bisects the line PQ.*

Take O as the origin, let the radii of the two circles be R and R', and let the lines joining their centres to O make angles α and α' with the initial line.

The equations to the two circles are therefore, [Art. 172 (2)]

$$r = 2R \cos (\theta - \alpha) \quad \text{and} \quad r = 2R' \cos (\theta - \alpha')$$

Hence, if S be the middle point of PQ, we have

$$2OS = OP + OQ = 2R \cos (\theta - \alpha) + 2R' \cos (\theta - \alpha')$$

The locus of the point S is therefore,

$$r = R \cos (\theta - \alpha) + R' \cos (\theta - \alpha')$$
$$= (R \cos \alpha + R' \cos \alpha') \cos \theta + (R \sin \alpha + R' \sin \alpha') \sin \theta$$
$$= 2R'' \cos (\theta - \alpha'') \qquad \qquad ...(1)$$

where $2R'' \cos \alpha'' = R \cos \alpha + R' \cos \alpha'$,

and $2R'' \sin \alpha'' = R \sin \alpha + R' \sin \alpha'$

Hence, $R'' = \dfrac{1}{2} \sqrt{R^2 + R'^2 + 2RR' \cos (\alpha - \alpha')}$

and $\tan \alpha'' = \dfrac{R \sin \alpha + R' \sin \alpha'}{R \cos \alpha + R' \cos \alpha'}$

From (1) the locus of S is a circle, whose radius is R'', which passes through the origin O and is such that the line joining O to its centre is inclined at an angle α'' to the initial line.

EXAMPLES XXII

1. A point moves so that the sum of the squares of its distances from the four sides of a square is constant; prove that it always lies on a circle.
2. A point moves so that the sum of the squares of the perpendiculars let fall from it on the sides of an equilateral triangle is constant; prove that its locus is a circle.
3. A point moves so that the sum of the squares of its distances from the angular points of a triangle is constant; prove that its locus is a circle.
4. Find the locus of a point which moves so that the square of the tangent drawn from it to the circle $x^2 + y^2 = a^2$ is equal to c times its distance from the straight line $lx + my + n = 0$.

5. Find the locus of a point whose distance from a fixed point is in a constant ratio to the tangent drawn from it to a given circle.

6. Find the locus of the vertex of a triangle, given (1) its base and the sum of the squares of its sides, (2) its base and the sum of m times the square of one side and n times the square of the other.

7. A point moves so that the sum of the squares of its distances from n fixed points is given. Prove that its locus is a circle.

8. Whatever be the value of α, prove that the locus of the intersection of the straight lines, $x \cos \alpha + y \sin \alpha = a$ and $x \sin \alpha - y \cos \alpha = b$ is a circle.

9. From a point P on a circle perpendiculars PM and PN are drawn to two radii of the circle which are not at right angles; find the locus of the middle point of MN.

10. Tangents are drawn to a circle from a point which always lies on a given line; prove that the locus of the middle point of the chord of contact is another circle.

11. Find the locus of the middle points of chords of the circle $x^2 + y^2 = a^2$ which pass through the fixed point (h, k).

12. Find the locus of the middle points of chords of the circle $x^2 + y^2 = a^2$ which subtend a right angle at the point $(c, 0)$.

13. O is a fixed point and P any point on a fixed circle; on OP is taken a point Q such that OQ is in a constant ratio to OP; prove that the locus of Q is a circle.

14. O is a fixed point and P any point on a given straight line; OP is joined and on it is taken a point Q such that $OP \cdot OQ = k^2$; prove that the locus of Q, i.e., the inverse of the given straight line with respect to O, is a circle which passes through O.

15. One vertex of a triangle of given species is fixed, and another moves along the circumference of a fixed circle; prove that the locus of the remaining vertex is a circle and find its radius.

16. O is any point in the plane of a circle, and OP_1P_2 any chord of the circle which passes through O and meets the circle in P_1 and P_2. On this chord is taken a point Q such that OQ is equal to (1) the arithmetic, (2) the geometric, and (3) the harmonic mean between OP_1 and OP_2; in each case find the equation to the locus of Q.

17. Find the locus of the point of intersection of the tangent to a given circle and the perpendicular let fall on this tangent from a fixed point on the circle.

18. A circle touches the axis of x and cuts off a constant length $2l$ from the axis of y; prove that the equation of the locus of its centre is $y^2 - x^2 = l^2 \cosec^2 \omega$, the axes being inclined at an angle ω.

19. A straight line moves so that the product of the perpendiculars on it from two fixed points is constant. Prove that the locus of the feet of the perpendiculars from each of these points upon the straight line is a circle, the same for each.

20. O is a fixed point and AP and BQ are two fixed parallel straight lines; BOA is perpendicular to both and POQ is a right angle. Prove that the locus of the foot of the perpendicular drawn from O upon PQ is the circle on AB as diameter.

21. Two rods, of lengths a and b, slide along the axes, which are rectangular, in such a manner that their ends are always concyclic; prove that the locus of the centre of the circle passing through these ends is the curve $4(x^2 - y^2) = a^2 - b^2$.

22. Shew that the locus of a point, which is such that the tangents from it to two given concentric circles are inversely as the radii, is a concentric circle, the square of whose radius is equal to the sum of the squares of the radii of the given circles.

23. Shew that if the length of the tangent from a point P to the circle $x^2 + y^2 = a^2$ be four times the length of the tangent from it to the circle $(x - a)^2 + y^2 = a^2$, then P lies on the circle,
$$15x^2 + 15y^2 - 32ax + a^2 = 0$$
Prove also that these three circles pass through two points and that the distance between the centres of the first and third circles is sixteen times the distance between the centres of the second and third circles.

24. Find the locus of the foot of the perpendicular let fall from the origin upon any chord of the circle $x^2 + y^2 + 2gx + 2fy + c = 0$ which subtends a right angle at the origin.
Find also the locus of the middle points of these chords.

25. Through a fixed point O are drawn two straight lines OPQ and ORS to meet a circle in P and Q, and R and S, respectively. Prove that the locus of the point of intersection of PS and QR, as also that of the point of intersection of PR and QS, is the polar of O with respect to the circle.

26. A, B, C and D are four points in a straight line; prove that the locus of a point P, such that the angles APB and CPD are equal, is a circle.

27. The polar of P with respect to the circle $x^2 + y^2 = a^2$ touches the circle $(x - \alpha)^2 + (y - \beta)^2 = b^2$; prove that its locus is the curve given by the equation, $(\alpha x + \beta y - a^2)^2 = b^2(x^2 + y^2)$.

28. A tangent is drawn to the circle $(x - a)^2 + y^2 = b^2$ and a perpendicular tangent to the circle $(x + a)^2 + y^2 = c^2$; find the locus of their point of intersection, and prove that the bisector of the angle between them always touches one or other of two fixed circles.

29. In any circle prove that the perpendicular from any point of it on the line joining the points of contact of two tangents is a mean proportional between the perpendiculars from the point upon the two tangents.

30. From any point on the circle
$$x^2 + y^2 + 2gx + 2fy + c = 0$$
tangents are drawn to the circle
$$x^2 + y^2 + 2gx + 2fy + c \sin^2 \alpha + (g^2 + f^2) \cos^2 \alpha = 0;$$
prove that the angle between them is 2α.

31. The angular points of a triangle are the points $(a \cos \alpha, a \sin \alpha)$, $(a \cos \beta, a \sin \beta)$, and $(a \cos \gamma, a \sin \gamma)$; prove that the coordinates of the orthocentre of the triangle are

$$a (\cos \alpha + \cos \beta + \cos \gamma) \text{ and } a (\sin \alpha + \sin \beta + \sin \gamma).$$

Hence prove that if A, B, C, and D be four points on a circle the orthocentres of the four triangles ABC, BCD, CDA, and DAB lie on a circle.

32. A variable circle passes through the point of intersection O of any two straight lines and cuts off from them portions OP and OQ such that $m . OP + n . OQ$ is equal to unity; prove that this circle always passes through a fixed point.

33. Find the length of the common chord of the circles, whose equations are $(x - a)^2 + y^2 = a^2$ and $x^2 + (y - b)^2 = b^2$, and prove that the equation to the circle whose diameter is this common chord is

$$(a^2 + b^2) (x^2 + y^2) = 2ab (bx + ay).$$

34. Prove that the length of the common chord of the two circles whose equations are

$$(x - a)^2 + (y - b)^2 = c^2 \text{ and } (x - b)^2 + (y - a)^2 = c^2$$
is $\sqrt{4c^2 - 2 (a - b)^2}.$

Hence find the condition that the two circles may touch.

35. Find the length of the common chord of the circles

$$x^2 + y^2 - 2ax - 4ay - 4a^2 = 0 \text{ and } x^2 + y^2 - 3ax + 4ay = 0.$$

Find also the equations of the common tangents and shew that the length of each is $4a$.

36. Find the equations to the common tangents of the circles
(1) $x^2 + y^2 - 2x - 6y + 9 = 0$ and $x^2 + y^2 + 6x - 2y + 1 = 0$,
(2) $x^2 + y^2 = c^2$ and $(x - a)^2 + y^2 = b^2$.

9

SYSTEMS OF CIRCLES

(This chapter may be omitted by the student on a first reading of the subject)

➤ **182. Orthogonal circles. Def.:** Two circles are said to intersect orthogonally when the tangents at their points of intersection are at right angles.

If the two circles intersect at P, the radii O_1P and O_2P, which are perpendicular to the tangents at P, must also be at right angles.

Hence, $$O_1O_2^2 = O_1P^2 + O_2P^2$$

i.e., the square of the distance between the centres must be equal to the sum of the squares of the radii.

Also the tangent from O_2 to the other circle is equal to the radius a_2, *i.e.*, if two circles be orthogonal the length of the tangent drawn from the centre of one circle to the second circle is equal to the radius of the first.

Either of these two conditions will determine whether the circles are orthogonal.

The centres of the circles,

$$x^2 + y^2 + 2gx + 2fy + c = 0 \quad \text{and} \quad x^2 + y^2 + 2g'x + 2f'y + c' = 0,$$

are the points $(-g, -f)$ and $(-g', -f')$; also the squares of their radii are $g^2 + f^2 - c$ and $g'^2 + f'^2 - c'$.

They therefore, cut orthogonally if

$$(-g + g')^2 + (-f + f')^2 = g^2 + f^2 - c + g'^2 + f'^2 - c',$$

i.e., if $$2gg' + 2ff' = c + c'.$$

➤ **183. Radical Axis. Def.** The radical axis of two circles is the locus of a point which moves so that the lengths of the tangents drawn from it to the two circles are equal.

Let the equations to the circles be

$$x^2 + y^2 + 2gx + 2fy + c = 0 \qquad \ldots(1)$$

and $$x^2 + y^2 + 2g_1x + 2f_1y + c_1 = 0 \qquad \ldots(2)$$

and let (x_1, y_1) be any point such that the tangents from it to these circles are equal.

By Art. 168, we have

$$x_1^2 + y_1^2 + 2gx_1 + 2fy_1 + c = x_1^2 + y_1^2 + 2g_1x_1 + 2f_1y_1 + c_1$$

i.e., $$2x_1(g - g_1) + 2y_1(f - f_1) + c - c_1 = 0$$

But this is the condition that the point (x_1, y_1) should lie on the locus

$$2x(g - g_1) + 2y(f - f_1) + c - c_1 = 0 \qquad \ldots(3)$$

This is therefore the equation to the radical axis, and it is clearly a straight line.

It is easily seen that the radical axis is perpendicular to the line joining the centres of the circles. For these centres are the points $(-g, -f)$ and $(-g_1, -f_1)$. The "m" of the line joining them is therefore,

$$\frac{-f_1 - (-f)}{-g_1 - (-g)}, \quad i.e., \quad \frac{f - f_1}{g - g_1}.$$

The "m" of the line (3) is $-\dfrac{g - g_1}{f - f_1}$.

The product of these two "m's" is -1.

Hence, by Art. 69, the radical axis and the line joining the centres are perpendicular.

▶ **184. A geometrical construction** can be given for the radical axis of two circles.

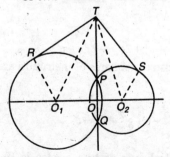
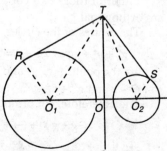

If the circles intersect in real points, P and Q, as in Fig. 1, the radical axis is clearly the straight line PQ. For if T be any point on PQ and TR and TS be the tangents from it to the circles we have

$$TR^2 = TP \cdot TQ = TS^2.$$

If they do not intersect in real points, as in the second figure, let their radii be a_1 and a_2, and let T be a point such that the tangents TR and TS are equal in length.

Draw TO perpendicular to O_1O_2.

Since,
$$TR^2 = TS^2,$$

We have
$$TO_1^2 - O_1R^2 = TO_2^2 - O_2S^2,$$

i.e.,
$$TO^2 + O_1O^2 - a_1^2 = TO^2 + OO_2^2 - a_2^2$$

i.e.,
$$O_1O^2 - OO_2^2 = a_1^2 - a_2^2,$$

i.e.,
$$(O_1O - OO_2)(O_1O + OO_2) = a_1^2 - a_2^2$$

i.e.,
$$O_1O - OO_2 = \frac{a_1^2 - a_2^2}{O_1O_2} = \text{a constant quantity}$$

Hence, O is a fixed point, since it divides the fixed straight line O_1O_2 into parts whose difference is constant.

Therefore, since O_1OT is a right angle, the locus of T, i.e., the radical axis, is a fixed straight line perpendicular to the line joining the centres.

➤ **185.** If the equations to the circles in Art. 183 be written in the form $S = 0$ and $S' = 0$, the equation (3) to the radical axis may be written $S - S' = O$ and therefore, the radical axis passes through the common points, real or imaginary, of the circles $S = 0$ and $S' = 0$.

In the last article we saw that this was true geometrically for the case in which the circles meet in real points.

When the circles do not geometrically intersect, as in Fig. 2, we must then look upon the straight line TO as passing through the imaginary points of intersection of the two circles.

➤ **186.** *The radical axes of three circles, taken in pairs, meet in a point.*

Let the equations to the three circles be
$$S = 0 \qquad \qquad \text{...(1)}$$
$$S' = 0 \qquad \qquad \text{...(2)}$$
and
$$S'' = 0 \qquad \qquad \text{...(3)}$$

The radical axis of the circles (1) and (2) is the straight line
$$S - S' = 0 \qquad \qquad \text{...(4)}$$

The radical axis of (2) and (3) is the straight line
$$S' - S'' = 0 \qquad \qquad \text{...(5)}$$

If we add equation (5) to equation (4) we shall have the equation of a straight line through their points of intersection.

Hence, $\qquad\qquad\qquad S - S'' = 0 \qquad\qquad$ ...(6)

is a straight line through the intersection of (4) and (5).

But (6) is the radical axis of the circles (3) and (1).

Hence, the three radical axes of the three circles, taken in pairs, meet in a point.

This point is called the **Radical Centre** of the three circles.

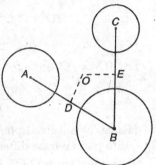

This may also be easily proved geometrically. For let the three circles be called A, B, and C, and let the radical axis of A and B and that of B and C meet in a point O.

By the definition of the radical axis, the tangent from O to the circle A = the tangent from O to the circle B, and the tangent from O to the circle B = tangent from it to the circle C.

Hence, the tangent from O to the circle A = the tangent from it to the circle C, *i.e.*, O is also a point on the radical axis of the circles A and C.

➤ **187.** *If $S = 0$ and $S' = 0$ be the equations of two circles, the equation of any circle through their points of intersection is $S = \lambda S'$. Also the equation to any circle, such that the radical axis of it and $S = 0$ is $u = 0$, is $S + \lambda u = 0$.*

For wherever $S = 0$ and $S' = 0$ are *both* satisfied the equation $S = \lambda S'$ is clearly satisfied, so that $S = \lambda S'$ is some locus through the intersections of $S = 0$ and $S' = 0$.

Also in both S and S' the coefficients of x^2 and y^2 are equal and the coefficient of xy is zero. The same statement is therefore true for the equation $S = \lambda S'$. Hence, the proposition.

Again, since u is only of the first degree, therefore, in $S + \lambda u$ the coefficients of x^2 and y^2 are equal and the coefficient of xy is zero, so that $S + \lambda u = 0$ is clearly a circle. Also it passes through the intersections of $S = 0$ and $u = 0$.

EXAMPLES XXIII

Prove that the following pairs of circles intersect orthogonally:

1. $x^2 + y^2 - 2ax + c = 0$ and $x^2 + y^2 + 2by - c = 0$
2. $x^2 + y^2 - 2ax + 2by + c = 0$ and $x^2 + y^2 + 2bx + 2ay - c = 0$

3. Find the equation to the circle which passes through the origin and cuts orthogonally each of the circles

$$x^2 + y^2 - 6x + 8 = 0 \quad \text{and} \quad x^2 + y^2 - 2x - 2y = 7$$

Find the radical axis of the pairs of circles

4. $x^2 + y^2 = 144$ and $x^2 + y^2 - 15x + 11y = 0$

5. $x^2 + y^2 - 3x - 4y + 5 = 0$ and $3x^2 + 3y^2 - 7x + 8y + 11 = 0$

6. $x^2 + y^2 - xy + 6x - 7y + 8 = 0$ and $x^2 + y^2 - xy - 4 = 0$, the axes being inclined at 120°.

Find the radical centre of the sets of circles

7. $x^2 + y^2 + x + 2y + 3 = 0$, $x^2 + y^2 + 2x + 4y + 5 = 0$

   and $\qquad\qquad\qquad x^2 + y^2 - 7x - 8y - 9 = 0$

8. $(x - 2)^2 + (y - 3)^2 = 36$, $(x + 3)^2 + (y + 2)^2 = 49$

   and $\qquad\qquad\qquad (x - 4)^2 + (y + 5)^2 = 64$

9. Prove that the square of the tangent that can be drawn from any point on one circle to another circle is equal to twice the product of the perpendicular distance of the point from the radical axis of the two circles, and the distance between their centres.

10. Prove that a common tangent to two circles is bisected by the radical axis. [Hence, by joining the middle points of any two of the common tangents, we have a construction for the radical axis.]

11. Find the general equation of all circles any pair of which have the same radical axis as the circles

$$x^2 + y^2 = 4 \quad \text{and} \quad x^2 + y^2 + 2x + 4y = 6$$

12. Find the equations to the straight lines joining the origin to the points of intersection of

$$x^2 + y^2 - 4x - 2y = 4 \quad \text{and} \quad x^2 + y^2 - 2x - 4y - 4 = 0$$

13. The polars of a point P with respect to two fixed circles meet in the point Q. Prove that the circle on PQ as diameter passes through two fixed points, and cuts both the given circles at right angles.

14. Prove that the two circles, which pass through the two points $(0, a)$ and $(0, -a)$ and touch the straight line $y = mx + c$, will cut orthogonally if $c^2 = a^2(2 + m^2)$,

15. Find the locus of the centre of the circle which cuts two given circles orthogonally.

16. If two circles cut orthogonally, prove that the polar of any point P on the first circle with respect to the second passes through the other end of the diameter of the first circle which goes through P.

Hence, (by considering the orthogonal circle of three circles as the locus of a point such that its polars with respect to the circles meet in a point) prove that the orthogonal circle of three circles, given by the general equation is

$$\begin{vmatrix} x + g_1, & y + f_1, & g_1 x + f_1 y + c_1 \\ x + g_2, & y + f_2, & g_2 x + f_2 y + c_2 \\ x + g_3, & y + f_3, & g_3 x + f_3 y + c_3 \end{vmatrix} = 0$$

➤ **188. Coaxal Circles. Def.** A system of circles is said to be coaxal when they have a common radical axis, *i.e.*, when the radical axis of each pair of circles of the system is the same.

To find the equation of a system of coaxal circles.

Since, by Art. 183, the radical axis of any pair of the circles is perpendicular to the line joining their centres, it follows that the centres of all the circles of a coaxal system must lie on a straight line which is perpendicular to the radical axis.

Take the line of centres as the axis of x and the radical axis as the axis of y (Figs. I and II, Art. 190), so that O is the origin.

The equation to any circle with its centre on the axis of x is

$$x^2 + y^2 - 2gx + c = 0 \qquad \qquad ...(1)$$

Any point on the radical axis is $(0, y_1)$.

The square on the tangent from it to the circle (1) is by Art. 168, $y_1^2 + c$.

Since, this quantity is to be the same for all circles of the system it follows that c is the same for all such circles; the different circles are therefore obtained by giving different values to g in the equation (1).

The intersections of equation (1) with the radical axis are then obtained by putting $x = 0$ in equation (1), and we have

$$y = \pm \sqrt{-c}.$$

If c be negative, we have two real points of intersection as in Fig. I. of Art. 190. In such cases the circles are said to be of the Intersecting Species.

If c be positive, we have two imaginary points of intersection as in Fig. II.

➤ **189. Limiting points of a coaxal system.**

The equation (1) of the previous article which gives any circle of the system may be written in the form

$$(x - g)^2 + y^2 = g^2 - c = [\sqrt{g^2 - c}]^2.$$

It therefore, represents a circle whose centre is the point $(g, 0)$ and whose radius is $\sqrt{g^2 - c}$.

This radius vanishes, *i.e.*, the circle becomes a point circle, when $g^2 = c$, *i.e.*, when $g = \pm \sqrt{c}$.

Hence, at the particular points $(\pm \sqrt{c}, 0)$ we have point-circles which belong to the system. These point-circles are called the Limiting Points of the system.

If c be negative, these points are imaginary.

But it was shown in the last article that when c is negative the circles intersect in real points as in Fig. I., Art. 190.

If c be positive, the limiting points L_1 and L_2 (Fig. II.) are real, and in this case the circles intersect in imaginary points.

The limiting points are therefore real or imaginary according as the circles of the system intersect in imaginary or real points.

▶ **190. Orthogonal circles of a coaxal system.**

Let T be *any* point on the common radical axis of a system of coaxal circles, and let TR be the tangent from it to any circle of the system.

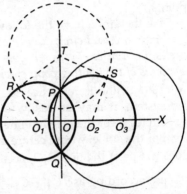

Then a circle, whose centre is T and whose radius is TR, will cut each circle of the coaxal system orthogonally.

[For the radius TR of this circle is at right angles to the radius O_1R, and so for its intersection with *any* other circle of the system.]

Fig. I

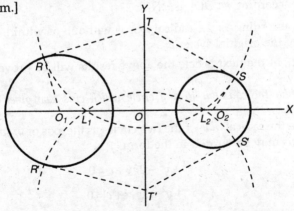

Fig. II

Hence, the limiting points (being point-*circles* of the system) are on this orthogonal circle.

The limiting points are therefore the intersections with the line of centres of *any* circle whose centre is on the common radical axis and whose radius is the tangent from it to any of the circles of the system.

Since, in Fig. I., the limiting points are imaginary these orthogonal circles do not meet the line of centres in real points.

In Fig. II they pass through the limiting points L_1 and L_2.

These orthogonal circles (since they all pass through two points, real or imaginary) are therefore a coaxal system.

Also if the original circles, as in Fig. I., intersect in real points, the orthogonal circles intersect in imaginary points; in Fig. II the original circles intersect in imaginary points, and the orthogonal circles in real points.

We therefore, have the following theorem:

A set of coaxal circles can be cut orthogonally by another set of coaxal circles, the centres of each set lying on the radical axis of the other set; also one set is of the limiting point species and the other set of the other species.

➤ **191.** Without reference to the limiting points of the original system, it may be easily found whether or not the orthogonal circles meet the original line of centres.

For the circle, whose centre is T and whose radius is TR, meets or does not meet the line O_1O_2 according as TR^2 is $>$ or $< TO^2$,

i.e., according as $TO_1{}^2 - O_1R^2$ is $\rightleftharpoons TO^2$,

i.e., according as $TO^2 + OO_1{}^2 - O_1R^2$ is $\rightleftharpoons TO^2$,

i.e., according as OO_1 is $\rightleftharpoons O_1R$,

i.e., according as the radical axis is without, or within, each of the circles of the original system.

➤ **192.** In the next article the above results will be proved analytically.

To find the equation to any circle which cuts two given circles orthogonally.

Take the radical axis of the two circles as the axis of y, so that their equations may be written in the form

$$x^2 + y^2 - 2gx + c = 0 \qquad \ldots(1)$$

and

$$x^2 + y^2 - 2g_1x + c = 0 \qquad \ldots(2)$$

the quantity c being the same for each.

Let the equation to any circle which cuts them orthogonally be

$$(x - A)^2 + (y - B)^2 = R^2 \qquad \ldots(3)$$

The equation (1) can be written in the form

$$(x - g^2) + y^2 = [\sqrt{g^2 - c}]^2 \qquad \ldots(4)$$

The circles (3) and (4) cut orthogonally if the square of the distance between their centres is equal to the sum of the squares of their radii,

i.e., if $\qquad (A - g)^2 + B^2 = R^2 + [\sqrt{g^2 - c}]^2$

i.e., if $\qquad A^2 + B^2 - 2Ag = R^2 - c \qquad$ ...(5)

Similarly, (3) will cut (2) orthogonally if

$$A^2 + B^2 - 2Ag_1 = R^2 - c \qquad ...(6)$$

Subtracting (6) from (5), we have $A(g - g_1) = 0$

Hence, $\qquad A = 0 \quad$ and $\quad R^2 = B^2 + c$

Substituting these values in (3), the equation to the required orthogonal circle is

$$x^2 + y^2 - 2By - c = 0 \qquad ...(7)$$

where B is any quantity whatever.

Whatever be the value of B the equation (7) represents a circle whose centre is on the axis of y and which passes through the points $(\pm \sqrt{c}, 0)$.

But, the latter points are the limiting points of the coaxal system to which the two circles belong. [Art. 189]

Hence, any pair of circles belonging to a coaxal system is cut at right angles by any circle of another coaxal system; also the centres of the circles of the latter system lie on the common radical axis of the original system, and all the circles of the latter system pass through the limiting points (real or imaginary) of the first system.

Also the centre of the circle (7) is the point $(0, B)$ and its radius is $\sqrt{B^2 + c}$.

The square of the tangent drawn from $(0, B)$ to the circle $(1) = B^2 + c$ (by Art. 168).

Hence, the radius of any circle of the second system is equal to the length of the tangent drawn from its centre to any circle of the first system.

▶ **193.** The equation to the system of circles which cut a given coaxal system orthogonally may also be obtained by using the result of Art. 182.

For any circle of the coaxal system is, by Art. 188, given by

$$x^2 + y^2 - 2gx + c = 0 \qquad ...(1)$$

where c is the same for all circles.

Any point on the radical axis is $(0, y')$.

The square on the tangent drawn from it to (1) is therefore, $y'^2 + c$.

The equation to *any* circle cutting (1) orthogonally is therefore

$$x^2 + (y - y')^2 = y'^2 + c$$

i.e., $$x^2 + y^2 - 2yy' - c = 0$$

Whatever be the value of y' this circle passes through the points $(\pm \sqrt{c}, 0)$, *i.e.*, through the limiting points of the system of circles given by (1).

➤ **194.** We can now deduce an easy construction for the circle that cuts any three circles orthogonally.

Consider the three circles in the figure of Art. 186.

By Art. 192 any circle cutting A and B orthogonally has its centre on their common radical axis, *i.e.*, on the straight line OD.

Similarly, any circle cutting B and C orthogonally has its centre on the radical axis OE.

Any circle cutting all three circles orthogonally must therefore, have its centre at the intersection of OD and OE, *i.e.*, at the radical centre O. Also its radius must be the length of the tangent drawn from the radical centre to any one of the three circles.

Example *Find the equation to the circle which cuts orthogonally each of the three circles*

$$x^2 + y^2 + 2x + 17y + 4 = 0 \qquad \qquad ...(1)$$
$$x^2 + y^2 + 7x + 6y + 11 = 0 \qquad \qquad ...(2)$$
$$x^2 + y^2 - x + 22y + 3 = 0 \qquad \qquad ...(3)$$

The radical axis of (1) and (2) is

$$5x - 11y + 7 = 0$$

The radical axis of (2) and (3) is

$$8x - 16y + 8 = 0$$

These two straight lines meet in the point (3, 2) which is therefore the radical centre.

The square of the length of the tangent from the point (3, 2) to each of the given circles = 57.

The required equation is therefore $(x - 3)^2 + (y - 2)^2 = 57$,

i.e., $$x^2 + y^2 - 6x - 4y - 44 = 0$$

➤ **195.**

Example *Find the locus of a point which moves so that the length of the tangent drawn from it to one given circle is λ times the length of the tangent from it to another given circle.*

As in Art. 188 take as axes of x and y the line joining the centres of the two circles and the radical axis. The equations to the two circles are therefore,

$$x^2 + y^2 - 2g_1x + c = 0 \qquad \ldots(1)$$

and
$$x^2 + y^2 - 2g_2x + c = 0 \qquad \ldots(2)$$

Let (h, k) be a point such that the length of the tangent from it to (1) is always λ times the length of the tangent from it to (2).

Then, $h^2 + k^2 - 2g_1h + c = \lambda^2[h^2 + k^2 - 2g_2h + c]$

Hence, (h, k) always lies on the circle

$$x^2 + y^2 - 2x\frac{g_2\lambda^2 - g_1}{\lambda^2 - 1} + c = 0 \qquad \ldots(3)$$

This circle is clearly a circle of the coaxal system to which (1) and (2) belong.

Again, the centre of (1) is the point $(g_1, 0)$, the centre of (2) is $(g_2, 0)$, whilst the centre of (3) is $\left(\dfrac{g_2\lambda^2 - g_1}{\lambda^2 - 1}, 0\right)$

Hence, if these three centres be called O_1, O_2, and O_3, we have

$$O_1O_3 = \frac{g_2\lambda^2 - g_1}{\lambda^2 - 1} - g_1 = \frac{\lambda^2}{\lambda^2 - 1}(g_2 - g_1)$$

and
$$O_2O_3 = \frac{g_2\lambda^2 - g_1}{\lambda^2 - 1} - g_2 = \frac{1}{\lambda^2 - 1}(g_2 - g_1)$$

So that,
$$O_1O_3 : O_2O_3 :: \lambda^2 : 1.$$

The required locus is therefore a circle coaxal with the two given circles and whose centre divides externally, in the ratio $\lambda^2 : 1$, the line joining the centres of the two given circles.

EXAMPLES XXIV

1. Prove that a common tangent to two circles of a coaxal system subtends a right angle at either limiting point of the system.
2. Prove that the polar of a limiting point of a coaxal system with respect to any circle of the system is the same for all circles of the system.
3. Prove that the polars of any point with respect to a system of coaxal circles all pass through a fixed point, and that the two points are equidistant from the radical axis and subtend a right angle at a limiting point of the system. If the first point be one limiting point of the system prove that the second point is the other limiting point.
4. A fixed circle is cut by a series of circles all of which pass through

two given points; prove that the straight line joining the intersections of the fixed circle with any circle of the system always passes through a fixed point.

5. Prove that tangents drawn from any point of a fixed circle of a coaxal system to two other fixed circles of the system are in a constant ratio.

6. Prove that a system of coaxal circles inverts with respect to either limiting point into a system of concentric circles and find the position of the common centre.

7. A straight line is drawn touching one of a system of coaxal circles in P and cutting another in Q and R. Shew that PQ and PR subtend equal or supplementary angles at one of the limiting points of the system.

8. Find the locus of the point of contact of parallel tangents which are drawn to each of a series of coaxal circles.

9. Prove that the circle of similitude of the two circles

$$x^2 + y^2 - 2kx + \delta = 0 \quad \text{and} \quad x^2 + y^2 - 2k'x + \delta = 0$$

(*i.e.*, the locus of the points at which the two circles subtend the same angle) is the coaxal circle

$$x^2 + y^2 - 2\frac{kk' + \delta}{k + k'} x + \delta = 0$$

10. From the preceding question shew that the centres of similitude (*i.e.*, the points in which the common tangents to two circles meet the line of centres) divide the line joining the centres internally and externally in the ratio of the radii.

11. If $x + y\sqrt{-1} = \tan(u + v\sqrt{-1})$, where $x, y, u,$ and v are all real, prove that the curves $u =$ constant give a family of coaxal circles passing through the points $(0, \pm 1)$, and that the curves $v =$ constant give a system of circles cutting the first system orthogonally.

12. Find the equation to the circle which cuts orthogonally each of the circles

$$x^2 + y^2 + 2gx + c = 0, \quad x^2 + y^2 + 2g'x + c = 0,$$

and $\qquad\qquad x^2 + y^2 + 2hx + 2ky + a = 0$

13. Find the equation to the circle cutting orthogonally the three circles

$$x^2 + y^2 = a^2, \quad (x - c)^2 + y^2 = a^2, \text{ and } x^2 + (y - b)^2 = a^2$$

14. Find the equation to the circle cutting orthogonally the three circles

$$x^2 + y^2 - 2x + 3y - 7 = 0, \quad x^2 + y^2 + 5x - 5y + 9 = 0,$$

and $\qquad\qquad x^2 + y^2 + 7x - 9y + 29 = 0$

15. Shew that the equation to the circle cutting orthogonally the circles

$$(x - a)^2 + (y - b)^2 = b^2, \quad (x - b)^2 + (y - a)^2 = a^2$$

and $\qquad\qquad (x - a - b - c)^2 + y^2 = ab + c^2,$

is $x^2 + y^2 - 2x(a + b) - y(a + b) + a^2 + 3ab + b^2 = 0.$

CONIC SECTIONS

10

THE PARABOLA

▶ **196. Conic Section. Def.** The locus of a point P, which moves so that its distance from a fixed point is always in a constant ratio to its perpendicular distance from a fixed straight line, is called a Conic Section.

The fixed point is called the **Focus** and is usually denoted by S.
The constant ratio is called the **Eccentricity** and is denoted by e.
The fixed straight line is called the **Directrix**.
The straight line passing through the Focus and perpendicular to the Directrix is called the **Axis**.

When the eccentricity e is equal to unity, the Conic Section is called a **Parabola**.

When e is less than unity, it is called an **Ellipse**.

When e is greater than unity, it is called a **Hyperbola**.

[The name Conic Section is derived from the fact that these curves were first obtained by cutting a cone in various ways.]

▶ **197.** *To find the equation to a Parabola.*

Let S be the fixed point and ZM the directrix. We require therefore, the locus of a point P which moves so that its distance from S is always equal to PM, its perpendicular distance from ZM.

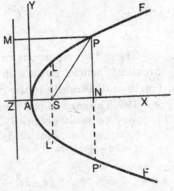

Draw SZ perpendicular to the directrix and bisect SZ in the point A; produce ZA to X.

The point A is clearly a point on the curve and is called the **Vertex** of the Parabola.

Take A as origin, AX as the axis of x, and AY, perpendicular to it, as the axis of y.

Let the distance ZA, or AS, be called a, and let P be any point on the curve whose coordinates are x and y.

Join SP, and draw PN and PM perpendicular respectively to the axis and directrix.

We have then, $SP^2 = PM^2$,

i.e., $$(x - a)^2 + y^2 = ZN^2 = (a + x)^2,$$

∴ $$y^2 = 4ax \qquad\qquad \text{...(1)}$$

This being the relation which exists between the coordinates of any point P on the parabola is, by Art. 42, the equation to the parabola.

Cor. : The equation (1) is equivalent to the geometrical proposition

$$PN^2 = 4AS \cdot AN$$

➤ **198.** The equation of the preceding article is the simplest possible equation to the parabola. Throughout this chapter this standard form of the equation is assumed unless the contrary is stated.

If instead of AX and AY we take the axis and the directrix ZM as the axes of coordinates, the equation would be

$$(x - 2a)^2 + y^2 = x^2$$

i.e., $$y^2 = 4a(x - a) \qquad\qquad \text{...(1)}$$

Similarly, if the axis SX and a perpendicular line SL be taken as the axes of coordinates, the equation is

$$x^2 + y^2 = (x + 2a)^2,$$

i.e., $$y^2 = 4a(x + a) \qquad\qquad \text{...(2)}$$

These two equations may be deduced from the equation of the previous article by transforming the origin, firstly to the point $(-a, 0)$ and secondly to the point $(a, 0)$.

➤ **199.** The equation to the parabola referred to any focus and directrix may be easily obtained. Thus, the equation to the parabola, whose focus is the point $(2, 3)$ and whose directrix is the straight line $x - 4y + 3 = 0$, is

$$(x - 2)^2 + (y - 3)^2 = \left\{ \frac{x - 4y + 3}{\sqrt{1^2 + 4^2}} \right\}^2$$

i.e., $17[x^2 + y^2 - 4x - 6y + 13] = \{x^2 + 16y^2 + 9 - 8xy + 6x - 24y\}$,

i.e., $16x^2 + y^2 + 8xy - 74x - 78y + 212 = 0$

➤ **200.** *To trace the curve*

$$y^2 = 4ax \qquad\qquad ...(1)$$

If x be negative, the corresponding values of y are imaginary (since the square root of a negative quantity is unreal); hence there is no part of the curve to the left of the point A.

If y be zero, so also is x, so that the axis of x meets the curve at the point A only.

If x be zero, so also is y, so that the axis of y meets the curve at the point A only.

For every positive value of x we see from (1), by taking the square root, that y has two equal and opposite values.

Hence, corresponding to any point P on the curve there is another point P' on the other side of the axis which is obtained by producing PN to P' so that PN and NP' are equal in magnitude. The line PP' is called a double ordinate.

As x increases in magnitude, so do the corresponding values of y ; finally, when x becomes infinitely great, y becomes infinitely great also.

By taking a large number of values of x and the corresponding values of y it will be found that the curve is as in the figure of Art. 197.

The two branches never meet but are of infinite length.

➤ **201.** *The quantity $y'^2 - 4ax'$ is negative, zero, or positive according as the point (x', y') is within, upon, or without the parabola.*

Let Q be the point (x', y') and let it be within the curve, *i.e.*, be between the curve and the axis AX. Draw the ordinate QN and let it meet the curve in P.

Then (by Art. 197), $PN^2 = 4a \cdot x'$.

Hence, y'^2, *i.e.*, QN^2, is $< PN^2$, and hence, is $< 4ax'$.

∴ $y'^2 - 4ax'$ is negative.

Similarly, if Q be without the curve, then y'^2, *i.e.*, QN^2, is $> PN^2$, and hence is $> 4ax'$.

Hence, the proposition.

➤ **202. Latus Rectum. Def.** The latus rectum of any conic is the double ordinate LSL' drawn through the focus S.

In the case of the parabola we have $SL =$ distance of L from the directrix $= SZ = 2a$.

Hence,   the latus rectum $= 4a$.

When the latus rectum is given it follows that the equation to the parabola is completely known in its standard form, and the size and shape of the curve determined.

The quantity $4a$ is also often called the **principal parameter** of the curve.

Focal distance of any point. The focal distance of any point P is the distance SP.

This focal distance $= PM = ZN = ZA + AN = a + x$.

EXAMPLE *Find the vertex, axis, focus, and latus rectum of the parabola*

$$4y^2 + 12x - 20y + 67 = 0.$$

The equation can be written

$$y^2 - 5y = -3x - \frac{67}{4},$$

i.e.,

$$\left(y - \frac{5}{2}\right)^2 = -3x - \frac{67}{4} + \frac{25}{4} = -3\left(x + \frac{7}{2}\right).$$

Transform this equation to the point $\left(-\frac{7}{2}, \frac{5}{2}\right)$ and it becomes

$y^2 = -3x$, which represents a parabola, whose axis is the axis of x and whose concavity is turned towards the negative end of this axis. Also its latus rectum is 3.

Referred to the original axes the vertex is the point $\left(-\frac{7}{2}, \frac{5}{2}\right)$, the axis

is $y = \frac{5}{2}$ and the focus is the point $\left(-\frac{7}{2} - \frac{3}{4}, \frac{5}{2}\right)$, *i.e.,* $\left(-\frac{17}{4}, \frac{5}{2}\right)$.

EXAMPLES XXV

Find the equation to the parabola with
1. focus $(3, -4)$ and directrix $6x - 7y + 5 = 0$
2. focus (a, b) and directrix $\dfrac{x}{a} + \dfrac{y}{b} = 1$

Find the vertex, axis, latus rectum, and focus of the parabolas:
3. $y^2 = 4x + 4y$
4. $x^2 + 2y = 8x - 7$
5. $x^2 - 2ax + 2ay = 0$
6. $y^2 = 4y - 4x$
7. Draw the curves
   (i) $y^2 = -4ax$, (ii) $x^2 = 4ay$, and (iii) $x^2 = -4ay$.

8. Find the value of p when the parabola $y^2 = 4px$ goes through the point (i) $(3, -2)$, and (ii) $(9, -12)$.

9. For what point of the parabola, $y^2 = 18x$ is the ordinate equal to three times the abscissa?

10. Prove that the equation to the parabola, whose vertex and focus are on the axis of x at distances a and a' from the origin respectively, is

$$y^2 = 4(a' - a)(x - a).$$

11. In the parabola $y^2 = 6x$, find (1) the equation to the chord through the vertex and the negative end of the latus rectum, and (2) the equation to any chord through the point on the curve whose abscissa is 24.

12. Prove that the equation $y^2 + 2Ax + 2By + C = 0$ represents a parabola, whose axis is parallel to the axis of x, and find its vertex and the equation to its latus rectum.

13. Prove that the locus of the middle points of all chords of the parabola $y^2 = 4ax$ which are drawn through the vertex is the parabola $y^2 = 2ax$.

14. Prove that the locus of the centre of a circle, which intercepts a chord of given length $2a$ on the axis of x and passes through a given point on the axis of y distant b from the origin, is the curve

$$x^2 - 2yb + b^2 = a^2.$$

Trace this parabola.

15. PQ is a double ordinate of a parabola. Find the locus of its points of trisection.

16. Prove that the locus of a point, which moves so that its distance from a fixed line is equal to the length of the tangent drawn from it to a given circle, is a parabola. Find the position of the focus and directrix.

17. If a circle be drawn so as always to touch a given straight line and also a given circle, prove that the locus of its centre is a parabola.

18. The vertex A of a parabola is joined to any point P on the curve and PQ is drawn at right angles to AP to meet the axis in Q. Prove that the projection of PQ on the axis is always equal to the latus rectum.

19. If on a given base triangles be described such that the sum of the tangents of the base angles is constant, prove that the locus of the vertices is a parabola.

20. A double ordinate of the curve $y^2 = 4px$ is of length $8p$; prove that the lines from the vertex to its two ends are at right angles.

21. Two parabolas have a common axis and concavities in opposite directions; if any line parallel to the common axis meet the parabolas in P and P', prove that the locus of the middle point of PP' is another parabola, provided that the latera recta of the given parabolas are unequal.

22. A parabola is drawn to pass through A and B, the ends of a diameter of a given circle of radius a, and to have as directrix a tangent to a concentric circle of radius b ; the axis being AB and a perpendicular diameter, prove that the locus of the focus of the parabola is

$$\frac{x^2}{b^2} + \frac{y^2}{b^2 - a^2} = 1.$$

▶ **203.** *To find the points of intersection of any straight line with the parabola*

$$y^2 = 4ax \qquad \qquad \dots(1)$$

The equation to any straight line is

$$y = mx + c \qquad \qquad \dots(2)$$

The coordinates of the points common to the straight line and the parabola satisfy both equations (1) and (2), and are therefore, found by solving them.

Substituting the value of y from (2) in (1), we have

$$(mx + c)^2 = 4ax$$

i.e., $\qquad m^2x^2 + 2x(mc - 2a) + c^2 = 0 \qquad \qquad \dots(3)$

This is a quadratic equation for x and therefore, has two roots, real, coincident, or imaginary.

The straight line therefore, meets the parabola in two points, real, coincident, or imaginary.

The roots of (3) are real or imaginary according as

$$\{2(mc - 2a)\}^2 - 4m^2c^2$$

is positive or negative, *i.e.,* according as $-amc + a^2$ is positive or negative, *i.e.,* according as mc is $\lessgtr a$.

▶ **204.** *To find the length of the chord intercepted by the parabola on the straight line*

$$y = mx + c \qquad \qquad \dots(1)$$

If (x_1, y_1) and (x_2, y_2) be the common points of intersection, then, as in Art. 154, we have, from equation (3) of the last article,

$$(x_1 - x_2)^2 = (x_1 + x_2)^2 - 4x_1x_2$$

$$= \frac{4(mc - 2a)^2}{m^4} - \frac{4c^2}{m^2} = \frac{16a(a - mc)}{m^4},$$

and $\qquad \qquad y_1 - y_2 = m(x_1 - x_2)$

Hence, the required length $= \sqrt{(y_1 - y_2)^2 + (x_1 - x_2)^2}$

$$= \sqrt{1 + m^2}\,(x_1 - x_2) = \frac{4}{m^2}\sqrt{1 + m^2}\,\sqrt{a(a - mc)}$$

➤ **205.** *To find the equation to the tangent at any point (x', y') of the parabola $y^2 = 4ax$.*

The definition of the tangent is given in Art. 149.

Let P be the point (x', y') and Q a point (x'', y'') on the parabola. The equation to the line PQ is

$$y - y' = \frac{y'' - y'}{x'' - x'} (x - x') \qquad \ldots(1)$$

Since, P and Q both lie on the curve, we have

$$y'^2 = 4ax' \qquad \ldots(2)$$

and

$$y''^2 = 4ax'' \qquad \ldots(3)$$

Hence, by subtraction, we have

$$y''^2 - y'^2 = 4a(x'' - x'),$$

i.e.,

$$(y'' - y')(y'' + y') = 4a(x'' - x')$$

and hence,

$$\frac{y'' - y'}{x'' - x'} = \frac{4a}{y'' + y'}.$$

Substituting this value in equation (1), we have, as the equation to any secant PQ,

$$y - y' = \frac{4a}{y'' + y'} (x - x')$$

i.e.,

$$y(y' + y'') = 4ax + y'y'' + y'^2 - 4ax'$$

$$= 4ax + y'y'' \qquad \ldots(4)$$

To obtain the equation of the tangent at (x', y') we take Q indefinitely close to P, and hence, in the limit, put $y'' = y'$.

The equation (4) then becomes

$$2yy' = y'^2 + 4ax = 4ax + 4ax',$$

i.e.,

$$yy' = 2a(x + x').$$

Cor. It will be noted that the equation to the tangent is obtained from the equation to the curve by the rule of Art. 152.

EXAMPLE *The equation to the tangent at the point $(2, -4)$ of the parabola $y^2 = 8x$ is*

$$y(-4) = 4(x + 2)$$

i.e.,

$$x + y + 2 = 0$$

The equation to the tangent at the point $\left(\dfrac{a}{m^2}, \dfrac{2a}{m} \right)$ of the parabola $y^2 = 4ax$ is

$$y \cdot \frac{2a}{m} = 2a \left(x + \frac{a}{m^2} \right)$$

i.e., $$y = mx + \frac{a}{m}$$

➤ **206.** *To find the condition that the straight line*

$$y = mx + c \qquad \qquad \dots(1)$$

may touch the parabola $\qquad y^2 = 4ax \qquad \qquad \dots(2)$

The abscissae of the points in which the straight line (1) meets the curve (2) are as in Art. 203, given by the equation

$$m^2x^2 + 2x(mc - 2a) + c^2 = 0 \qquad \qquad \dots(3)$$

The line (1) will touch (2) if it meet it in two points which are indefinitely close to one another, *i.e.,* in two points which ultimately coincide.

The roots of equations (3) must, therefore, be equal.

The condition for this is

$$4(mc - 2a)^2 = 4m^2c^2$$

i.e., $$a^2 - amc = 0$$

so that $$c = \frac{a}{m}$$

Substituting this value of c in (1) we have as the equation to a tangent,

$$y = mx + \frac{a}{m}$$

In this equation m is the tangent of the angle which the tangent makes with the axis of x.

The foregoing proposition may also be obtained from the equation of Art. 205.

For equation (4) of that article may be written

$$y = \frac{2a}{y'} x + \frac{2ax'}{y'} \qquad \qquad \dots(1)$$

In this equation put $\dfrac{2a}{y'} = m$, *i.e.,* $y' = \dfrac{2a}{m}$,

and hence $$x' = \frac{y'^2}{4a} = \frac{a}{m^2} \quad \text{and} \quad \frac{2ax'}{y'} = \frac{a}{m}$$

The equation (1) then becomes $y = mx + \dfrac{a}{m}$.

Also, it is the tangent at the point (x', y'), *i.e.,* $\left(\dfrac{a}{m^2}, \dfrac{2a}{m} \right)$.

➤ **207.** *Equation to the normal at* (x', y'). The required normal is the straight line which passes through the point (x', y') and is perpendicular to the tangent, *i.e.*, to the straight line

$$y = \frac{2a}{y'}(x + x')$$

Its equation, is therefore,

$$y - y' = m'(x - x'),$$

where

$$m' \times \frac{2a}{y'} = -1, \quad i.e., \quad m' = -\frac{y'}{2a} \qquad \text{(Art. 69)}$$

and the equation to the normal is

$$y - y' = \frac{-y'}{2a}(x - x') \qquad \qquad ...(1)$$

➤ **208.** *To express the equation of the normal in the form*

$$y = mx - 2am - am^3.$$

In equation (1) of the last article put

$$\frac{-y'}{2a} = m, \quad i.e., \quad y' = -2am.$$

Hence,

$$x' = \frac{y'^2}{4a} = am^2.$$

The normal is therefore

$$y + 2am = m(x - am^2),$$

i.e.,

$$y = mx - 2am - am^3,$$

and it is a normal at the point $(am^2, -2am)$ of the curve.

In this equation m is the tangent of the angle which the *normal* makes with the axis. It must be carefully distinguished from the m of Art. 206 which is the tangent of the angle which the *tangent* makes with the axis. The "m" of this article is -1 divided by the "m" of Art. 206.

➤ **209. Subtangent and Subnormal. Def.** If the tangent and normal at any point P of a conic section meet the axis in T and G respectively and PN be the ordinate at P, then NT is called the Subtangent and NG the Subnormal of P.

To find the length of the subtangent and subnormal.

If P be the point (x', y') the equation to TP is, by Art. 205,

$$yy' = 2a(x + x') \qquad \qquad ...(1)$$

To obtain the length of AT, we have to find the point where this straight line meets the axis of x, *i.e.*, we put $y = 0$ in (1) and we have

$$x = -x' \qquad \qquad ...(2)$$

Hence, $\qquad\qquad AT = AN$

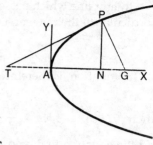

[The negative sign in equation (2) shews that T and N always lie on opposite sides of the vertex A.]

Hence, the subtangent $NT = 2AN =$ twice the abscissa of the point P.

Since, TPG is a right-angled triangle, we have

$$PN^2 = TN \cdot NG$$

Hence, the subnormal $NG = \dfrac{PN^2}{TN} = \dfrac{PN^2}{2AN} = 2a$.

The subnormal is, therefore, constant for all points on the parabola and is equal to the semi-latus rectum.

➤ **210.**

EXAMPLE 1 *If a chord which is normal to the parabola at one end subtend a right angle at the vertex, prove that it is inclined at an angle* $\tan^{-1}\sqrt{2}$ *to the axis.*

The equation to any chord which is normal, is

$$y = mx - 2am - am^3,$$

i.e., $\qquad\qquad mx - y = 2am + am^3$

The parabola is, $\qquad\qquad y^2 = 4ax$

The straight lines joining the origin to the intersections of these two are, therefore, given by the equation

$$y^2(2am + am^3) - 4ax(mx - y) = 0.$$

If these be at right angles, then

$$2am + am^3 - 4am = 0,$$

i.e., $\qquad\qquad m = \pm\sqrt{2}$

EXAMPLE 2 *From the point where any normal to the parabola* $y^2 = 4ax$ *meets the axis is drawn a line perpendicular to this normal; prove that this line always touches an equal parabola.*

The equation of any normal to the parabola is

$$y = mx - 2am - am^3.$$

This meets the axis in the point $(2a + am^2, 0)$.

The equation to the straight line through this point perpendicular to the normal is

$$y = m_1(x - 2a - am^2),$$

where
$$m_1 m = -1$$

the equation is therefore,

$$y = m_1\left(x - 2a - \frac{a}{m_1^2}\right),$$

i.e.,
$$y = m_1(x - 2a) - \frac{a}{m_1}.$$

This straight line, as in Art. 206, always touches the equal parabola
$$y^2 = -4a(x - 2a),$$

whose vertex is the point $(2a, 0)$ and whose concavity is towards the negative end of the axis of x.

EXAMPLES XXVI

Write down the equations to the tangent and normal

1. at the point $(4, 6)$ of the parabola $y^2 = 9x$.
2. at the point of the parabola $y^2 = 6x$ whose ordinate is 12.
3. at the ends of the latus rectum of the parabola $y^2 = 12x$
4. at the ends of the latus rectum of the parabola $y^2 = 4a(x - a)$.
5. Find the equation to that tangent to the parabola $y^2 = 7x$ which is parallel to the straight line $4y - x + 3 = 0$. Find also its point of contact.
6. A tangent to the parabola $y^2 = 4ax$ makes an angle of 60° with the axis; find its point of contact.
7. A tangent to the parabola $y^2 = 8x$ makes an angle of 45° with the straight line $y = 3x + 5$. Find its equation and its point of contact.
8. Find the points of the parabola $y^2 = 4ax$ at which (i) the tangent, and (ii) the normal is inclined at 30° to the axis.
9. Find the equation to the tangents to the parabola $y^2 = 9x$ which goes through the point $(4, 10)$.
10. Prove that the straight line $x + y = 1$ touches the parabola $y = x - x^2$.
11. Prove that the straight line $y = mx + c$ touches the parabola $y^2 = 4a(x + a)$ if $c = ma + \dfrac{a}{m}$.
12. Prove that the straight line $lx + my + n = 0$ touches the parabola $y^2 = 4ax$ if $ln = am^2$.
13. For what point of the parabola $y^2 = 4ax$ is (1) the normal equal to twice the subtangent, (2) the normal equal to the difference between the subtangent and the subnormal?
    Find the equations to the common tangents of
14. the parabolas $y^2 = 4ax$ and $x^2 = 4by$,

15. the circle $x^2 + y^2 = 4ax$ and the parabola $y^2 = 4ax$.

16. Two equal parabolas have the same vertex and their axes are at right angles; prove that the common tangent touches each at the end of a latus rectum.

17. Prove that two straight lines, one a tangent to the parabola $y^2 = 4a(x + a)$ and the other to the parabola $y^2 = 4a'(x + a')$, which are at right angles to one another, meet on the straight line $x + a + a' = 0$.

    Shew also that this straight line is the common chord of the two parabolas.

18. PN is an ordinate of the parabola; a straight line is drawn parallel to the axis to bisect NP and meets the curve in Q; prove that NQ meets the tangent at the vertex in a point T such that $AT = \dfrac{2}{3} NP$.

19. Prove that the chord of the parabola $y^2 = 4ax$, whose equation is $y - x\sqrt{2} + 4a\sqrt{2} = 0$, is a normal to the curve and that its length is $6\sqrt{3}a$.

20. If perpendiculars be drawn on any tangent to a parabola from two fixed points on the axis, which are equidistant from the focus, prove that the difference of their squares is constant.

21. If P, Q, and R be three points on a parabola whose ordinates are in geometrical progression, prove that the tangents at P and R meet on the ordinate of Q.

22. Tangents are drawn to a parabola at points whose abscissae are in the ratio $\mu : 1$; prove that they intersect on the curve
    $$y^2 = (\mu^{1/4} + \mu^{-1/4})^2 ax.$$

23. If the tangents at the points (x', y') and (x'', y'') meet at the point (x_1, y_1) and the normals at the same points, in (x_2, y_2), prove that

    1. $x_1 = \dfrac{y'y''}{4a}$ and $y_1 = \dfrac{y' + y''}{2}$,

    2. $x_2 = 2a + \dfrac{y'^2 + y'y'' + y''^2}{4a}$ and $y_2 = -y'y''\dfrac{y' + y''}{8a^2}$,

    and hence, that

    3. $x_2 = 2a + \dfrac{y_1^2}{a} - x_1$ and $y_2 = -\dfrac{x_1 y_1}{a}$.

24. From the preceding question prove that, if tangents be drawn to the parabola $y^2 = 4ax$ from any point on the parabola $y^2 = a(x + b)$, then the normals at the points of contact meet on a fixed straight line.

25. Find the lengths of the normals drawn from the point on the axis of the parabola $y^2 = 8ax$ whose distance from the focus is $8a$.

26. Prove that the locus of the middle point of the portion of a normal intersected between the curve and the axis is a parabola whose

vertex is the focus and whose latus rectum is one quarter of that of the original parabola.

27. Prove that the distance between a tangent to the parabola and the parallel normal is $a \csc \theta \sec^2 \theta$, where θ is the angle that either makes with the axis.

28. PNP' is a double ordinate of the parabola; prove that the locus of the point of intersection of the normal at P and the straight line through P' parallel to the axis is the equal parabola $y^2 = 4a(x - 4a)$.

29. The normal at any point P meets the axis in G and the tangent at the vertex in G'; if A be the vertex and the rectangle $AGQG'$ be completed, prove that the equation to the locus of Q is

$$x^3 = 2ax^2 + ay^2.$$

30. Two equal parabolas have the same focus and their axes are at right angles; a normal to one is perpendicular to a normal to the other; prove that the locus of the point of intersection of these normals is another parabola.

31. If a normal to a parabola make an angle ϕ with the axis, shew that

it will cut the curve again at an angle $\tan^{-1}\left(\dfrac{1}{2}\tan\phi\right)$.

32. Prove that the two parabolas $y^2 = 4ax$ and $y^2 = 4c(x - b)$ cannot have a common normal, other than the axis, unless $\dfrac{b}{a - c} > 2$.

33. If $a^2 > 8b^2$, prove that a point can be found such that the two tangents from it to the parabola $y^2 = 4ax$ are normals to the parabola $x^2 = 4by$.

34. Prove that three tangents to a parabola, which are such that the tangents of their inclinations to the axes are in a given harmonical progression, form a triangle whose area is constant.

35. Prove that the parabolas $y^2 = 4ax$ and $x^2 = 4by$ cut one another at an

angle $\tan^{-1}\dfrac{3a^{1/3}b^{1/3}}{2(a^{2/3} + b^{2/3})}$.

36. Prove that two parabolas, having the same focus and their axes in opposite directions, cut at right angles.

37. Shew that the two parabolas

$$x^2 + 4a(y - 2b - a) = 0 \quad \text{and} \quad y^2 = 4b(x - 2a + b)$$

intersect at right angles at the common end of the latus rectum of each.

38. A parabola is drawn touching the axis of x at the origin and having its vertex at a given distance k from this axis. Prove that the axis of the parabola is a tangent to the parabola $x^2 = -8k(y - 2k)$.

➤ **211. Some Properties of the Parabola**

(a) *If the tangent and normal at any point P of the parabola meet the axis in T and G respectively, then*

$$ST = SG = SP,$$

and the tangent at P is equally inclined to the axis and the focal distance of P.

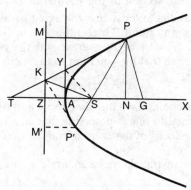

Let P be the point (x', y').

Draw PM perpendicular to the directrix.

By Art. 209, we have $AT = AN$.

$\therefore \qquad TS = TA + AS = AN + ZA = ZN = MP = SP,$

and hence, $\qquad\qquad \angle STP = \angle SPT.$

By the same article, $NG = 2AS = ZS.$

$\therefore \qquad SG = SN + NG = ZS + SN = MP = SP.$

(b) *If the tangent at P meet the directrix in K, then KSP is a right angle.*

For $\qquad\qquad \angle SPT = \angle PTS = \angle KPM.$

Hence, the two triangles KPS and KPM have the two sides KP PS and the angle KPS equal respectively to the two sides KP, PM and the angle KPM.

Hence, $\qquad\qquad \angle KSP = \angle KMP = $ a right angle.

Also, $\qquad\qquad \angle SKP = \angle MKP.$

(c) *Tangents at the extremities of any focal chord intersect at right angles in the directrix.*

For, if PS be produced to meet the curve in P', then, since $\angle P'SK$ is a right angle, the tangent at P' meets the directrix in K.

Also, by (β), $\qquad\qquad \angle MKP = \angle SKP,$

and, similarly, $\qquad\qquad \angle M'KP' = \angle SKP'$

Hence, $\angle PKP' = \dfrac{1}{2} \angle SKM + \dfrac{1}{2} \angle SKM' = $ a right angle.

(d) *If SY be perpendicular to the tangent at P, then Y lies on the tangent at the vertex and $SY^2 = AS \cdot SP$.*

For the equation to any tangent is

$$y = mx + \frac{a}{m} \qquad \qquad \ldots(1)$$

The equation to the perpendicular to this line passing through the focus is

$$y = -\frac{1}{m}(x - a) \qquad \qquad \ldots(2)$$

The lines (1) and (2) meet where

$$mx + \frac{a}{m} = -\frac{1}{m}(x - a) = -\frac{1}{m}x + \frac{a}{m},$$

i.e., where $x = 0$.

Hence, Y lies on the tangent at the vertex.

Also, by geometry,

$$SY^2 = SA \cdot ST = AS \cdot SP$$

➤ **212.** *To prove that through any given point (x_1, y_1) there pass, in general, two tangents to the parabola.*

The equation to any tangent is (by Art. 206)

$$y = mx + \frac{a}{m} \qquad \qquad \ldots(1)$$

If this pass through the fixed point (x_1, y_1), we have

$$y_1 = mx_1 + \frac{a}{m}$$

i.e., $$m^2 x_1 - my_1 + a = 0 \qquad \qquad \ldots(2)$$

For any given values of x_1 and y_1 this equation is in general a quadratic equation and gives two values of m (real or imaginary).

Corresponding to each value of m we have, by substituting in (1), a different tangent.

The roots of (2) are real and different if $y_1^2 - 4ax_1$ be positive, *i.e.*, by Art. 201, if the point (x_1, y_1) lie without the curve.

They are equal, *i.e.*, the *two* tangents coalesce into one tangent, if $y_1^2 - 4ax_1$ be zero, *i.e.* if the point (x_1, y_1) lie on the curve.

The two roots are imaginary if $y_1^2 - 4ax_1$ be negative, *i.e.*, if the point (x_1, y_1) lie within the curve.

➤ **213.** *Equation to the* **chord of contact** *of tangents drawn from a point* (x_1, y_1).

The equation to the tangent at any point Q, whose coordinates are x' and y', is

$$yy' = 2a(x + x')$$

Also the tangent at the point R, whose coordinates are x'' and y'', is

$$y'' = 2a(x + x'')$$

If these tangents meet at the point T, whose coordinates are x_1 and y_1, we have

$$y_1y' = 2a(x_1 + x') \qquad \text{...(1)}$$

and

$$y_1y'' = 2a(x_1 + x'') \qquad \text{...(2)}$$

The equation to QR is then

$$yy_1 = 2a(x + x_1) \qquad \text{...(3}$$

For, since (1) is true, the point (x', y') lies on (3).

Also, since (2) is true, the point (x'', y'') lies on (3).

Hence (3) must be the equation to the straight line joining (x', y') to the point (x'', y''), *i.e.*, it must be the equation to QR the chord o contact of tangents from the point (x_1, y_1).

➤ **214.** The polar of any point with respect to a parabola is define as in Art. 162.

To find the equation of the **polar** *of the point* (x_1, y_1) *with respect to th parabola* $y^2 = 4ax$.

Let Q and R be the points in which any chord drawn through th point P, whose coordinates are (x_1, y_1), meets the parabola.

Let the tangents at Q and R meet in the point whose coordinate are (h, k).

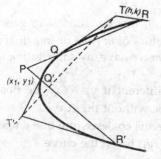
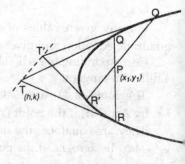

We require the locus of (h, k).

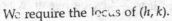

Since, QR is the chord of contact of tangents from (h, k), its equation (Art. 213) is

$$ky = 2a(x + h)$$

Since, this straight line passes through the point (x_1, y_1), we have

$$ky_1 = 2a(x_1 + h) \qquad \ldots(1)$$

Since, the relation (1) is true, it follows that the point (h, k) always lies on the straight line

$$yy_1 = 2a(x + x_1) \qquad \ldots(2)$$

Hence, (2) is the equation to the polar of (x_1, y_1).

Cor. : The equation to the polar of the focus, *viz.*, the point $(a, 0)$, is $0 = x + a$, so that the polar of the focus is the directrix.

▶ **215.** When the point (x_1, y_1) lies without the parabola the equation to its polar is the same as the equation to the chord of contact tangents drawn from (x_1, y_1).

When (x_1, y_1) is on the parabola the polar is the same as the tangent at the point.

As in Art. 164, the polar of (x_1, y_1) might have been defined as the chord of contact of the tangents (real or imaginary) that can be drawn from it to the parabola.

▶ **216.** *Geometrical construction for the polar of a point* (x_1, y_1).

Let T be the point (x_1, y_1), so that its polar is

$$yy_1 = 2a(x + x_1) \qquad \ldots(1)$$

Through T draw a straight line parallel to the axis; its equation is therefore,

$$y = y_1 \qquad \ldots(2)$$

Let this straight line meet the polar in V and the curve in P.

The coordinates of V, which is the intersection of (1) and (2), are therefore,

$$\frac{y_1^2}{2a} - x_1 \quad \text{and} \quad y_1 \qquad \ldots(3)$$

Also P is the point on the curve whose ordinate is y_1, and whose coordinates are therefore,

$$\frac{y_1}{4a} \quad \text{and} \quad y_1$$

Since abscissa of $P = \dfrac{\text{abscissa of } T + \text{abscissa of } V}{2}$, therefore, by Art. 22, Cor., P is the middle point of TV.

Also the tangent at P is

$$yy_1 = 2a\left(x + \frac{y_1^2}{4a}\right),$$

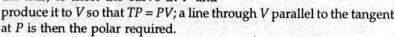

which is parallel to (1).

Hence, the polar of T is parallel to the tangent at P.

To draw the polar of T we therefore, draw a line through T, parallel to the axis, to meet the curve in P and produce it to V so that $TP = PV$; a line through V parallel to the tangent at P is then the polar required.

➤ **217.** *If the polar of a point P passes through the point T, then the polar of T goes through P.* (Fig. Art. 214).

Let P be the point (x_1, y_1) and T the point (h, k).

The polar of P is $yy_1 = 2a(x + x_1)$.

Since, it passes, through T, we have

$$y_1k = 2a(x_1 + h) \qquad \qquad ...(1)$$

The polar of T is, $yk = 2a(x + h)$.

Since, (1) is true, this equation is satisfied by the coordinates x_1 and y_1.

Hence, the proposition.

Cor. : The point of intersection, T, of the polars of two points, P and Q, is the pole of the line PQ.

➤ **218.** *To find the   pole of a given straight line with respect to the parabola.*

Let the given straight line be

$$Ax + By + C = 0$$

If its pole be the point (x_1, y_1), it must be the same straight line as,

$$yy_1 = 2a(x + x_1)$$

i.e., $2ax - yy_1 + 2ax_1 = 0$

Since, these straight lines are the same, we have

$$\frac{2a}{A} = \frac{-y_1}{B} = \frac{2ax_1}{C}$$

i.e., $\qquad x_1 = \dfrac{C}{A}$ and $\qquad y_1 = -\dfrac{2Ba}{A}$

➤ **219.** *To find the equation to the pair of tangents that can be drawn to the parabola from the point* (x_1, y_1).

Let (h, k) be any point on *either* of the tangents drawn from (x_1, y_1). The equation to the line joining (x_1, y_1) to (h, k) is

$$y - y_1 = \frac{k - y_1}{h - x_1}(x - x_1),$$

i.e.,

$$y = \frac{k - y_1}{h - x_1}x + \frac{hy_1 - kx_1}{h - x_1}.$$

If this be a tangent it must be of the form

$$y = mx + \frac{a}{m}$$

so that, $\qquad \dfrac{k - y_1}{h - x_1} = m$ and $\qquad \dfrac{hy_1 - kx_1}{h - x_1} = \dfrac{a}{m}.$

Hence, by multiplication,

$$a = \frac{k - y_1}{h - x_1}\frac{hy_1 - kx_1}{h - x_1}$$

i.e., $\qquad a(h - x_1)^2 = (k - y_1)(hy_1 - kx_1).$

The locus of the point (h, k), (*i.e.,* the *pair* of tangents required) is therefore,

$$a(x - x_1)^2 = (y - y_1)(xy_1 - yx_1) \qquad \ldots(1)$$

It will be seen that this equation is the same as

$$(y^2 - 4ax)(y_1{}^2 - 4ax_1) = \{yy_1 - 2a(x + x_1)\}^2.$$

➤ **220.** *To prove that the middle points of a system of parallel chords of a parabola all lie on a straight line which is parallel to the axis.*

Since, the chords are all parallel, they all make the same angle with the axis of x. Let the tangent of this angle be m.

The equation to QR, any one of these chords, is therefore

$$y = mx + c \qquad \ldots(1)$$

where c is different for the several chords, but m is the same.

This straight line meets the parabola $y^2 = 4ax$ in points whose ordinates are given by

$$my^2 = 4a(y - c),$$

i.e., $\qquad y^2 - \dfrac{4a}{m}y + \dfrac{4ac}{m} = 0 \qquad \ldots(2)$

Let the roots of this equation, *i.e.*, the ordinates of Q and R, be y' and y'', and let the coordinates of V, the middle point of QR, be (h, k).

Then, by Art. 22,

$$k = \frac{y' + y''}{2} = \frac{2a}{m},$$

from equation (2).

The coordinates of V, therefore, satisfy the equation

$$y = \frac{2a}{m},$$

so that the locus of V is a straight line parallel to the axis of the curve.

The straight line $y = \frac{2a}{m}$ meets the curve in a point P, whose

ordinate is $\frac{2a}{m}$ and whose abscissa is therefore, $\frac{a}{m^2}$.

The tangent at this point is, by Art. 205,

$$y = mx + \frac{a}{m},$$

and is therefore, parallel to each of the given chords.

Hence, the locus of the middle points of a system of parallel chords of a parabola is a straight line which is parallel to the axis and meets the curve at a point the tangent at which is parallel to the given system.

➤ **221.** *To find the equation to the chord of the parabola which is bisected at any point* (h, k).

By the last article the required chord is parallel to the tangent at the point P where a line through (h, k) parallel to the axis meets the curve.

Also, by Art. 216, the polar of (h, k) is parallel to the tangent at this same point P.

The required chord is therefore parallel to the polar $yk = 2a(x + h)$.

Hence, since it goes through (h, k), its equation is

$$k(y - k) = 2a(x - h) \qquad \text{(Art. 67).}$$

➤ **222. Diameter. Def.** The locus of the middle points of a system of parallel chords of a parabola is called a diameter and the chords are called its double ordinates.

Thus, in the figure of Art. 220, PV is a diameter and QR and all the parallel chords are ordinates to this diameter.

The proposition of that article may therefore, be stated as follows:

Any diameter of a parabola is parallel to the axis and the tangent at the point where it meets the curve is parallel to its ordinates.

➤ **223.** *The tangents at the ends of any chord meet on the diameter which bisects the chord.*

Let the equation of QR (Fig., Art. 220) be

$$y = mx + c \qquad \qquad \text{...(1)}$$

and let the tangents at Q and R meet at the point T (x_1, y_1).

Then QR is the chord of contact of tangents drawn from T, and hence its equation is

$$yy_1 = 2a(x + x_1) \qquad \qquad \text{(Art. 213).}$$

Comparing this with equation (1), we have

$$\frac{2a}{y_1} = m, \quad \text{so that} \quad y_1 = \frac{2a}{m},$$

and therefore T lies on the straight line

$$y = \frac{2a}{m}.$$

But this straight line was proved, in Art. 220, to be the diameter PV which bisects the chord.

➤ **224.** *To find the equation to a parabola, the axes being any diameter and the tangent to the parabola at the point where this diameter meets the curve.*

Let PVX be the diameter and PV the tangent at P meeting the axis in T.

Take any point Q on the curve, and draw QM perpendicular to the axis meeting the diameter PV in L.

Let PV be x and VQ be y.

Draw PN perpendicular to the axis of the curve, and let

$$\theta = \angle YPX = \angle PTM$$

Then,

$$4AS \cdot AN = PN^2 = NT^2 \tan^2 \theta = 4AN^2 \cdot \tan^2 \theta$$

$$\therefore \qquad AN = AS \cdot \cot^2 \theta = a \cot^2 \theta,$$

and

$$PN = \sqrt{4AS \cdot AN} = 2a \cot \theta$$

Now, $\qquad QM^2 = 4AS \cdot AM = 4a \cdot AM$ ...(1)

Also, $QM = NP + LQ = 2a \cot \theta + VQ \sin \theta = 2a \cot \theta + y \sin \theta$,

and $\qquad AM = AN + PV + VL = a \cot^2 \theta + x + y \cos \theta$

Substituting these values in (1), we have

$$(2a \cot \theta + y \sin \theta)^2 = 4a(a \cot^2 \theta + x + y \cos \theta),$$

i.e., $\qquad\qquad y^2 \sin^2 \theta = 4ax$

The required equation is therefore

$$y^2 = 4px \qquad\qquad ...(2)$$

where $\qquad p = \dfrac{a}{\sin^2 \theta} = a(1 + \cot^2 \theta) = a + AN = SP$ (by Art. 202).

The equation to the parabola referred to the above axes is therefore, of the same form as its equation referred to the rectangular axes of Art. 197.

The equation (2) states that

$$QV^2 = 4SP \cdot PV$$

➤ **225.** The quantity $4p$ is called the parameter of the diameter PV. It is equal in length to the chord which is parallel to PY and passes through the focus.

For if $Q'V'R'$ be the chord, parallel to PY and passing through the focus and meeting PV in V', we have

$$PV' = ST = SP = p,$$

so that $\qquad Q'V'^2 = 4p \cdot PV' = 4p^2,$

and hence, $\qquad Q'R' = 2Q'V' = 4p.$

➤ **226.** Just as in Art. 205 it could now be shown that the tangent at any point (x', y') of the above curve is

$$yy' = 2p(x + x')$$

Similarly, for the equation to the polar of any point.

═══════ EXAMPLES XXVII ═══════

1. Prove that the length of the chord joining the points of contact of tangents drawn from the point (x_1, y_1) is

$$\frac{\sqrt{y_1^2 + 4a^2}\,\sqrt{y_1^2 - 4ax_1}}{a}.$$

2. Prove that the area of the triangle formed by the tangents from the point (x_1, y_1) and the chord of contact is $(y_1^2 - 4ax_1)^{3/2} \div 2a$.

3. If a perpendicular be let fall from any point P upon its polar prove that the distance of the foot of this perpendicular from the focus is equal to the distance of the point P from the directrix.

4. What is the equation to the chord of the parabola $y^2 = 8x$ which is bisected at the point $(2, -3)$?

5. The general equation to a system of parallel chords in the parabola $y^2 = \dfrac{25}{7} x$ is $4x - y + k = 0$. What is the equation to the corresponding diameter?

6. P, Q, and R are three points on a parabola and the chord PQ cuts the diameter through R in V. Ordinates PM and QN are drawn to this diameter. Prove that $RM \cdot RN = RV^2$.

7. Two equal parabolas with axis in opposite directions touch at a point O. From a point P on one of them are drawn tangents PQ and PQ' to the outher. Prove that QQ' will touch the first parabola in P' where PP' is parallel to the common tangent at O.

Coordinates of any point on the parabola expressed in terms of one variable

➤ **227.** It is often convenient to express the coordinates of any point on the curve in terms of one variable.

It is clear that the values

$$x = \frac{a}{m^2}, \quad y = \frac{2a}{m}$$

always satisfy the equation to the curve.

Hence, for all values of m, the point

$$\left(\frac{a}{m^2}, \frac{2a}{m} \right)$$

lies on the curve. By Art. 206, this m is equal to the tangent of the angle which the tangent at the point makes with the axis.

The equation to the tangent at this point is

$$y = mx + \frac{a}{m},$$

and the normal is, by Art. 207, found to be

$$my + x = 2a + \frac{a}{m^2}.$$

➤ **228.** The coordinates of the point could also be expressed in terms of the m of the normal at the point; in this case its coordinates are am^2 and $-2am$.

The equation of the tangent at the point $(am^2, -2am)$ is, by Art. 205.

$$my + x + am^2 = 0,$$

and the equation to the normal is

$$y = mx - 2am - am^3$$

➤ **229.** The simplest substitution (avoiding both negative signs and fractions) is

$$x = at^2 \quad \text{and} \quad y = 2at.$$

These values satisfy the equation $y^2 = 4ax$.

The equations to the tangent and normal at the point $(at^2, 2at)$ are, by Arts. 205 and 207,

$$ty = x + at^2,$$

and $$y + tx = 2at + at^3$$

The equation to the straight line joining

$$(at_1^2, 2at_1) \quad \text{and} \quad (at_2^2, 2at_2)$$

is easily found to be

$$y(t_1 + t_2) = 2x + 2at_1t_2$$

The tangents at the points

$$(at_1^2, 2at_1) \quad \text{and} \quad (at_2^2, 2at_2)$$

are $$t_1y = x + at_1^2,$$

and $$t_2y = x + at_2^2.$$

The point of intersection of these two tangents is clearly

$$\{at_1t_2, a(t_1 + t_2)\}$$

The point whose coordinates are $(at^2, 2at)$ may, for brevity, be called the point "t".

In the following articles we shall prove some important properties of the parabola making use of the above substitution.

➤ **230.** *If the tangents at P and Q meet in T, prove that*

1. TP and TQ subtend equal angles at the focus S,

2. $ST^2 = SP \cdot SQ$,

and 3. the triangles SPT and STQ are similar.

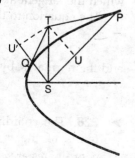

Let P be the point $(at_1^2, 2at_1)$ and Q be the point $(at_2^2, 2at_2)$, so that (Art. 229) T is the point $\{at_1t_2, a(t_1 + t_2)\}$.

1. The equation to SP is

$$y = \frac{2at_1}{at_1^2 - a}(x - a)$$

i.e., $\qquad (t_1^2 - 1)y - 2t_1 x + 2at_1 = 0.$

The perpendicular, TU, from T on this straight line

$$= \frac{a(t_1^2 - 1)(t_1 + t_2) - 2t_1 \cdot at_1 t_2 + 2at_1}{\sqrt{(t_1^2 - 1)^2 + 4t_1^2}}$$

$$= a\frac{(t_1^3 - t_1^2 t_2) + (t_1 - t_2)}{t_1^2 + 1}$$

$$= a(t_1 - t_2)$$

Similarly, TU' has the same numerical value.

The angles PST and QST are therefore, equal.

2. By Art. 202, we have $SP = a(1 + t_1^2)$ and $SQ = a(1 + t_2^2)$.

Also, $ST^2 = (at_1 t_2 - a)^2 + a^2(t_1 + t_2)^2$

$$= a^2[t_1^2 t_2^2 + t_1^2 + t_2^2 + 1] = a^2(1 + t_1^2)(1 + t_2^2).$$

Hence, $\qquad ST^2 = SP \cdot SQ.$

3. Since, $\dfrac{ST}{SP} = \dfrac{SQ}{ST}$ and the angles TSP and TSQ are equal, the triangles SPT and STQ are similar, so that

$$\angle SQT = \angle STP \quad \text{and} \quad \angle STQ = \angle SPT.$$

▶ **231.** *The area of the triangle formed by three points on a parabola is twice the area of the triangle formed by the tangents at these points.*

Let the three points on the parabola be

$$(at_1^2, 2at_1), (at_2^2, 2at_2), \text{ and } (at_3^2, 2at_3)$$

The area of the triangle formed by these points, by Art. 25,

$$= \frac{1}{2}[at_1^2(2at_2 - 2at_3) + at_2^2(2at_3 - 2at_1) + at_3^2(2at_1 - 2at_2)]$$

$$= -a^2(t_2 - t_3)(t_3 - t_1)(t_1 - t_2)$$

The intersections of the tangents at these points are (Art. 229) the points

$$\{at_2 t_3, a(t_2 + t_3)\}, \{at_3 t_1, a(t_3 + t_1)\}, \text{ and } \{at_1 t_2, a(t_1 + t_2)\}.$$

The area of the triangle formed by these three points

$$= \frac{1}{2}\{at_2 t_3(at_3 - at_2) + at_3 t_1(at_1 - at_3) + at_1 t_2(at_2 - at_1)\}$$

$$= \frac{1}{2} a^2 (t_2 - t_3)(t_3 - t_1)(t_1 - t_2)$$

The first of these areas is double the second.

➤ **232.** *The circle circumscribing the triangle formed by any three tangents to a parabola passes through the focus.*

Let P, Q and R be the points at which the tangents are drawn and let their coordinates be

$$(at_1^2, 2at_1), (at_2^2, 2at_2), \text{ and } (at_3^2, 2at_3).$$

As in Art. 229, the tangents at Q and R intersect in the point

$$\{at_2t_3, a(t_2 + t_3)\}.$$

Similarly, the other pairs of tangents meet at the points

$$\{at_3t_1, a(t_3 + t_1)\} \quad \text{and} \quad \{at_1t_2, a(t_1 + t_2)\}.$$

Let the equation to the circle be

$$x^2 + y^2 + 2gx + 2fy + c = 0 \qquad \qquad \text{...(1)}$$

Since, it passes through the above three points, we have

$$a^2 t_2^2 t_3^2 + a^2(t_2 + t_3)^2 + 2gat_2t_3 + 2fa(t_2 + t_3) + c = 0 \qquad \text{...(2)}$$

$$a^2 t_3^2 t_1^2 + a^2(t_3 + t_1)^2 + 2gat_3t_1 + 2fa(t_3 + t_1) + c = 0 \qquad \text{...(3)}$$

and $\qquad a^2 t_1^2 t_2^2 + a^2(t_1 + t_2)^2 + 2gat_1t_2 + 2fa(t_1 + t_2) + c = 0 \qquad \text{...(4)}$

Subtracting (3) from (2) and dividing by $a(t_2 - t_1)$, we have

$$a\{t_3^2(t_1 + t_2) + t_1 + t_2 + 2t_3\} + 2gt_3 + 2f = 0$$

Similarly, from (3) and (4), we have

$$a\{t_1^2(t_2 + t_3) + t_2 + t_3 + 2t_1\} + 2gt_1 + 2f = 0$$

From these two equations, we have

$$2g = -a(1 + t_2t_3 + t_3t_1 + t_1t_2) \text{ and } 2f = -a[t_1 + t_2 + t_3 - t_1t_2t_3]$$

Substituting these values in (2), we obtain

$$c = a^2(t_2t_3 + t_3t_1 + t_1t_2)$$

The equation to the circle is therefore,

$$x^2 + y^2 - ax(1 + t_2t_3 + t_3t_1 + t_1t_2) - ay(t_1 + t_2 + t_3 - t_1t_2t_3)$$
$$+ a^2(t_2t_3 + t_3t_1 + t_1t_2) = 0,$$

which clearly goes through the focus $(a, 0)$.

➤ **233.** *If O be any point on the axis and POP' be any chord passing through O, and if PM and $P'M'$ be the ordinates of P and P', prove that $AM \cdot AM' = AO^2$, and $PM \cdot P'M' = -4a \cdot AO$.*

Let O be the point $(h, 0)$, and let P and P' be the points

$$(at_1^2, 2at_1) \quad \text{and} \quad (at_2^2, 2at_2)$$

The equation to PP' is, by Art. 229,

$$(t_2 + t_1)y - 2x = 2at_1t_2.$$

If this pass through the point $(h, 0)$, we have

$$-2h = 2at_1t_2$$

i.e.,
$$t_1t_2 = -\frac{h}{a}.$$

Hence, $\quad AM \cdot AM' = at_1^2 \cdot at_2^2 = a^2 \cdot \dfrac{h^2}{a^2} = h^2 = AO^2,$

and $\qquad PM \cdot PM' = 2at_1 \cdot 2at_2 = 4a^2\left(-\dfrac{h}{a}\right) = -4a \cdot AO$

Cor. : If O be the focus, $AO = a$, and we have

$$t_1t_2 = -1, \quad i.e., \quad t_2 = -\frac{1}{t_1}.$$

The points $(at_1^2, 2at_1)$ and $\left(\dfrac{a}{t_1^2}, \dfrac{-2a}{t_1}\right)$ are therefore, at the ends of a focal chord.

▶ **234.** *To prove that the orthocentre of any triangle formed by three tangents to a parabola lies on the directrix.*

Let the equations to the three tangents be

$$y = m_1x + \frac{a}{m_1} \qquad \qquad \text{...(1)}$$

$$y = m_2x + \frac{a}{m_2} \qquad \qquad \text{...(2)}$$

and
$$y = m_3x + \frac{a}{m_3} \qquad \qquad \text{...(3)}$$

The point of intersection of (2) and (3) is found, by solving them, to be

$$\left\{\frac{a}{m_2m_3}, a\left(\frac{1}{m_2} + \frac{1}{m_3}\right)\right\}.$$

The equation to the straight line through this point perpendicular to (1) is (Art. 69)

$$y - a\left(\frac{1}{m_2} + \frac{1}{m_3}\right) = -\frac{1}{m_1}\left[x - \frac{a}{m_2m_3}\right],$$

i.e., $$y + \frac{x}{m_1} = a\left[\frac{1}{m_2} + \frac{1}{m_3} + \frac{1}{m_1 m_2 m_3}\right] \qquad \ldots(4)$$

Similarly, the equation to the straight line through the intersection of (3) and (1) perpendicular to (2) is

$$y + \frac{x}{m_2} = a\left(\frac{1}{m_3} + \frac{1}{m_1} + \frac{1}{m_1 m_2 m_3}\right) \qquad \ldots(5)$$

and the equation to the straight line through the intersection of (1) and (2) perpendicular to (3) is

$$y + \frac{x}{m_3} = a\left(\frac{1}{m_1} + \frac{1}{m_2} + \frac{1}{m_1 m_2 m_3}\right) \qquad \ldots(6)$$

The point which is common to the straight lines (4), (5) and (6)] *i.e.*, the orthocentre of the triangle, is easily seen to be the point whose coordinates are

$$x = -a, \quad y = a\left(\frac{1}{m_1} + \frac{1}{m_2} + \frac{1}{m_3} + \frac{1}{m_1 m_2 m_3}\right),$$

and this point lies on the directrix.

EXAMPLES XXVIII

1. If ω be the angle which a focal chord of a parabola makes with the axis, prove that the length of the chord is $4a \operatorname{cosec}^2 \omega$ and that the perpendicular on it from the vertex is $a \sin \omega$.

2. A point on a parabola, the foot of the perpendicular from it upon the directrix, and the focus are the vertices of an equilateral triangle. Prove that the focal distance of the point is equal to the latus rectum.

3. Prove that the semi-latus-rectum is a harmonic mean between the segments of any focal chord.

4. If T be any point on the tangent at any point P of a parabola, and if TL be perpendicular to the focal radius SP and TN be perpendicular to the directrix, prove that $SL = TN$.

   Hence, obtain a geometrical construction for the pair of tangents drawn to the parabola from any point T.

5. Prove that on the axis of any parabola there is a certain point K which has the property that, if a chord PQ of the parabola be drawn through it, then

$$\frac{1}{PK^2} + \frac{1}{QK^2}$$

is the same for all positions of the chord.

6. The normal at the point $(at_1^2, 2at_1)$ meets the parabola again in the point $(at_2^2, 2at_2)$; prove that

$$t_2 = -t_1 - \frac{2}{t_1}.$$

7. A chord is a normal to a parabola and is inclined at an angle θ to the axis; prove that the area of the triangle formed by it and the tangents at its extremities is $4a^2 \sec^3 \theta \csc^3 \theta$.

8. If PQ be a normal chord of the parabola and if S be the focus, prove that the locus of the centroid of the triangle SPQ is the curve

$$36ay^2(3x - 5a) - 81y^4 = 128a^4.$$

9. Prove that the length of the intercept on the normal at the point $(at^2, 2at)$ made by the circle which is described on the focal distance of the given point as diameter is $a\sqrt{1 + t^2}$.

10. Prove that the area of the triangle formed by the normals to the parabola at the points $(at_1^2, 2at_1)$, $(at_2^2, 2at_2)$ and $(at_3^2, 2at_3)$ is

$$\frac{a^2}{2}(t_2 - t_3)(t_3 - t_1)(t_1 - t_2)(t_1 + t_2 + t_3)^2.$$

11. Prove that the normal chord at the point whose ordinate is equal to its abscissa subtends a right angle at the focus.

12. A chord of a parabola passes through a point on the axis (outside the parabola) whose distance from the vertex is half the latus rectum; prove that the normals at its extremities meet on the curve.

13. The normal at a point P of a parabola meets the curve again in Q, and T is the pole of PQ; shew that T lies on the diameter passing through the other end of the focal chord passing through P, and that PT is bisected by the directrix.

14. If from the vertex of a parabola a pair of chords be drawn at right angles to one another and with these chords as adjacent sides a rectangle be made, prove that the locus of the further angle of the rectangle is the parabola

$$y^2 = 4a(x - 8a)$$

15. A series of chords is drawn so that their projections on a straight line which is inclined at an angle α to the axis are all of constant length c; prove that the locus of their middle point is the curve

$$(y^2 - 4ax)(y \cos \alpha + 2a \sin \alpha)^2 + a^2c^2 = 0$$

16. Prove that the locus of the poles of chords which subtend a right angle at a fixed point (h, k) is

$$ax^2 - hy^2 + (4a^2 + 2ah)x - 2aky + a(h^2 + k^2) = 0$$

17. Prove that the locus of the middle points of all tangents drawn from points on the directrix to the parabola is
$$y^2(2x + a) = a(3x + a)^2$$

18. Prove that the orthocentres of the triangles formed by three tangents and the corresponding three normals to a parabola are equidistant from the axis.

19. T is the pole of the chord PQ; prove that the perpendiculars from P, T, and Q upon any tangent to the parabola are in geometrical progression.

20. If r_1 and r_2 be the lengths of radii vectors of the parabola which are drawn at right angles to one another from the vertex, prove that
$$r_1^{4/3} r_2^{4/3} = 16a^2(r_1^{2/3} + r_2^{2/3}).$$

21. A parabola touches the sides of a triangle ABC in the points D, E and F respectively; if DE and DF cut the diameter through the point A in b and c respectively, prove that Bb and Cc are parallel.

22. Prove that all circles described on focal chords as diameters touch the directrix of the curve, and that all circles on focal radii as diameters touch the tangent at the vertex.

23. A circle is described on a focal chord as diameter; if m be the tangent of the inclination of the chord to the axis, prove that the equation to the circle is
$$x^2 + y^2 - 2ax\left(1 + \frac{2}{m^2}\right) - \frac{4ay}{m} - 3a^2 = 0$$

24. LOL' and MOM' are two chords of a parabola passing through a point O on its axis. Prove that the radical axis of the circles described on LL' and MM' as diameters passes through the vertex of the parabola.

25. A circle and a parabola intersect in four points; shew that the algebraic sum of the ordinates of the four points is zero.

Shew also that the line joining one pair of these four points and the line joining the other pair are equally inclined to the axis.

26. Circles are drawn through the vertex of the parabola to cut the parabola orthogonally at the other point of intersection. Prove that the locus of the centres of the circles is the curve
$$2y^2(2y^2 + x^2 - 12ax) = ax(3x - 4a)^2$$

27. Prove that the equation to the circle passing through the points $(at_1^2, 2at_1)$ and $(at_2^2, 2at_2)$ and the intersection of the tangents to the parabola at these points is
$$x^2 + y^2 - ax[(t_1 + t_2)^2 + 2] - ay(t_1 + t_2)(1 - t_1t_2) + a^2t_1t_2(2 - t_1t_2) = 0$$

28. TP and TQ are tangents to the parabola and the normals at P and Q meet at a point R on the curve; prove that the centre of the circle circumscribing the triangle TPQ lies on the parabola
$$2y^2 = a(x - a)$$

29. Through the vertex A of the parabola $y^2 = 4ax$ two chords AP and AQ are drawn, and the circles on AP and AQ as diameters intersect in R. Prove that, if θ_1, θ_2, and ϕ be the angles made with the axis by the tangents at P and Q and by AR, then

$$\cot \theta_1 + \cot \theta_2 + 2 \tan \phi = 0$$

30. A parabola is drawn such that each vertex of a given triangle is the pole of the opposite side; shew that the focus of the parabola lies on the nine-point circle of the triangle, and that the orthocentre of the triangle formed by joining the middle points of the sides lies on the directrix.

11

THE PARABOLA (CONTINUED)

[On a first reading of this Chapter, the student may, with advantage, omit from Art. 239 to the end.]

SOME EXAMPLES OF LOCI CONNECTED WITH THE PARABOLA

➤ **235.**

EXAMPLE 1 *Find the locus of the intersection of tangents to the parabola* $y^2 = 4ax$, *the angle between them being always a given angle* α.

The straight line $y = mx + \dfrac{a}{m}$ is always a tangent to the parabola.

If it pass through the point T (h, k), we have

$$m^2h - mk + a = 0 \qquad \dots(1)$$

If m_1 and m_2 be the roots of this equation, we have (by Art. 2)

$$m_1 + m_2 = \frac{k}{h} \qquad \dots(2)$$

and

$$m_1 m_2 = \frac{a}{h} \qquad \dots(3)$$

and the equations to TP and PQ are, then

$$y = m_1 x + \frac{a}{m_1} \quad \text{and} \quad y = m_2 x + \frac{a}{m_2}$$

Hence, by Art. 66, we have

$$\tan \alpha = \frac{m_1 - m_2}{1 + m_1 m_2} = \frac{\sqrt{(m_1 + m_2)^2 - 4m_1 m_2}}{1 + m_1 m_2}$$

$$= \frac{\sqrt{\dfrac{k^2}{h^2} - \dfrac{4a}{h}}}{1 + \dfrac{a}{h}} = \frac{\sqrt{k^2 - 4ah}}{a + h} \quad \text{by (2) and (3)}$$

$$\therefore \qquad k^2 - 4ah = (a + h)^2 \tan^2 \alpha$$

Hence, the coordinates of the point T always satisfy the equation

$$y^2 - 4ax = (a + x)^2 \tan^2 \alpha$$

We shall find in a later chapter that this curve is a hyperbola.

As a particular case let the tangents intersect at right angles, so that $m_1 m_2 = -1$.

From (3), we then have $h = -a$, so that in this case the point T lies on the straight line $x = -a$, which is the directrix.

Hence, the locus of the point of intersection of tangents, which cut at right angles, is the directrix.

EXAMPLE 2 *Prove that the locus of the poles of chords which are normal to the parabola $y^2 = 4ax$ is the curve*

$$y^2 (x + 2a) + 4a^3 = 0$$

Let PQ be a chord which is normal at P. Its equation is then

$$y = mx - 2am - am^3 \qquad \text{...(1)}$$

Let the tangents at P and Q intersect in T, whose coordinates are h and k, so that we require the locus of T.

Since, PQ is the polar of the point (h, k) its equation is

$$yk = 2a (x + h) \qquad \text{...(2)}$$

Now the equations (1) and (2) represent the same straight line, so that they must be equivalent.

Hence, $\qquad m = \dfrac{2a}{k}, \quad$ and $\quad -2am - am^3 = \dfrac{2ah}{k}$

Eliminating m, *i.e.,* substituting the value of m from the first of these equations in the second, we have

$$-\frac{4a^2}{k} - \frac{8a^4}{k^3} = \frac{2ah}{k}$$

i.e., $\qquad k^2 (h + 2a) + 4a^3 = 0$

The locus of the point T is therefore,

$$y^2 (x + 2a) + 4a^3 = 0$$

EXAMPLE 3 *Find the locus of the middle points of chords of a parabola which subtend a right angle at the vertex, and prove that these chords all pass through a fixed point on the axis of the curve.*

First method : Let PQ be any such chord, and let its equation be

$$y = mx + c \qquad \text{...(1)}$$

The lines joining the vertex with the points of intersection of this straight line with the parabola

$$y^2 = 4ax \qquad \text{...(2)}$$

are given by the equation

$$y^2 c = 4ax (y - mx) \qquad \text{(Art. 122)}$$

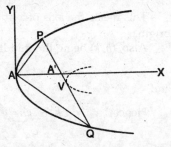

These straight lines are at right angles if

$$c + 4am = 0 \qquad \text{(Art. 111)}$$

Substituting this value of c in (1), the equation to PQ is

$$y = m (x - 4a) \qquad \ldots(3)$$

This straight line cuts the axis of x at a constant distance $4a$ from the vertex, i.e., $AA' = 4a$.

If the middle point of PQ be (h, k) we have, by Art. 220.

$$k = \frac{2a}{m} \qquad \ldots(4)$$

Also the point (h, k) lies on (3), so that we have

$$k = m (h - 4a) \qquad \ldots(5)$$

If between (4) and (5) we eliminate m, we have

$$k = \frac{2a}{k} (h - 4a)$$

i.e., $$k^2 = 2a (h - 4a)$$

so, that (h, k) always lies on the parabola

$$y^2 = 2a (x - 4a)$$

This is a parabola one half the size of the original, and whose vertex is at the point A' through which all the chords pass.

Second method : Let P be the point $(at_1^2, 2at_1)$ and Q be the point $(at_2^2, 2at_2)$.

The tangents of the inclinations of AP and AQ to the axis are

$$\frac{2}{t_1} \quad \text{and} \quad \frac{2}{t_2}$$

Since, AP and AQ are at right angles, therefore

$$\frac{2}{t_1} \cdot \frac{2}{t_2} = -1$$

i.e., $$t_1 t_2 = -4 \qquad \ldots(6)$$

As in Art. 229, the equation to PQ is

$$(t_1 + t_2) y = 2x + 2at_1 t_2 \qquad \ldots(7)$$

This meets the axis of x at a distance $-at_1 t_2$ i.e., by (6), $4a$, from the origin.

Also, (h, k) being the middle point of PQ, we have

$$2h = a (t_1^2 + t_2^2)$$

and $$2k = 2a(t_1 + t_2)$$

Hence, $$k^2 - 2ah = a^2 (t_1 + t_2)^2 - a^2 (t_1^2 + t_2^2)$$

$$= 2a^2 t_1 t_2 = -8a^2$$

so, that the locus of (h, k) is, as before, the parabola

$$y^2 = 2a\,(x - 4a)$$

Third method. The equation to the chord which is bisected at the point (h, k) is, by Art. 221,

$$k\,(y - k) = 2a\,(x - h)$$

i.e., $\qquad\qquad ky - 2ax = k^2 - 2ah$ $\qquad\qquad\qquad$ ...(8)

As in Art. 122 the equation to the straight lines joining its points of intersection with the parabola to the vertex is

$$(k^2 - 2ah)\,y^2 = 4ax\,(ky - 2ax)$$

These lines are at right angles if

$$(k^2 - 2ah) + 8a^2 = 0$$

Hence, the locus as before
Also the equation (8) becomes

$$ky - 2ax = -8a^2$$

This straight line always goes through the point $(4a, 0)$.

EXAMPLES XXIX

From an external point P tangents are drawn to the parabola; find the equation to the locus of P when these tangents make angles θ_1 and θ_2 with the axis, such that

1. $\tan\theta_1 + \tan\theta_2$ is constant $(= b)$
2. $\tan\theta_1 \tan\theta_2$ is constant $(= c)$
3. $\cot\theta_1 + \cot\theta_2$ is constant $(= d)$
4. $\theta_1 + \theta_2$ is constant $(= 2\alpha)$
5. $\tan^2\theta_1 + \tan^2\theta_2$ is constant $(= \lambda)$
6. $\cos\theta_1 \cos\theta_2$ is constant $(= \mu)$
7. Two tangents to a parabola meet at an angle of $45°$; prove that the locus of their point of intersection is the curve

$$y^2 - 4ax = (x + a)^2$$

   If they meet at an angle of $60°$, prove that the locus is

$$y^2 - 3x^2 - 10ax - 3a^2 = 0$$

8. A pair of tangents are drawn which are equally inclined to a straight line whose inclination to the axis is α; prove that the locus of their point of intersection is the straight line

$$y = (x - a)\tan 2\alpha.$$

9. Prove that the locus of the point of intersection of two tangents

which intercept a given distance $4c$ on the tangent at the vertex is an equal parabola.

10. Shew that the locus of the point of intersection of two tangents which with the tangent at the vertex form a triangle of constant area c^2, is the curve $x^2(y^2 - 4ax) = 4c^4$.

11. If the normals at P and Q meet on the parabola, prove that the point of intersection of the tangents at P and Q lies either on a certain straight line, which is parallel to the tangent at the vertex, or on the curve whose equation is $y^2(x + 2a) + 4a^3 = 0$.

12. Two tangents to a parabola intercept on a fixed tangent segments whose product is constant; prove that the locus of their point of intersection is a straight line.

13. Shew that the locus of the poles of chords which subtend a constant angle α at the vertex is the curve.

$$(x + 4a)^2 = 4\cot^2\alpha\,(y^2 - 4ax)$$

14. In the preceding questions if the constant angle be a right angle the locus is a straight line perpendicular to the axis.

15. A point P is such that the straight line drawn through it perpendicular to its polar with respect to the parabola $y^2 = 4ax$ touches the parabola $x^2 = 4by$. Prove that its locus is the straight line

$$2ax + by + 4a^2 = 0$$

16. Two equal parabolas, A and B, have the same vertex and axis but have their concavities turned in opposite directions; prove that the locus of poles with respect to B of tangents to A is the parabola A.

17. Prove that the locus of the poles of tangents to the parabola $y^2 = 4ax$ with respect to the circle $x^2 + y^2 = 2ax$ is the circle $x^2 + y^2 = ax$.

18. Shew the locus of the poles of tangents to the parabola $y^2 = 4ax$ with respect to the parabola $y^2 = 4bx$ is the parabola

$$y^2 = \frac{4b^2}{a}x$$

Find the locus of the middle points of chords of the parabola which

19. pass through the focus.

20. pass through the fixed point (h, k).

21. are normal to the curve.

22. subtend a constant angle α at the vertex.

23. are of given length l.

24. are such that the normals at their extremities meet on the parabola.

25. through each point of the straight line $x = my + h$ is drawn the chord of the parabola $y^2 = 4ax$ which is bisected at the point; prove that it always touches the parabola

$$(y + 2am)^2 = 8a(x - h)$$

26. Two parabolas have the same axis and tangents are drawn to the second from points on the first; prove that the locus of the middle points of the chords of contact with the second parabola all lie on a fixed parabola.

27. Prove that the locus of the feet of the perpendiculars drawn from the vertex of the parabola upon chords, which subtend an angle of 45° at the vertex, is the curve

$$r^2 - 24ar \cos \theta + 16 a^2 \cos 2\theta = 0$$

▶ **236.** *To prove that, in general, three normals can be drawn from any point to the parabola and that the algebraic sum of the ordinates of the feet of these three normals is zero.*

The straight line

$$y = mx - 2am - am^3 \quad \ldots(1)$$

is, by Art. 208, a normal to the parabola at the points whose coordinates are

$$am^2 \text{ and } -2am \quad \ldots(2)$$

If this normal passes through the fixed point O, whose coordinates are h and k, we have

$$k = mh - 2am - am^3$$

i.e., $$am^3 + (2a - h) m + k = 0 \quad \ldots(3)$$

This equation, being of the third degree, has three roots, real or imaginary. Corresponding to each of these roots, we have, on substitution in (1), the equation to a normal which passes through the point O.

Hence, three normals, real or imaginary, pass through any point O.

If m_1, m_2 and m_3 be the roots of the equation (3), we have by Art. 2, Ex. 2,

$$m_1 + m_2 + m_3 = 0$$

If the ordinates of the feet of these normals be y_1, y_2 and y_3, we then have by (2),

$$y_1 + y_2 + y_3 = -2a (m_1 + m_2 + m_3) = 0$$

Hence, the second part of the proposition.

We shall find, in a subsequent chapter, that for certain positions of the point O, all three normals are real; for other positions of O, one normal only will be real, and the other two imaginary.

▶ **237.**

EXAMPLE *Find the locus of a point which is such that (α) two of the normals drawn from it to the parabola are at right angles, (β) the three normals through it cut the axis in points whose distances from the vertex are in arithmetical progression.*

Any normal is $y = mx - 2am - am^3$, and this passes through the point (h, k), if

$$am^3 + (2a - h)m + k = 0 \qquad \ldots(1)$$

It then m_1, m_2 and m_3 be the roots, we have, by Art. 2,

$$m_1 + m_2 + m_3 = 0 \qquad \ldots(2)$$

$$m_2 m_3 + m_3 m_1 + m_1 m_2 = \frac{2a - h}{a} \qquad \ldots(3)$$

and

$$m_1 m_2 m_3 = -\frac{k}{a} \qquad \ldots(4)$$

(a) If two of the normals, say m_1 and m_2, be at right angles, we have $m_1 m_2 = -1$, and hence, from (4), $m_3 = \dfrac{k}{a}$

The quantity $\dfrac{k}{a}$ is therefore, a root of (1) and hence, by substitution, we have

$$\frac{k^3}{a^2} + (2a - h)\frac{k}{a} + k = 0$$

i.e.,

$$k^2 = a(h - 3a)$$

The locus of the point (h, k) is therefore the parabola $y^2 = a(x - 3a)$ whose vertex is the point $(3a, 0)$ and whose latus rectum is one-quarter that of the given parabola.

The student should draw the figure of both parabolas.

(β) The normal $y = mx - 2am - am^3$ meets the axis of x at a point whose distance from the vertex is $2a + am^2$. The conditions of the question then give

$$(2a + am_1^2) + (2a + am_3^2) = 2(2a + am_2^2)$$

i.e.,

$$m_1^2 + m_3^2 = 2m_2^2 \qquad \ldots(5)$$

If we eliminate m_1, m_2 and m_3 from the equations (2), (3) (4), and (5), we shall have a relation between h and k.

From (2) and (3), we have

$$\frac{2a - h}{a} = m_1 m_3 + m_2(m_1 + m_3) = m_1 m_3 - m_2^2 \qquad \ldots(6)$$

Also, (5) and (2) give

$$2m_2^2 = (m_1 + m_3)^2 - 2m_1 m_3 = m_2^2 - 2m_1 m_3$$

i.e.,

$$m_2^2 + 2m_1 m_3 = 0 \qquad \ldots(7)$$

Solving (6) and (7), we have

$$m_1 m_3 = \frac{2a - h}{3a}, \quad \text{and} \quad m_2^2 = -2 \times \frac{2a - h}{3a}$$

Substituting these values in (4), we have

$$\frac{2a-h}{3a}\sqrt{-2\frac{2a-h}{3a}} = -\frac{k}{a}$$

i.e.,
$$27ak^2 = 2(h-2a)^3$$

so that the required locus is

$$27ay^2 = 2(x-2a)^3$$

➤ **238.**

EXAMPLE *If the normals at three points P, Q and R meet in a point O and S be the focus, prove that* $SP \cdot SQ \cdot SR = a \cdot SO^2$.

As in the previous question we know that the normals at the points $(am_1^2, -2am_1)$, $(am_2^2, -2am_2)$ and $(am_3^2, -2am_3)$ meet in the point (h, k), if

$$m_1 + m_2 + m_3 = 0 \qquad \qquad \ldots(1)$$

$$m_2m_3 + m_3m_1 + m_1m_2 = \frac{2a-h}{a} \qquad \ldots(2)$$

and
$$m_1m_2m_3 = -\frac{k}{a} \qquad \qquad \ldots(3)$$

By Art. 202, we have

$$SP = a(1+m_1^2),\ SQ = a(1+m_2^2),\ \text{and}\ SR = a(1+m_3^2)$$

Hence,
$$\frac{SP \cdot SQ \cdot SR}{a^3} = (1+m_1^2)(1+m_2^2)(1+m_3^2)$$

$$= 1 + (m_1^2 + m_2^2 + m_3^2) + (m_2^2 m_3^2 + m_3^2 m_1^2 + m_1^2 m_2^2) + m_1^2 m_2^2 m_3^2$$

Also, from (1) and (2), we have

$$m_1^2 + m_2^2 + m_3^2 = (m_1 + m_2 + m_3)^2 - 2(m_2m_3 + m_3m_1 + m_1m_2)$$

$$= 2\frac{h-2a}{a}$$

and
$$m_2^2 m_3^2 + m_3^2 m_1^2 + m_1^2 m_2^2 = (m_2m_3 + m_3m_1 + m_1m_2)^2$$
$$- 2m_1m_2m_3(m_1 + m_2 + m_3)$$

$$= \left(\frac{h-2a}{a}\right)^2, \qquad \text{by (1) and (2)}$$

Hence,
$$\frac{SP \cdot SQ \cdot SR}{a^3} = 1 + 2\frac{h-2a}{a} + \left(\frac{h-2a}{a}\right)^2 + \frac{k^2}{a^2}$$

$$= \frac{(h-a)^2 + k^2}{a^2} = \frac{SO^2}{a^2}$$

i.e.,
$$SP \cdot SQ \cdot SR = SO^2 \cdot a$$

Examples XXX

Find the locus of a point O when the three normals drawn from it are such that

1. two of them make complementary angles with the axis.
2. two of them make angles with the axis the product of whose tangents is 2.
3. one bisects the angle between the other two.
4. two of them make equal angles with the given line $y = mx + c$.
5. the sum of the three angles made by them with the axis is constant.
6. the area of the triangle formed by their feet is constant.
7. the line joining the feet of two of them is always in a given direction.

The normals at three points P, Q and R of the parabola $y^2 = 4ax$ meet in a point O whose coordinates are h and k; prove that

8. the centroid of the triangle PQR lies on the axis.
9. the point O and the orthocentre of the triangle formed by the tangents at P, Q and R are equidistant from the axis.
10. if OP and OQ make complementary angles with the axis, then tangent at R is parallel to SO.
11. the sum of the intercepts which the normals cut off from the axis is $2(h + a)$.
12. the sum of the squares of the sides of the triangle PQR is equal to $2(h - 2a)(h + 210a)$.
13. the circle circumscribing the triangle PQR goes through the vertex and its equation is $2x^2 + 2y^2 - 2x(h + 2a) - ky = 0$
14. if P be fixed, then QR is fixed in direction and the locus of the centre of the circle circumscribing PQR is a straight line.
15. Three normals are drawn to the parabola $y^2 = 4ax \cos \alpha$ from any point lying on the straight line $y = b \sin \alpha$. Prove that the locus of the orthocentre of the triangles formed by the corresponding tangents is the curve $\dfrac{x^2}{a^2} + \dfrac{y^2}{b^2} = 1$, the angle α being variable.
16. Prove that the sum of the angles which the three normals, drawn from any point O, make with the axis exceeds the angle which the focal distance of O makes with the axis by a multiple of π.
17. Two of the normals drawn from a point O to the curve make complementary angles with the axis; prove that the locus of O and the curve which is touched by its polar are parabolas such that their latera recta and that of the original parabola form a geometrical progression. Sketch the three curves.
18. Prove that the normals at the points where the straight line $lx + my = 1$ meets the parabola, meet on the normal at the point $\left(\dfrac{4am^2}{l^2} \quad \dfrac{4am}{l} \right)$ of the parabola.

19. If the normals at the three points P, Q and R meet in a point and if PP', QQ' and RR' be chords parallel to QR, RP and PQ respectively, prove that the normals at P', Q' and R' also meet in a point.

20. If the normals drawn from any point to the parabola cut the line $x = 2a$ in points whose ordinates are in arithmetical progression, prove that the tangents of the angles which the normals make with the axis are in geometrical progression.

21. PG, the normal at P to a parabola, cuts the axis in G and is produced to Q so that $GQ = \frac{1}{2} PG$; prove that the other normals which pass through Q intersect at right angles.

22. Prove that the equation to the circle, which passes through the focus and touches the parabola $y^2 = 4ax$ at the point $(at^2, 2at)$, is

$$x^2 + y^2 - ax(3t^2 + 1) - ay(3t - t^3) + 3a^2t^2 = 0$$

Prove also that the locus of its centre is the curve

$$27ay^2 = (2x - a)(x - 5a)^2$$

23. Shew that three circles can be drawn to touch a parabola and also to touch at the focus a given straight line passing through the focus and prove that the tangents at the point of contact with the parabola form an equilateral triangle.

24. Through a point P are drawn tangents PQ and PR to a parabola and circles are drawn through the focus to touch the parabola in Q and R respectively; prove that the common chord of these circles passes through the centroid of the triangle PQR.

25. Prove that the locus of the centre of the circle, which passes through the vertex of a parabola and through its intersections with a normal chord, is the parabola $2y^2 = ax - a^2$.

26. A circle is described whose centre is the vertex and whose diameter is three-quarters of the latus rectum of a parabola; prove that the common chord of the circle and parabola bisects the distance between the vertex and the focus.

27. Prove that the sum of the angles which the four common tangents to a parabola and a circle make with the axis is equal to $n\pi + 2\alpha$, where α is the angle which the radius from the focus to the centre of the circle makes with the axis and n is an integer.

28. PR and QR are chords of parabola which are normals at P and Q. Prove that two of the common chords of the parabola and the circle circumscribing the triangle PRQ meet on the directrix.

29. The two parabolas $y^2 = 4a(x - l)$ and $x^2 = 4a(y - l')$ always touch one another, the quantities l and l' being both variable; prove that the locus of their point of contact is the curve $xy = 4a^2$.

30. A parabola, of latus rectum l, touches a fixed equal parabola, the axes of the two curves being parallel, prove that the locus of the vertex of the moving curve is a parabola of latus rectum $2l$.

31. The sides of a triangle touch a parabola, and two of its angular points lie on another parabola with its axis in the same direction; prove that the locus of the third angular points is another parabola.

➤ **239.** In Art. 197, we obtained the simplest possible form of the equation to a parabola.

We shall now transform the origin and axes in the most general manner.

Let the new origin have as coordinates (h, k) and let the new axis of x be inclined at θ to the original axis, and let the new angle between the axes be ω'.

By Art. 133 we have for x and y, to substitute

$$x \cos \theta + y \cos (\omega' + \theta) + h,$$

and $\qquad x \sin \theta + y \sin (\omega' + \theta) + k$

respectively.

The equation of Art. 197, then becomes

$$\{x \sin \theta + y \sin (\omega' + \theta) + k\}^2 = 4a \{x \cos \theta + y \cos (\omega' + \theta) + h\}$$

i.e., $\{x \sin \theta + y \sin (\omega' + \theta)\}^2 + 2x \{k \sin \theta - 2a \cos \theta\}$

$$+ 2y \{k \sin (\omega' + \theta) - 2a \cos (\omega' + \theta)\} + k^2 - 4ah = 0 \qquad \ldots(1)$$

This equation is therefore the most general form of the equation to a parabola.

We notice that in it the terms of the second degree always form a perfect square.

➤ **240.** *To find the equation to a parabola, any two tangents to it being the axes of coordinates and the points of contact being distant a and b from the origin.*

By the last article, the most general form of the equation to any parabola is

$$(Ax + By)^2 + 2gx + 2fy + c = 0 \qquad \ldots(1)$$

This meets the axis of x in points whose abscissae are given by

$$A^2x^2 + 2gx + c = 0 \qquad \ldots(2)$$

If the parabola touch the axis of x at a distance a from the origin, this equation must be equivalent to

$$A^2 (x - a)^2 = 0 \qquad \ldots(3)$$

Comparing equations (2) and (3), we have

$$g = - A^2a, \text{ and } c = A^2a^2 \qquad \ldots(4)$$

Similarly, since the parabola is to touch the axis of y at a distance b from the origin, we have

$$f = - B^2b \text{ and } c = B^2b^2 \qquad \ldots(5)$$

From (4) and (5), equating the values of c, we have

$$B^2b^2 = A^2a^2$$

so that

$$B = \pm A\frac{a}{b} \qquad \qquad \ldots(6)$$

Taking the negative sign, we have

$$B = -A\frac{a}{b}, \quad g = -A^2a, \quad f = -A^2\frac{a^2}{b}, \quad \text{and} \quad c = A^2a^2$$

Substituting these values in (1), we have, as the required equation,

$$\left(x - \frac{a}{b}y\right)^2 - 2ax - 2\frac{a^2}{b}y + a^2 = 0$$

i.e.,

$$\left(\frac{x}{a} - \frac{y}{b}\right)^2 - \frac{2x}{a} - \frac{2y}{b} + 1 = 0 \qquad \qquad \ldots(7)$$

This equation can be written in the form

$$\left(\frac{x}{a} + \frac{y}{b}\right)^2 - 2\left(\frac{x}{a} + \frac{y}{b}\right) + 1 = \frac{4xy}{ab}$$

i.e.,

$$\frac{x}{a} + \frac{y}{b} - 1 = \pm 2\sqrt{\frac{xy}{ab}}$$

i.e.,

$$\left(\sqrt{\frac{x}{a}} \mp \sqrt{\frac{y}{b}}\right)^2 = 1$$

i.e.,

$$\sqrt{\frac{x}{a}} + \sqrt{\frac{y}{b}} = 1 \qquad \qquad \ldots(8)$$

[The radical signs in (8) can clearly have both the positive and negative signs prefixed. The different equations thus obtained correspond to different portions of the curve. In the figure of Art. 243, the abscissa of any point on the portion PAQ is $< a$, and the ordinate $< b$, so that for this portion of the curve we must take both signs positive. For the part beyond P the abscissa is $> a$, and $\frac{x}{a} > \frac{y}{b}$, so that the signs must be $+$ and $-$. For the part beyond Q the ordinate is $> b$, and $\frac{y}{b} > \frac{x}{a}$, so that the signs must be $-$ and $+$. There is clearly no part of the curve corresponding to two negative signs.]

➤ **241.** If in the previous article we took the positive sign in (6), the equation would reduce to

$$\left(\frac{x}{a}+\frac{y}{b}\right)^2 - 2\frac{x}{a} - \frac{2y}{b} + 1 = 0$$

i.e.,
$$\left(\frac{x}{a}+\frac{y}{b}-1\right)^2 = 0$$

This gives us (Fig., Art. 243) the pair of coincident straight lines *PQ*. This pair of coincident straight lines is also a conic meeting the axes in two concident points at *P* and *Q*, but is not the parabola required.

➤ **242.** *To find the equation to the tangent at any point* (x', y') *of the parabola*

$$\sqrt{\frac{x}{a}} + \sqrt{\frac{y}{b}} = 1$$

Let (x'', y'') be any point on the curve close to (x', y'). The equation to the line joining these two points is

$$y - y' = \frac{y'' - y'}{x'' - x'}(x - x') \qquad \qquad ...(1)$$

But, since these points lie on the curve, we have

$$\sqrt{\frac{x'}{a}} + \sqrt{\frac{y'}{b}} = 1 = \sqrt{\frac{x''}{a}} + \sqrt{\frac{y''}{b}} \qquad \qquad ...(2)$$

so that
$$\frac{\sqrt{y''} - \sqrt{y'}}{\sqrt{x''} - \sqrt{x'}} = -\frac{\sqrt{b}}{\sqrt{a}} \qquad \qquad ...(3)$$

The equation (1), is therefore,

$$y - y' = \frac{\sqrt{y''} - \sqrt{y'}}{\sqrt{x''} - \sqrt{x'}} \cdot \frac{\sqrt{y''} + \sqrt{y'}}{\sqrt{x''} + \sqrt{x'}}(x - x')$$

or, by equation (3),

$$y - y' = -\frac{\sqrt{b}}{\sqrt{a}} \cdot \frac{\sqrt{y''} + \sqrt{y'}}{\sqrt{x''} + \sqrt{x'}}(x - x') \qquad \qquad ...(4)$$

The equation to the tangent at (x', y') is then obtained by putting $x'' = x'$ and $y'' = y'$, and is

$$y - y' = -\frac{\sqrt{b}}{\sqrt{a}} \cdot \frac{\sqrt{y'}}{\sqrt{x'}}(x - x')$$

i.e.,
$$\frac{x}{\sqrt{ax'}} + \frac{y}{\sqrt{by'}} = \sqrt{\frac{x'}{a}} + \sqrt{\frac{y'}{b}} = 1 \qquad \qquad ...(5)$$

This is the required equation.

[In the foregoing we have assumed that (x', y') lies on the portion *PAQ* (Fig., Art. 243). If it lie on either of the other portions the proper signs must be affixed to the radicals, as in Art., 240.]

EXAMPLE *To find the condition that the straight line $\dfrac{x}{f} + \dfrac{y}{g} = 1$ may be a tangent.*

This line will be the same as (5), if

$$f = \sqrt{ax'} \quad \text{and} \quad g = \sqrt{by'}$$

so that

$$\sqrt{\dfrac{x'}{a}} = \dfrac{f}{a}, \quad \text{and} \quad \sqrt{\dfrac{y'}{b}} = \dfrac{g}{b}$$

Hence,

$$\dfrac{f}{a} + \dfrac{g}{b} = 1$$

This is the required condition; also since, $x' = \dfrac{f^2}{a}$ and $y' = \dfrac{g^2}{b}$, the

point of contact of the given line is $\left(\dfrac{f^2}{a}, \dfrac{g^2}{b} \right)$.

Similarly, the straight line $lx + my = n$ will touch the parabola if

$\dfrac{n}{al} + \dfrac{n}{bm} = 1$.

➤ **243.** *To find the **focus** of the parabola*

$$\sqrt{\dfrac{x}{a}} + \sqrt{\dfrac{y}{b}} = 1$$

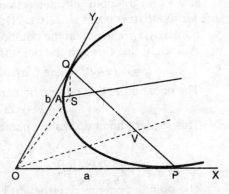

Let S be the focus, O the origin, and P and Q the points of contact of the parabola with the axes.

Since, by Art. 230, the triangles OSP and QSO are similar, the angle SOP = angle SQO.

Hence, if we describe a circle through O, Q and S, then by geometry, OP is the tangent to it at O.

Hence, S lies on the circle passing through the origin O, the point Q, $(0, b)$, and touching the axis of x at the origin.

The equation to this circle is

$$x^2 + 2xy \cos \omega + y^2 = by \qquad \text{...(1)}$$

Similarly, since $\angle SOQ = \angle SPO$, S will lie on the circle through O and P and touching the axis of y at the origin *i.e.*, on the circle

$$x^2 + 2xy \cos \omega + y^2 = ax \qquad \text{...(2)}$$

The intersections of (1) and (2) give the point required.

On solving (1) and (2), we have as the focus the point

$$\left(\frac{ab^2}{a^2 + 2ab \cos \omega + b^2}, \ \frac{a^2b}{a^2 + 2ab \cos \omega + b^2}\right)$$

➤ **244.** *To find the equation to the* **axis.**

If V be the middle point of PQ, we know, by Art. 223, that OV is parallel to the axis.

Now, V is the point $\left(\dfrac{a}{2}, \dfrac{b}{2}\right)$.

Hence, the equation to OV is $y = \dfrac{b}{a} x$.

The equation to the axis (a line through S parallel to OV) is therefore,

$$y - \frac{a^2b}{a^2 + 2ab \cos \omega + b^2} = \frac{b}{a}\left(x - \frac{ab^2}{a^2 + 2ab \cos \omega + b^2}\right)$$

i.e., $ay - bx = \dfrac{ab(a^2 - b^2)}{a^2 + 2ab \cos \omega + b^2}$

➤ **245.** *To find the equation to the* **directrix.**

If we find the point of intersection of OP and a tangent perpendicular to OP, this point will (Art. 211, γ) be on the directrix.

Similarly, we can obtain the point on OQ which is on the directrix.

A straight line through the point $(f, 0)$ perpendicular to OX is

$$y = m(x - f), \text{ where (Art. 93) } 1 + m \cos \omega = 0$$

The equation to this perpendicular straight line is, then

$$x + y \cos \omega = f \qquad \qquad \text{...(1)}$$

This straight line touches the parabola if (Art. 242)

$$\frac{f}{a} + \frac{f}{b \cos \omega} = 1, \qquad i.e., \text{ if } \quad f = \frac{ab \cos \omega}{a + b \cos \omega}$$

The point $\left(\dfrac{ab \cos \omega}{a + b \cos \omega}, 0\right)$ therefore lies on the directrix.

Similarly, the point $\left(0, \dfrac{ab \cos \omega}{b + a \cos \omega}\right)$ is on it.

The equation to the directrix is therefore,

$$x(a + b \cos \omega) + y(b + a \cos \omega) = ab \cos \omega \qquad \text{...(2)}$$

The latus rectum being twice the perpendicular distance of the focus from the directrix = twice the distance of the point

$$\left(\frac{ab^2}{a^2 + 2ab \cos \omega + b^2}, \frac{a^2b}{a^2 + 2ab \cos \omega + b^2}\right)$$

from the straight line (2)

$$= \frac{4a^2b^2 \sin^2 \omega}{(a^2 + 2ab \cos \omega + b^2)^{3/2}}$$

by Art. 96 after some reduction.

➤ **246.** *To find the coordinates of the* **vertex** *and the equation to the tangent at the vertex.*

The vertex is the intersection of the axis and the curve, *i.e.*, its coordinates are given by

$$\frac{y}{b} - \frac{x}{a} = \frac{a^2 - b^2}{a^2 + 2ab \cos \omega + b^2} \qquad \qquad \text{...(1)}$$

and by

$$\left(\frac{x}{a} - \frac{y}{b}\right)^2 - \frac{2x}{a} - \frac{2y}{b} + 1 = 0 \qquad \text{(Art. 240)}$$

i.e., by

$$\left(\frac{x}{a} - \frac{y}{b} + 1\right)^2 = \frac{4x}{a} \qquad \qquad \text{...(2)}$$

From (1) and (2), we have

$$x = \frac{a}{4}\left[1 - \frac{a^2 - b^2}{a^2 + 2ab \cos \omega + b^2}\right]^2 = \frac{ab^2 (b + a \cos \omega)^2}{(a^2 + 2ab \cos \omega + b^2)^2}$$

Similarly,

$$y = \frac{a^2b (a + b \cos \omega)^2}{(a^2 + 2ab \cos \omega + b^2)^2}$$

These are the coordinates of the vertex.

The tangent at the vertex being parallel to the directrix, its equation is

$$(a + b \cos \omega)\left[x - \frac{ab^2 (b + a \cos \omega)^2}{(a^2 + 2ab \cos \omega + b^2)^2}\right]$$

$$+ (b + a \cos \omega)\left[y - \frac{a^2b (a + b \cos \omega)^2}{(a^2 + 2ab \cos \omega + b^2)^2}\right] = 0$$

i.e.,

$$\frac{x}{b + a \cos \omega} + \frac{y}{a + b \cos \omega} = \frac{ab}{a^2 + 2ab \cos \omega + b^2}$$

[The equation of the tangent at the vertex may also be written down by means of the example of Art. 242.]

EXAMPLES XXXI

1. If a parabola, whose latus rectum is 4c, slide between two rectangular axes, prove that the locus of its focus is $x^2y^2 = c^2 (x^2 + y^2)$, and that the curve traced out by its vertex is

$$x^{2/3} y^{2/3} (x^{2/3} + y^{2/3}) = c^2$$

2. Parabolas are drawn to touch two given rectangular axes and their foci are all at a constant distance c from the origin. Prove that the locus of the vertices of these parabolas is the curve
$$x^{2/3} + y^{2/3} = c^{2/3}$$

3. The axes being rectangular, prove that the locus of the focus of the parabola $\left(\dfrac{x}{a} + \dfrac{y}{b} - 1\right)^2 = \dfrac{4xy}{ab}$, a and b being variables such that $ab = c^2$, is the curve $(x^2 + y^2)^2 = c^2xy$.

4. Parabolas are drawn to touch two given straight lines which are inclined at an angle ω; if the chords of contact all pass through a fixed point, prove that
   (i) their directrices all pass through another fixed point, and
   (ii) their foci all lie on a circle which goes through the intersection of the two given straight lines.

5. A parabola touches two given straight lines at given points; prove that the locus of the middle point of the portion of any tangent which is intercepted between the given straight lines is a straight line.

6. TP and TQ are any two tangents to a parabola and the tangent at a third point R cuts them in P' and Q'; prove that
$$\frac{TP'}{TP} + \frac{TQ'}{TQ} = 1 \quad \text{and} \quad \frac{QQ'}{Q'T} = \frac{TP'}{P'P} = \frac{Q'R}{RP'}$$

7. If a parabola touch three given straight lines, prove that each of the lines joining the points of contact passes through a fixed point.

8. A parabola touches two given straight lines; if its axis pass through the point (h, k), the given lines being the axes of coordinates, prove that the locus of the focus is the curve
$$x^2 - y^2 - hx + ky = 0$$

9. A parabola touches two given straight lines, which meet at O, in given points and a variable tangent meets the given lines in P and Q respectively; prove that the locus of the centre of the circumcircle of the triangle OPQ is a fixed straight line.

10. The sides AB and AC of a triangle ABC are given in position and the harmonic mean between the lengths AB and AC is also given; prove that the locus of the focus of the parabola touching the sides at B and C is a circle whose centre lies on the line bisecting the angle BAC.

11. Parabolas are drawn to touch the axes, which are inclined at an angle ω, and their directrices all pass through a fixed point (h, k). Prove that all the parabolas touch the straight line
$$\frac{x}{h + k \sec \omega} + \frac{y}{k + h \sec \omega} = 1$$

12

THE ELLIPSE

➤ **247.** The ellipse is a conic section in which the eccentricity e is less than unity.

To find the equation to an ellipse.

Let ZK be the directrix, S the focus, and let SZ be perpendicular to the directrix.

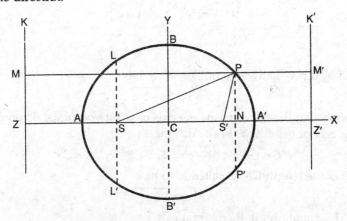

There will be a point A on SZ, such that

$$SA = e \cdot AZ \qquad \ldots(1)$$

Since, $e < 1$, there will be another point A', in ZS produced, such that

$$SA' = e \cdot A'Z \qquad \ldots(2)$$

Let the length AA' be called $2a$, and let C be the middle point of AA'. Adding equations (1) and (2), we have

$$2a = AA' = e \, (AZ + A'Z) = 2 \cdot e \cdot CZ$$

i.e. $$CZ = \frac{a}{e} \qquad \ldots(3)$$

Subtracting equations (1) and (2), we have

$$e \, (A'Z - AZ) = SA' - SA = (SC + CA') - (CA - CS)$$

i.e., $e \cdot AA' = 2CS$

and hence, $CS = a \cdot e$ ...(4)

Let C be the origin, CA' the axis of x, and a line through C perpendicular to AA' the axis of y.

Let P be any point on the curve, whose coordinates are x and y, and let PM be the perpendicular upon the directrix, and PN the perpendicular upon AA'.

The focus S is the point $(-ae, 0)$

The relation $SP^2 = e^2 \cdot PM^2 = e^2 \cdot ZN^2$, then gives

$$(x + ae)^2 + y^2 = e^2 \left(x + \frac{a}{e} \right)^2 \qquad \text{(Art. 20)}$$

i.e., $x^2 (1 - e^2) + y^2 = a^2 (1 - e^2)$

i.e., $\dfrac{x^2}{a^2} + \dfrac{y^2}{a^2 (1 - e^2)} = 1$ ...(5)

If in this equation we put $x = 0$, we have

$$y = \pm a \sqrt{1 - e^2},$$

shewing that the curve meets the axis of y in two points, B and B', lying on opposite sides of C, such that

$$B'C = CB = a \sqrt{1 - e^2}, \quad \text{*i.e.,*} \quad CB^2 = CA^2 - CS^2$$

Let the length CB be called b, so that

$$b = a \sqrt{1 - e^2}$$

The equation (5), then becomes

$$\frac{x^2}{a^2} + \frac{y^2}{b^2} = 1 \qquad \qquad ...(6)$$

➤ **248.** The equation (6) of the previous article may be written

$$\frac{y^2}{b^2} = 1 - \frac{x^2}{a^2} = \frac{a^2 - x^2}{a^2} = \frac{(a + x)(a - x)}{a^2}$$

i.e., $\dfrac{PN^2}{b^2} = \dfrac{AN \cdot NA'}{a^2}$

i.e., $PN^2 : AN \cdot NA' :: BC^2 : AC^2$

Def.: The points A and A' are called the vertices of the curve, AA' is called the major axis, and BB' the minor axis. Also C is called the centre.

➤ **249.** Since S is the point $(-ae, 0)$, the equation to the ellipse referred to S as origin is (Art. 128),

$$\frac{(x - ae)^2}{a^2} + \frac{y^2}{b^2} = 1$$

The equation referred to A as origin, and AX and a perpendicular line as axes, is

$$\frac{(x - a)^2}{a^2} + \frac{y^2}{b^2} = 1$$

i.e.,

$$\frac{x^2}{a^2} + \frac{y^2}{b^2} - \frac{2x}{a} = 0$$

Similarly, the equation referred to ZX and ZK as axes is, since $CZ = -\dfrac{a}{e}$,

$$\frac{\left(x - \dfrac{a}{e}\right)^2}{a^2} + \frac{y^2}{b^2} = 1$$

The equation to the ellipse, whose focus and directrix are any given point and line, and whose eccentricity is known, is easily written down.

For example, if the focus be the point $(-2, 3)$, the directrix be the line $2x + 3y + 4 = 0$, and the eccentricity be $\dfrac{4}{5}$, the required equation is

$$(x + 2)^2 + (y - 3)^2 = \left(\frac{4}{5}\right)^2 \frac{(2x + 3y + 4)^2}{2^2 + 3^2}$$

i.e., $261x^2 + 181y^2 - 192\,xy + 1044x - 2334y + 3969 = 0$

Generally, the equation to the ellipse, whose focus is the point (f, g), whose directrix is $Ax + By + C = 0$, and whose eccentricity is e, is

$$(x - f)^2 + (y - g)^2 = e^2 \frac{(Ax + By + C)^2}{A^2 + B^2}$$

▶ **250.** *There exist a second focus and a second directrix for the curve.*

On the positive side of the origin take a point S', which is such that $SC = CS' = ae$, and another point Z', such that

$$ZC = CZ' = \frac{a}{e}$$

Draw $Z'K'$ perpendicular to ZZ', and PM' perpendicular to $Z'K'$. The equation (5) of Art. 247, may be written in the form

$$x^2 - 2aex + a^2e^2 + y^2 = e^2x^2 - 2aex + a^2,$$

i.e.,
$$(x - ae)^2 + y^2 = e^2 \left(\frac{a}{e} - x \right)^2$$

i.e.,
$$S'P^2 = e^2 \cdot PM'^2$$

Hence, any point P of the curve is such that its distance from S' is e times its distance from $Z'K'$, so that we should have obtained the same curve, if we had started with S' as focus, $Z'K'$ as directrix, and the same eccentricity.

➤ **251.** *The sum of the focal distances of any point on the curve is equal to the major axis.*

For (Fig. Art. 247), we have
$$SP = e \cdot PM, \quad \text{and} \quad S'P = e \cdot PM'$$

Hence, $SP + S'P = e (PM + PM') = e \cdot MM'$

$$= e \cdot ZZ' = 2e \cdot CZ = 2a \qquad \text{(Art. 247)}$$

$$= \text{the major axis.}$$

Also, $SP = e \cdot PM = e \cdot NZ = e \cdot CZ + e \cdot CN = a + ex'$

and $\qquad S'P = e \cdot PM' = e \cdot NZ' = e \cdot CZ' - e \cdot CN = a - ex'$

where x' is the abscissa of P referred to the centre.

➤ **252. Mechanical construction for an ellipse :** By the preceding article, we can get a simple mechanical method of constructing an ellipse.

Take a piece of thread, whose length is the major axis of the required ellipse, and fasten its ends at the points S and S' which are to be the foci.

Let the point of a pencil move on the paper, the point being always in contact with the string and keeping the two portions of the string between it and the fixed ends always tight. If the end of the pencil be moved about on the paper, so as to satisfy these conditions, it will trace out the curve on the paper. For the end of the pencil will be always in such a position that the sum of its distances from S and S' will be constant.

In practice, it is easier to fasten two drawing pins at S and S', and, to have an endless piece of string whose total length is equal to the sum of SS' and AA'. This string must be passed round the two pins at S and S' and then be kept stretched by the pencil as before. By this second arrangement it will be found that the portions of the curve near A and A' can be more easily described than in the first method.

➤ **253.** *Latus-rectum of the ellipse :* Let LSL' be the double ordinate of the curve which passes through the focus S. By the definition of the curve, the semi-latus-rectum SL

= e times the distance of L from the directrix

$= e \cdot SZ = e \, (CZ - CS) = e \cdot CZ - e \cdot CS$

$= a - ae^2$ (by equations (3) and (4) of Art. 247)

$= \dfrac{b^2}{a}$ (Art. 247)

➤ **254.** *To trace the curve*

$$\frac{x^2}{a^2} + \frac{y^2}{b^2} = 1 \qquad \ldots(1)$$

The equation may be written in either of the forms

$$y = \pm b \sqrt{1 - \frac{x^2}{a^2}} \qquad \ldots(2)$$

or

$$x = \pm a \sqrt{1 - \frac{y^2}{b^2}} \qquad \ldots(3)$$

From equation (2), it follows that if $x^2 > a^2$, i.e., if $x > a$ or $< -a$, then y is impossible. There is therefore, no part of the curve to the right of A' or to the left of A.

From equation (3), it follows, similarly, that, if $y > b$ or $< -b$, x is impossible and hence that there is no part of the curve above B or below B'.

If x lie between $-a$ and $+a$, the equation (2), gives two equal and opposite values for y, so that the curve is symmetrical with respect to the axis of x.

If y lie between $-b$ and $+b$, the equation (3) gives two equal and opposite values for x, so that the curve is symmetrical with respect to the axis of y.

If a number of values in succession be given to x, and the corresponding values of y be determined, we shall obtain a series of points which will all be found to lie on a curve of the shape given in the figure of Art. 247.

➤ **255.** *The quantity* $\dfrac{x'^2}{a^2} + \dfrac{y'^2}{b^2} - 1$ *is negative, zero or positive, according as the point (x', y') lies within, upon or without the ellipse.*

Let Q be the point (x', y'), and let the ordinate QN through Q meet the curve in P, so that, by equation (6) of Art. 247,

$$\frac{PN^2}{b^2} = 1 - \frac{x'^2}{a^2}$$

If Q be within the curve, then y', i.e., QN, is $< PN$, so that

$$\frac{y'^2}{b^2} < \frac{PN^2}{b^2}, \quad i.e., \ < 1 - \frac{x'^2}{a^2}$$

Hence, in this case,

$$\frac{x'^2}{a^2} + \frac{y'^2}{b^2} < 1$$

i.e., $\qquad\qquad \dfrac{x'^2}{a^2} + \dfrac{y'^2}{b^2} - 1$ is negative

Similarly, if Q' be without the curve, $y' > PN$, and then $\dfrac{x'^2}{a^2} + \dfrac{y'^2}{b^2} - 1$ is positive.

➤ **256.** *To find the length of a radius vector from the centre drawn in a given direction.*

The equation (6) of Art. 247 when transferred to polar coordinates becomes

$$\frac{r^2 \cos^2 \theta}{a^2} + \frac{r^2 \sin^2 \theta}{b^2} = 1$$

giving $\qquad\qquad r^2 = \dfrac{a^2 b^2}{b^2 \cos^2 \theta + a^2 \sin^2 \theta}$

We thus, have the value of the radius vector drawn at any inclination θ to the axis.

Since, $r^2 = \dfrac{a^2 b^2}{b^2 + (a^2 - b^2) \sin^2 \theta}$, we see that the greatest value of r is when $\theta = 0$, and then it is equal to a.

Similarly, $\theta = 90°$ gives the least value of r, viz. b.

Also, for each value of θ, we have two equal and opposite values of r, so that any line through the centre meets the curve in two points equidistant from it.

➤ **257. Auxiliary circle. Def.** The circle which is described on the major axis, AA', of an ellipse as diameter, is called the auxiliary circle of the ellipse.

Let NP be any ordinate of the ellipse, and let it be produced to meet the auxiliary circle in Q.

Since, the angle AQA' is a right angle, being the angle in a semicircle, we have, by geometry, $QN^2 = AN \cdot NA'$.

Hence, Art. 248 gives

$$PN^2 : QN^2 :: BC^2 : AC^2$$

so that
$$\frac{PN}{QN} = \frac{BC}{AC} = \frac{b}{a}$$

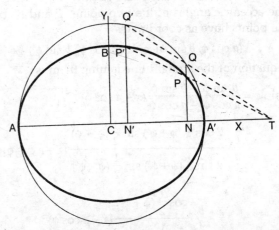

The point Q in which the ordinate NP meets the auxiliary circle is called the corresponding point to P.

The ordinates of any point on the ellipse and the corresponding point on the auxiliary circle are therefore to one another in the ratio $b : a$, i.e., in the ratio of the semi-minor to the semi-major axis of the ellipse.

The ellipse might therefore, have been defined as follows:

Take a circle and from each point of it draw perpendiculars upon a diameter; the locus of the points dividing these perpendiculars in a given ratio is an ellipse, of which the given circle is the auxiliary circle.

➤ **258. Eccentric Angle. Def.** The eccentric angle of any point P on the ellipse is the angle NCQ made with the major axis by the straight line CQ joining the centre C to the point Q on the auxiliary circle which corresponds to the point P.

This angle is generally called ϕ.

We have $\qquad CN = CQ \cdot \cos \phi = a \cos \phi.$

and $\qquad NQ = CQ \sin \phi = a \sin \phi.$

Hence, by the last article,
$$NP = \frac{b}{a} \cdot NQ = b \sin \phi.$$

The coordinates of any point P on the ellipse are therefore $a \cos \phi$ and $b \sin \phi$.

Since P is known when ϕ is given, it is often called "the point ϕ."

➤ **259.** *To obtain the equation of the straight line joining two points on the ellipse whose eccentric angles are given.*

Let the eccentric angles of the two points, P and P', be ϕ and ϕ', so that the points have as coordinates

$$(a \cos \phi, b \sin \phi) \text{ and } (a \cos \phi', b \sin \phi')$$

The equation of the straight line joining them is

$$y - b \sin \phi = \frac{b \sin \phi' - b \sin \phi}{a \cos \phi' - a \cos \phi} (x - a \cos \phi)$$

$$= \frac{b}{a} \cdot \frac{2 \cos \frac{1}{2}(\phi + \phi') \sin \frac{1}{2}(\phi' - \phi)}{2 \sin \frac{1}{2}(\phi + \phi') \sin \frac{1}{2}(\phi - \phi')} (x - a \cos \phi)$$

$$= -\frac{b}{a} \cdot \frac{\cos \frac{1}{2}(\phi + \phi')}{\sin \frac{1}{2}(\phi' + \phi)} (x - a \cos \phi)$$

i.e., $\dfrac{x}{a} \cos \dfrac{\phi + \phi'}{2} + \dfrac{y}{b} \sin \dfrac{\phi + \phi'}{2} = \cos \phi \cos \dfrac{\phi + \phi'}{2} + \sin \phi \sin \dfrac{\phi + \phi'}{2}$

$$= \cos \left[\phi - \frac{\phi + \phi'}{2} \right] = \cos \frac{\phi - \phi'}{2} \qquad \dots(1)$$

This is the required equation.

Cor. : The points on the auxiliary circle, corresponding to P and P', have as coordinates $(a \cos \phi, a \sin \phi)$ and $(a \cos \phi', a \sin \phi')$

The equation to the line joining them is therefore (Art. 178)

$$\frac{x}{a} \cos \frac{\phi + \phi'}{2} + \frac{y}{a} \sin \frac{\phi + \phi'}{2} = \cos \frac{\phi - \phi'}{2}$$

This straight line and equation (1) clearly make the same intercept on the major axis.

Hence, the straight line joining any two points on an ellipse, and the straight line joining the corresponding points on the auxiliary circle, meet the major axis in the same point.

EXAMPLES XXXII

1. Find the equation to the ellipses, whose centres are the origin, whose axes are the axes of coordinates, and which pass through
   (a) the points (2, 2) and (3, 1)
   and (b) the points (1, 4) and (–6, 1)

Find the equation of the ellipse referred to its centre

2. Whose latus rectum is 5 and whose eccentricity is $\frac{2}{3}$.

3. Whose minor axis is equal to the distance between the foci and whose latus rectum is 10.

4. Whose foci are the points $(4, 0)$ and $(-4, 0)$ and whose eccentricity is $\frac{1}{3}$.

5. Find the latus rectum, the eccentricity, and the coordinates of the foci, of the ellipses.

   (i) $x^2 + 3y^2 = a^2$ (ii) $5x^2 + 4y^2 = 1$, and
   (iii) $9x^2 + 5y^2 - 30y = 0$

6. Find the eccentricity of an ellipse, if its latus rectum be equal to one half its minor axis.

7. Find the equation to the ellipse, whose focus is the point $(-1, 1)$, whose directrix is the straight line $x - y + 3 = 0$, and whose eccentricity is $\frac{1}{2}$.

8. Is the point $(4, -3)$ within or without the ellipse
$$5x^2 + 7y^2 = 11?$$

9. Find the lengths oₗ and the equations to the focal radii drawn to the point $(4\sqrt{3}, 5)$ of the ellipse
$$25x^2 + 16y^2 = 1600$$

10. Prove that the sum of the squares of the reciprocals of two perpendicular diameter of an ellipse is constant.

11. Find the inclination to the major axis of the diameter of the ellipse the square of whose length is (1) the arithmetical mean, (2) the geometrical mean, and (3) the harmonical mean, between the squares on the major and minor axes.

12. Find the locus of the middle points of chords of an ellipse which are drawn through the positive end of the minor axis.

13. Prove that the locus of the intersection of AP with the straight line through A' perpendicular to $A'P$ is a straight line which is perpendicular to the major axis.

14. Q is the point on the auxiliary circle corresponding to P on the ellipse; PLM is drawn parallel to CQ to meet the axes in L and M; prove that $PL = b$ and $PM = a$.

15. Prove that the area of the triangle formed by three points on an ellipse, whose eccentric angles are θ, ϕ and ψ, is

$$2\,ab \sin\frac{\phi - \psi}{2} \sin\frac{\psi - \theta}{2} \sin\frac{\theta - \phi}{2}$$

Prove also that its area is to the area of the triangle formed by the corresponding points on the auxiliary circle as $b : a$, and hence that its area is a maximum when the latter triangle is equilateral, *i.e.*, when

$$\phi - \theta = \psi - \phi = \frac{2\pi}{3}.$$

16. Any point P of an ellipse is joined to the extremities of the major axis; prove that the portion of a directrix intercepted by them subtends a right angle at the corresponding focus.

17. Shew that the perpendiculars from the centre upon all chords, which join the ends of perpendicular diameters, are of constant length.

18. If α, β, γ and δ be the eccentric angles of the four points of intersection of the ellipse and any circle, prove that

$$\alpha + \beta + \gamma + \delta \text{ is an even multiple}$$

of π radians.

[See Trigonometry, Part II, Art. 31]

19. The tangent at any point P of a circle meets the tangent at a fixed point A in T, and T is joined to B, the other end of the diameter through A; prove that the locus of the intersection of AP and BT is an ellipse whose eccentricity is $\frac{1}{\sqrt{2}}$.

20. From any point P on the ellipse, PN is drawn perpendicular to the axis and produced to Q, so that NQ equals PS, where S is a focus; prove that the locus of Q is the two straight lines $y \pm ex + a = 0$.

21. Given the base of a triangle and the sum of its sides, prove that the locus of the centre of its incircle is an ellipse.

22. With a given point and line as focus and directrix, a series of ellipses are described; prove that the locus of the extremities of their minor axes is a parabola.

23. A line of fixed length $a + b$ moves so that its ends are always on two fixed perpendicular straight lines; prove that the locus of a point, which divides this line into portions of length a and b, is an ellipse.

24. Prove that the extremities of the latera recta of all ellipses having a given major axis $2a$, lie on the parabola $x^2 = -a(y - a)$, or on the parabola $x^2 = a(y + a)$.

➤ **260.** *To find the intersections of any straight line with the ellipse*

$$\frac{x^2}{a^2} + \frac{y^2}{b^2} = 1 \qquad \qquad \dots(1)$$

Let the equation of the straight line be

$$y = mx + c \qquad \qquad \dots(2)$$

The coordinates of the points of intersection of (1) and (2) satisfy both equations and are therefore, obtained by solving them as simultaneous equations.

Substituting for y in (1) from (2), the abscissae of the points of intersection are given by the equation

$$\frac{x^2}{a^2} + \frac{(mx+c)^2}{b^2} = 1$$

i.e., $\qquad x^2(a^2m^2+b^2) + 2a^2mcx + a^2(c^2-b^2) = 0 \qquad \qquad ...(3)$

This is a quadratic equation and hence has two roots, real, coincident, or imaginary.

Also corresponding to each value of x, we have from Eq. (2) one value of y.

The straight line therefore meets the curve in two points real, coincident, or imaginary.

The roots of the equation (3) are real, coincident, or imaginary according as

$(2a^2mc)^2 - 4(b^2+a^2m^2) \times a^2(c^2-b^2)$ is positive, zero or negative,

i.e., according as $b^2(b^2+a^2m^2) - b^2c^2$ is positive, zero, or negative,

i.e., according as c^2 is $< = $ or $> a^2m^2 + b^2$.

➤ **261.** *To find the length of the chord intercepted by the ellipse on the straight line $y = mx + c$.*

As in Art. 204, we have

$$x_1 + x_2 = -\frac{2a^2mc}{a^2m^2+b^2} \qquad \text{and} \qquad x_1x_2 = \frac{a^2(c^2-b^2)}{a^2m^2+b^2}$$

so that $\qquad\qquad x_1 - x_2 = \dfrac{2ab\sqrt{a^2m^2+b^2-c^2}}{a^2m^2+b^2}$

The length of the required chord therefore,

$$= \sqrt{(x_1-x_2)^2 + (y_1-y_2)^2} = (x_1-x_2)\sqrt{1+m^2}$$

$$= \frac{2ab\sqrt{1+m^2}\sqrt{a^2m^2+b^2-c^2}}{a^2m^2+b^2}$$

➤ **262.** *To find the equation to the* **tangent** *at any point (x', y') of the ellipse.*

Let P and Q be two points on the ellipse, whose coordinates are (x', y') and (x'', y'').

The equation to the straight line PQ is

$$y - y' = \frac{y''-y'}{x''-x'}(x-x') \qquad\qquad ...(1)$$

Since, both P and Q lie on the ellipse, we have

$$\frac{x'^2}{a^2} + \frac{y'^2}{b^2} = 1 \qquad \ldots(2)$$

and

$$\frac{x''^2}{a^2} + \frac{y''^2}{b^2} = 1 \qquad \ldots(3)$$

Hence, by subtraction,

$$\frac{x''^2 - x'^2}{a^2} + \frac{y''^2 - y'^2}{b^2} = 0$$

i.e.,

$$\frac{(y'' - y')(y'' + y')}{b^2} = -\frac{(x'' - x')(x'' + x')}{a^2}$$

i.e.,

$$\frac{y'' - y'}{x'' - x'} = -\frac{b^2}{a^2} \frac{x'' + x'}{y'' + y'}$$

On substituting in equation (1), the equation to any secant PQ becomes

$$y - y' = -\frac{b^2}{a^2} \frac{x'' + x'}{y'' + y'} (x - x') \qquad \ldots(4)$$

To obtain the equation to the tangent we take Q indefinitely close to P, and hence, in the limit, we put $x'' = x'$ and $y'' = y'$.

The equation (4) then becomes

$$y - y' = -\frac{b^2 x'}{a^2 y'} (x - x')$$

i.e.,

$$\frac{xx'}{a^2} + \frac{yy'}{b^2} = \frac{x'^2}{a^2} + \frac{y'^2}{b^2} = 1 \qquad \text{[by equation (2)]}$$

The required equation is therefore,

$$\frac{xx'}{a^2} + \frac{yy'}{b^2} = 1$$

Cor. : The equation to the tangent is therefore, obtained from the equation to the curve by the rule of Art. 152.

➤ **263.** *To find the equation to a tangent in terms of the tangent of its inclination to the major axis.*

As in Art. 260, the straight line

$$y = mx + c \qquad \ldots(1)$$

meets the ellipse in points whose abscissae are given by

$$x^2 (b^2 + a^2 m^2) + 2mca^2 x + a^2(c^2 - b^2) = 0$$

and by the same article, the roots of this equation are coincident if

$$c = \sqrt{a^2 m^2 + b^2}$$

In this case the straight line (1) is a tangent, and it becomes

$$y = mx + \sqrt{a^2m^2 + b^2} \qquad \text{...(2)}$$

This is the required equation.

Since, the radical sign on the right-hand of (2) may have either + or − prefixed to it, we see that there are two tangents to the ellipse having the same m, *i.e.*, there are two tangents parallel to any given direction.

The above form of the equation to the tangent may be deduced from the equation of Art. 262, as in the case of the parabola (Art. 206). It will be found that the point of contact is the point

$$\left(\frac{-a^2m}{\sqrt{a^2m^2 + b^2}}, \frac{b^2}{\sqrt{a^2m^2 + b^2}} \right)$$

➤ **264.** By a proof similar to that of the last article, it may be shewn that the straight line

$$x \cos \alpha + y \sin \alpha = p$$

ouches the ellipse, if

$$p^2 = a^2 \cos^2 \alpha + b^2 \sin^2 \alpha$$

Similarly, it may be shewn that the straight line

$$lx + my = n$$

touches the ellipse, if $a^2l^2 + b^2m^2 = n^2$.

➤ **265.** *Equation to the tangent at the point whose eccentric angle is* ϕ.

The coordinates of the point are $(a \cos \phi, b \sin \phi)$.

Substituting $x' = a \cos \phi$ and $y' = b \sin \phi$ in the equation of Art. 262, we have, as the required equation,

$$\frac{x}{a} \cos \phi + \frac{y}{b} \sin \phi = 1 \qquad \text{...(1)}$$

This equation may also be deduced from Art. 259.

For the equation of the tangent at the point "ϕ" is obtained by making $\phi' = \phi$ in the result of that article.

EXAMPLE *Find the intersection of the tangents at the points* ϕ *and* ϕ'.

The equations to the tangents are

$$\frac{x}{a} \cos \phi + \frac{y}{b} \sin \phi - 1 = 0$$

and

$$\frac{x}{a} \cos \phi' + \frac{y}{b} \sin \phi' - 1 = 0.$$

The required point is found by solving these equations.

We obtain

$$\frac{\dfrac{x}{a}}{\sin\phi - \sin\phi'} = \frac{\dfrac{y}{b}}{\cos\phi' - \cos\phi} = \frac{-1}{\sin\phi'\cos\phi - \cos\phi'\sin\phi} = \frac{1}{\sin(\phi - \phi')}$$

i.e.,

$$\frac{x}{2a\cos\dfrac{\phi+\phi'}{2}\sin\dfrac{\phi-\phi'}{2}} = \frac{y}{2b\sin\dfrac{\phi+\phi'}{2}\sin\dfrac{\phi-\phi'}{2}} = \frac{1}{2\sin\dfrac{\phi-\phi'}{2}\cos\dfrac{\phi-\phi'}{2}}$$

Hence, $\quad x = a\dfrac{\cos\dfrac{1}{2}(\phi+\phi')}{\cos\dfrac{1}{2}(\phi-\phi')}, \quad$ and $\quad y = b\dfrac{\sin\dfrac{1}{2}(\phi+\phi')}{\cos\dfrac{1}{2}(\phi-\phi')}$

➤ **266.** *Equation to the* **normal** *at the point* (x', y').

The required normal is the straight line which passes through the point (x', y') and is perpendicular to the tangent, *i.e.*, to the straight line

$$y = -\frac{b^2 x'}{a^2 y'}x + \frac{b^2}{y'}$$

Its equation is therefore,

$$y - y' = m(x - x')$$

where

$$m\left(-\frac{b^2 x'}{a^2 y'}\right) = -1$$

i.e., $\qquad\qquad\qquad m = \dfrac{a^2 y'}{b^2 x'} \qquad\qquad$ (Art. 69)

The equation to the normal is therefore, $y - y' = \dfrac{a^2 y'}{b^2 x'}(x - x')$

i.e.,

$$\frac{x - x'}{\dfrac{x'}{a^2}} = \frac{y - y'}{\dfrac{y'}{b^2}}$$

➤ **267.** *Equation to the normal at the point whose eccentric angle is* ϕ.

The coordinates of the point are $a\cos\phi$ and $b\sin\phi$

Hence, in the result of the last article putting

$$x' = a\cos\phi \quad \text{and} \quad y' = b\sin\phi$$

it becomes

$$\frac{x - a\cos\phi}{\dfrac{\cos\phi}{a}} = \frac{y - b\sin\phi}{\dfrac{\sin\phi}{b}}$$

i.e.,

$$\frac{ax}{\cos\phi} - a^2 = \frac{by}{\sin\phi} - b^2.$$

The required normal is therefore

$$ax \sec \phi - by \csc \phi = a^2 - b^2$$

> ***268.** *Equation to the normal in the form* $y = mx + c$

The equation to the normal at (x', y') is, as in Art. 266.

$$y = \frac{a^2 y'}{b^2 x'} x - y' \left(\frac{a^2}{b^2} - 1 \right).$$

Let $\dfrac{a^2 y'}{b^2 x'} = m$, so that $\dfrac{x'}{a} = \dfrac{ay'}{b^2 m}$.

Hence, since (x', y') satisfies the relation $\dfrac{x'^2}{a^2} + \dfrac{y'^2}{b^2} = 1$, we obtain

$$y' = \frac{b^2 m}{\sqrt{a^2 + b^2 m^2}}.$$

The equation to the normal is therefore,

$$y = mx - \frac{(a^2 - b^2) m}{\sqrt{a^2 + b^2 m^2}}.$$

This is not as important an equation as the corresponding equation in the case of the parabola. (Art. 208)

When it is desired to have the equation to the normal expressed in terms of one independent parameter it is generally better to use the equation of the previous article.

> **269.** *To find the length of the subtangent and subnormal.*

Let the tangent and normal at P, the point (x', y'), meet the axis in T and G respectively, and let PN be the ordinate of P.

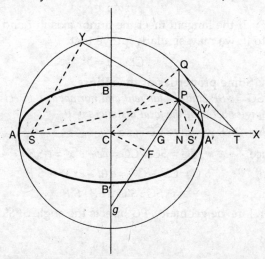

The equation to the tangent at P is (Art. 262)

$$\frac{xx'}{a^2} + \frac{yy'}{b^2} = 1 \qquad \qquad ...(1)$$

To find where the straight line meets the axis, we put $y = 0$ and have

$$x = \frac{a^2}{x'}, \quad i.e., \quad CT = \frac{a^2}{CN}$$

i.e., $\qquad \qquad CT \cdot CN = a^2 = CA^2 \qquad \qquad ...(2)$

Hence, the subtangent $NT = CT - CN = \dfrac{a^2}{x'} - x' = \dfrac{a^2 - x'^2}{x'}$.

The equation to the normal is (Art. 266)

$$\frac{x - x'}{\dfrac{x'}{a^2}} = \frac{y - y'}{\dfrac{y'}{b^2}}.$$

To find where it meets the axis, we put $y = 0$, and have

$$\frac{x - x'}{\dfrac{x'}{a^2}} = \frac{-y'}{\dfrac{y'}{b^2}} = -b^2$$

i.e., $\qquad CG = x = x' - \dfrac{b^2}{a^2} x' = \dfrac{a^2 - b^2}{a^2} x' = e^2 \cdot x' = e^2 \cdot CN \qquad ...(3)$

Hence, the subnormal $NG = CN - CG = (1 - e^2) CN$

i.e., $\qquad \qquad NG : NC :: 1 - e^2 : 1$

$$:: b^2 : a^2 \qquad \qquad \text{(Art. 247)}$$

Cor. : If the tangent meet the minor axis in t and Pn be perpendicular to it, we may, similarly, prove that

$$Ct \cdot Cn = b^2$$

➤ **270. Some properties of the ellipse.**

(a) *$SG = e \cdot SP$, and the tangent and normal at P bisect the external and internal angles between the focal distances of P.*

By Art. 269, we have $CG = e^2 x'$

Hence, $\qquad SG = SC + CG = ae + e^2 x' = e \cdot SP \qquad$ (by Art. 251)

Also, $\qquad S'G = CS' - CG = e(a - ex') = e \cdot S'P$

Hence, $\qquad SG : S'G :: SP : S'P$

Therefore, be geometry, PG bisects the angle SPS'.

It follows that the tangent bisects the exterior angle between SP and $S'P$.

(b) *If SY and S'Y' be the perpendiculars from the foci upon the tangent at any point P of the ellipse, then Y and Y' lie on the auxiliary circle, and SY. S'Y' = b². Also CY and S'P are parallel.*

The equation to any tangent is

$$x \cos \alpha + y \sin \alpha = p \qquad \ldots(1)$$

where $\qquad p = \sqrt{a^2 \cos^2 \alpha + b^2 \sin^2 \alpha} \qquad$ (Art. 264)

The perpendicular SY to (1) passes through the point $(-ae, 0)$ and its equation, by Art. 70, is therefore

$$(x + ae) \sin \alpha - y \cos \alpha = 0 \qquad \ldots(2)$$

If Y be the point (h, k) then, since Y lies on both (1) and (2), we have

$$h \cos \alpha + k \sin \alpha = \sqrt{a^2 \cos^2 \alpha + b^2 \sin^2 \alpha},$$

and $\qquad h \sin \alpha - k \cos \alpha = - ae \sin \alpha = - \sqrt{a^2 - b^2} \sin \alpha$

Squaring and adding these equations, we have $h^2 + k^2 = a^2$, so that Y lies on the auxiliary circle, $x^2 + y^2 = a^2$.

Similarly, it may be proved that Y' lies on this circle.

Again S is the point $(-ae, 0)$ and S' is $(ae, 0)$.

Hence, from equation (1)

$$SY = p + ae \cos \alpha, \text{ and } S'Y' = p - ae \cos \alpha \qquad \text{(Art. 75.)}$$

Thus $\quad SY \cdot S'Y' = p^2 - a^2 e^2 \cos^2 \alpha$

$$= a^2 \cos^2 \alpha + b^2 \sin^2 \alpha - (a^2 - b^2) \cos^2 \alpha$$

$$= b^2$$

Also, $\qquad\qquad CT = \dfrac{a^2}{CN}$

and therefore, $\qquad S'T = \dfrac{a^2}{CN} - ae = \dfrac{a(a - e\,CN)}{CN}$

$\therefore \qquad \dfrac{CT}{S'T} = \dfrac{a}{a - e \cdot CN} = \dfrac{CY}{S'P}.$

Hence, CY and $S'P$ are parallel. Similarly, CY' and SP are parallel.

(c) *If the normal at any point P meet the major and minor axes in G and g, and if CF be the perpendicular upon this normal, then PF·PG = b² and PF·Pg = a².*

The tangent at any point P (the point "ϕ") is

$$\frac{x}{a} \cos \phi + \frac{y}{b} \sin \phi = 1$$

Hence, $PF =$ perpendicular from C upon this tangent

$$= \frac{1}{\sqrt{\dfrac{\cos^2 \phi}{a^2} + \dfrac{\sin^2 \phi}{b^2}}} = \frac{ab}{\sqrt{b^2 \cos^2 \phi + a^2 \sin^2 \phi}} \qquad \ldots(1)$$

The normal at P is,

$$\frac{ax}{\cos \phi} - \frac{by}{\sin \phi} = a^2 - b^2 \qquad \ldots(2)$$

If we put $y = 0$, we have $CG = \dfrac{a^2 - b^2}{a} \cos \phi$

$$\therefore \qquad PG^2 = \left(a \cos \phi - \frac{a^2 - b^2}{a} \cos \phi\right)^2 + b^2 \sin^2 \phi$$

$$= \frac{b^4}{a^2} \cos^2 \phi + b^2 \sin^2 \phi$$

i.e., $PG = \dfrac{b}{a} \sqrt{b^2 \cos^2 \phi + a^2 \sin^2 \phi}$

From this and equation (1), we have $PF \cdot PG = b^2$.
If we put $x = 0$ in (2), we see that g is the point.

$$\left(0, -\frac{a^2 - b^2}{b} \sin \phi\right)$$

Hence, $Pg^2 = a^2 \cos^2 \phi + \left(b \sin \phi + \dfrac{a^2 - b^2}{b} \sin \phi\right)^2$

so that $Pg = \dfrac{a}{b} \sqrt{b^2 \cos^2 \phi + a^2 \sin^2 \phi}$

From this result and equation (1), we therefore, have

$$PF \cdot Pg = a^2$$

➤ **271.** *To find the locus of the point of intersection of tangents which meet at right angles.*
Any tangent to the ellipse is

$$y = mx + \sqrt{a^2 m^2 + b^2}$$

and a perpendicular tangent is

$$y = -\frac{1}{m}x + \sqrt{a^2\left(-\frac{1}{m}\right)^2 + b^2}$$

Hence, if (h, k) be their point of intersection, we have

$$k - mh = \sqrt{a^2m^2 + b^2} \qquad \qquad ...(1)$$

and $$mk + h = \sqrt{a^2 + b^2m^2} \qquad \qquad ...(2)$$

If between equations (1) and (2), we eliminate m, we shall have a relation between h and k. Squaring and adding these equations, we have

$$(k^2 + h^2)(1 + m^2) = (a^2 + b^2)(1 + m^2)$$

i.e., $$h^2 + k^2 = a^2 + b^2$$

Hence, the locus of the point (h, k) is the circle

$$x^2 + y^2 = a^2 + b^2$$

i.e., a circle whose centre is the centre of the ellipse, and whose radius is the length of the line joining the ends of the major and minor axis. This circle is called the **Director Circle.**

EXAMPLES XXXIII

Find the equation to the tangent and normal

1. At the point $(1, \frac{4}{3})$ of the ellipse $4x^2 + 9y^2 = 20$

2. At the point of the ellipse $5x^2 + 3y^2 = 137$ whose ordinate is 2,

3. At the ends of the latera recta of the ellipse $9x^2 + 16y^2 = 144$.

4. Prove that the straight line $y = x + \sqrt{\dfrac{7}{12}}$ touches the ellipse

$$3x^2 + 4y^2 = 1.$$

5. Find the equations to the tangents to the ellipse $4x^2 + 3y^2 = 5$ which are parallel to the straight line $y = 3x + 7$.

   Find also the coordinates of the points of contact of the tangents which are inclined at 60° to the axis of x.

6. Find the equations to the tangents at the ends of the latera recta of the ellipse $\dfrac{x^2}{a^2} + \dfrac{y^2}{b^2} = 1$, and shew that they pass through the intersections of the axis and the directrices.

7. Find the points on the ellipse such that the tangent at each of them

makes equal angles with the axes. Prove also that the length of the perpendicular from the centre on either of these tangents is

$$\sqrt{\frac{a^2 + b^2}{2}}$$

8. In an ellipse, referred to its centre, the length of the sub-tangent corresponding to the point $(3, \frac{12}{5})$ is $\frac{16}{3}$; prove that the eccentricity is $\frac{4}{5}$.

9. Prove that the sum of the squares of the perpendiculars on any tangent from two points on the minor axis, each distant $\sqrt{a^2 - b^2}$ from the centre, is $2a^2$.

10. Find the equations to the normals at the ends of the latera recta, and prove that each passes through an end of the minor axis if $e^4 + e^2 = 1$.

11. If any ordinate MP meet the tangent at L in Q, prove that MQ and SP are equal.

12. Two tangents to the ellipse intersect at right angles; prove that the sum of the squares of the chords which the auxiliary circle intercepts on them is constant, and equal to the square on the line joining the foci.

13. If P be a point on the ellipse, whose ordinate is y', prove that the angle between the tangent at P and the focal distance of P is $\tan^{-1} \frac{b^2}{aey'}$.

14. Shew that the angle between the tangents to the ellipse $\frac{x^2}{a^2} + \frac{y^2}{b^2} = 1$ and the circle $x^2 + y^2 = ab$ at their points of intersection is $\tan^{-1} \frac{a - b}{\sqrt{ab}}$.

15. A circle, of radius r, is concentric with the ellipse; prove that the common tangent is inclined to the major axis at an angle $\tan^{-1} \sqrt{\frac{r^2 - b^2}{a^2 - r^2}}$ and find its length.

16. Prove that the common tangent of the ellipses

$$\frac{x^2}{a^2} + \frac{y^2}{b^2} = \frac{2x}{c} \quad \text{and} \quad \frac{x^2}{b^2} + \frac{y^2}{a^2} + \frac{2x}{c} = 0$$

subtends a right angle at the origin.

17. Prove that $PG \cdot Pg = SP \cdot S'P$ and $CG \cdot CT = CS^2$.

18. The tangent at P meets the axes in T and t, and CY is the perpendicular on it from the centre; prove that (1) $Tt \cdot PY = a^2 - b^2$ and (2) the least value of Tt is $a + b$.

19. Prove that the perpendicular from the focus upon any tangent and the line joining the centre to the point of contact meet on the corresponding directrix.

20. Prove that the straight lines, joining each focus to the foot of the perpendicular from the other focus upon the tangent at any point P, meet on the normal PG and bisect it.

21. Prove that the circle on any focal distance as diameter touches the auxiliary circle.

22. Find the tangent of the angle between CP and the normal at P and prove that its greatest value is $\dfrac{a^2 - b^2}{2ab}$.

23. Prove that the straight line $lx + my = n$ is a normal to the ellipse, if
$$\frac{a^2}{l^2} + \frac{b^2}{m^2} = \frac{(a^2 - b^2)^2}{n^2}.$$

24. Find the locus of the point of intersection of the two straight lines
$$\frac{tx}{a} - \frac{y}{b} + t = 0 \quad \text{and} \quad \frac{x}{a} + \frac{ty}{b} - 1 = 0$$
Prove also that they meet at the point whose eccentric angle is $2 \tan^{-1} t$.

25. Prove that the locus of the middle points of the portions of tangents included between the axes is the curve
$$\frac{a^2}{x^2} + \frac{b^2}{y^2} = 4.$$

26. Any ordinate NP of an ellipse meets the auxiliary circle in Q; prove that the locus of the intersection of the normals at P and Q is the circle
$$x^2 + y^2 = (a + b)^2.$$

27. The normal at P meets the axes in G and g; shew that the loci of the middle points of PG and Gg are respectively the ellipses
$$\frac{4x^2}{a^2 (1 + e^2)^2} + \frac{4y^2}{b^2} = 1, \quad \text{and} \quad a^2 x^2 + b^2 y^2 = \frac{1}{4}(a^2 - b^2)^2.$$

28. Prove that the locus of the feet of the perpendicular drawn from the centre upon any tangent to the ellipse is
$$r^2 = a^2 \cos^2 \theta + b^2 \sin^2 \theta \qquad \text{[Use Art. 264]}$$

29. If a number of ellipses be described having the same major axis, but a variable minor axis, prove that the tangents at the ends of their latera recta pass through one or other of two fixed points.

30. The normal GP is produced to Q, so that $GQ = n \cdot GP$. Prove that the locus of Q is the ellipse $\dfrac{x^2}{a^2 (n + e^2 - ne^2)^2} + \dfrac{y^2}{n^2 b^2} = 1$.

31. If the straight line $y = mx + c$ meet the ellipse, prove that the equation to the circle, described on the line joining the points of intersection as diameter, is

$$(a^2m^2 + b^2)(x^2 + y^2) + 2ma^2cx - 2b^2cy + c^2(a^2 + b^2) - a^2b^2(1 + m^2) = 0.$$

32. PM and PN are perpendiculars upon the axes from any point P on the ellipse. Prove that MN is always normal to a fixed concentric ellipse.

33. Prove that the sum of the eccentric angles of the extremities of a chord, which is drawn in a given direction, is constant, and equal to twice the eccentric angle of the point at which the tangent is parallel to the given direction.

34. A tangent to the ellipse $\dfrac{x^2}{a^2} + \dfrac{y^2}{b^2} = 1$ meets the ellipse

$$\frac{x^2}{a} + \frac{y^2}{b} = a + b$$

in the points P and Q; prove that the tangents at P and Q are at right angles.

➤ **272.** *To prove that through any given point (x_1, y_1) there pass, in general, two tangents to an ellipse.*

The equation to any tangent is (by Art. 263)

$$y = mx + \sqrt{a^2m^2 + b^2} \qquad \qquad \dots(1)$$

If this pass through the fixed point (x_1, y_1), we have

$$y_1 - mx_1 = \sqrt{a^2m^2 + b^2}$$

i.e.,

$$y_1^2 - 2mx_1y_1 + m^2x_1^2 = a^2m^2 + b^2$$

i.e.,

$$m^2(x_1^2 - a^2) - 2mx_1y_1 + (y_1^2 - b^2) = 0 \qquad \qquad \dots(2)$$

For any given values of x_1 and y_1, this equation is in general a quadratic equation and gives two values of m (real or imaginary).

Corresponding to each value of m we have, by substituting in equation (1), a different tangent

The roots of equation (2) are real and different, if

$$(-2x_1y_1)^2 - 4(x_1^2 - a^2)(y_1^2 - b^2) \text{ be positive,}$$

i.e., if

$$b^2x_1^2 + a^2y_1^2 - a^2b^2 \text{ be positive}$$

i.e., if

$$\frac{x_1^2}{a^2} + \frac{y_1^2}{b^2} - 1 \text{ be positive}$$

i.e., if the point (x_1, y_1) be outside the curve.

The roots are equal if

$$b^2 x_1^2 + a^2 y_1^2 - a^2 b^2$$

be zero, *i.e.*, if the point (x_1, y_1) lie on the curve.

The roots are imaginary, if

$$\frac{x_1^2}{a^2} + \frac{y_1^2}{b^2} - 1$$

be negative, *i.e.*, if the point (x_1, y_1) lie within the curve (Art. 255)

▶ **273.** *Equation to the chord of contact of tangents drawn from a point* (x_1, y_1)

The equation to the tangent at any point Q, whose coordinates are x' and y', is

$$\frac{xx'}{a^2} + \frac{yy'}{b^2} = 1$$

Also the tangent at the point R, whose coordinates are x'' and y'', is

$$\frac{xx''}{a^2} + \frac{yy''}{b^2} = 1$$

If these tangents meet at the point T, whose coordinates are x_1 and y_1, we have

$$\frac{x_1 x'}{a^2} + \frac{y_1 y'}{b^2} = 1 \qquad \qquad ...(1)$$

and

$$\frac{x_1 x''}{a^2} + \frac{y_1 y''}{b^2} = 1 \qquad \qquad ...(2)$$

The equation to QR is then

$$\frac{xx_1}{a^2} + \frac{yy_1}{b^2} = 1 \qquad \qquad ...(3)$$

For, since (1) is true, the point (x', y') lies on (3).

Also, since (2) is true, the point (x'', y''), lies on (3).

Hence, (3) must be the equation to the straight line joining (x', y') and (x'', y''), *i.e.*, it must be the equation to QR the required chord of contact of tangents from (x_1, y_1).

▶ **274.** *To find the equation of the polar of the point* (x_1, y_1) *with respect to the ellipse*

$$\frac{x^2}{a^2} + \frac{y^2}{b^2} = 1 \qquad \qquad \text{[Art. 162]}$$

Let Q and R be the points in which any chord drawn through the point (x_1, y_1) meets the ellipse [Fig Art. 214].

Let the tangents at Q and R meet in the point whose coordinates are (h, k).

We require the locus of (h, k).

Since, QR is the chord of contact of tangents from (h, k), its equation (Art. 273) is

$$\frac{xh}{a^2} + \frac{yk}{b^2} = 1$$

Since this straight line passes through the point (x_1, y_1), we have

$$\frac{hx_1}{a^2} + \frac{ky_1}{b^2} = 1 \qquad \ldots(1)$$

Since, the relation (1) is true, it follows that the point (h, k) lies on the straight line

$$\frac{xx_1}{a^2} + \frac{yy_1}{b^2} = 1 \qquad \ldots(2)$$

Hence, (2) is the equation to the polar of the point (x_1, y_1).

Cor. : The polar of the focus $(ae, 0)$ is

$$\frac{x \cdot ae}{a^2} = 1, \quad i.e., \quad x = \frac{a}{e}$$

i.e., the corresponding directrix.

➤ **275.** When the point (x_1, y_1) lies outside the ellipse the equation to its polar is the same as the equation of the chord of contact of tangents from it.

When (x_1, y_1) is on the ellipse, its polar is the same as the tangent at it.

As in Art. 215, the polar of (x_1, y_1) might have been defined as the chord of contact of the tangents, real or imaginary, drawn from it.

➤ **276.** *By a proof similar to that of Art. 217 it can be shewn that if the polar of P pass through T, then the polar of T passes through P.*

➤ **277.** *To find the coordinates of the pole of any given line.*

$$Ax + By + C = 0 \qquad \ldots(1)$$

Let (x_1, y_1) be its pole. Then equation (1) must be the same as the polar of (x_1, y_1), *i.e.*,

$$\frac{xx_1}{a^2} + \frac{yy_1}{b^2} - 1 = 0 \qquad \ldots(2)$$

Comparing equations (1) and (2), as in Art. 218, the required pole is easily seen to be

$$\left(-\frac{Aa^2}{C}, -\frac{Bb^2}{C}\right).$$

➤ **278.** *To find the equation to the pair of tangents that can be drawn to the ellipse from the point* (x_1, y_1).

Let (h, k) be any point on either of the tangents that can be drawn to the ellipse.

The equation of the straight line joining (h, k) to (x_1, y_1) is

$$y - y_1 = \frac{k - y_1}{h - x_1}(x - x_1)$$

i.e.,
$$y = \frac{k - y_1}{h - x_1}x + \frac{hy_1 - kx_1}{h - x_1}$$

If this straight line touch the ellipse, it must be of the form

$$y = mx + \sqrt{a^2 m^2 + b^2} \qquad \text{[Art. 263]}$$

Hence, $\qquad m = \dfrac{k - y_1}{h - x_1},\qquad$ and $\qquad \left(\dfrac{hy_1 - kx_1}{h - x_1}\right)^2 = a^2 m^2 + b^2$

Hence, $\qquad \left(\dfrac{hy_1 - kx_1}{h - x_1}\right)^2 = a^2\left(\dfrac{k - y_1}{h - x_1}\right)^2 + b^2$

But this is the condition that the point (h, k) may lie on the locus

$$(xy_1 - x_1y)^2 = a^2(y - y_1)^2 + b^2(x - x_1)^2 \qquad \ldots(1)$$

This equation is therefore the equation to the required tangents. It would be found that equation (1) is equivalent to

$$\left(\frac{x^2}{a^2} + \frac{y^2}{b^2} - 1\right)\left(\frac{x_1^2}{a^2} + \frac{y_1^2}{b^2} - 1\right) = \left(\frac{xx_1}{a^2} + \frac{yy_1}{b^2} - 1\right)^2.$$

➤ **279.** *To find the locus of the middle points of parallel chords of the ellipse.*

Let the chords make with the axis an angle whose tangent is m, so that the equation to any one of them, QR, is

$$y = mx + c \qquad \ldots(1)$$

where c is different for the different chords.

This straight line meets the ellipse in points whose abscissae are given by the equation,

$$\frac{x^2}{a^2} + \frac{(mx+c)^2}{b^2} = 1$$

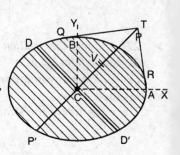

i.e., $x^2(a^2 m^2 + b^2) + 2a^2 mcx + a^2 (c^2 - b^2)$
$$= 0 \qquad \ldots(2)$$

Let the roots of this equation, i.e., the abscissae of Q and R, be x_1 and x_2, and let V, the middle point of QR, be the point (h, k).

Then, by Arts., 22 and 1, we have

$$h = \frac{x_1 + x_2}{2} = -\frac{a^2 mc}{a^2 m^2 + b^2} \qquad \ldots(3)$$

Also V lies on the straight line (1), so that

$$k = mh + c \qquad \ldots(4)$$

If between equations (3) and (4), we eliminate c, we have

$$h = -\frac{a^2 m (k - mh)}{a^2 m^2 + b^2}$$

i.e., $\qquad b^2 h = -a^2 mk \qquad \ldots(5)$

Hence, the point (h, k) always lies on the straight line

$$y = -\frac{b^2}{a^2 m} x \qquad \ldots(6)$$

The required locus is therefore the straight line

$$y = m_1 x, \text{ where } m_1 = -\frac{b^2}{a^2 m}$$

i.e., $\qquad mm_1 = -\frac{b^2}{a^2} \qquad \ldots(7)$

▶ **280.** *Equation to the chord whose middle point is (h, k).*

The required equation is (1) of the foregoing article, where m and c are given by equations (4) and (5), so that

$$m = -\frac{b^2 h}{a^2 k}, \text{ and } c = \frac{a^2 k^2 + b^2 h^2}{a^2 k}$$

The required equation is therefore,

$$y = -\frac{b^2 h}{a^2 k} x + \frac{a^2 k^2 + b^2 h^2}{a^2 k}$$

i.e.
$$\frac{k}{b^2}(y-k) + \frac{h}{a^2}(x-h) = 0$$

It is therefore parallel to the polar of (h, k).

▶ **281. Diameter. Def. :** The locus of the middle points of parallel chords of an ellipse is called a diameter, and the chords are called its double ordinates.

By equation (6) of Art. 279, we see that any diameter passes through the centre C.

Also, by Eq. (7), we see that the diameter $y = m_1 x$ bisects all chords parallel to the diameter $y = mx$, if

$$mm_1 = -\frac{b^2}{a^2} \qquad \qquad ...(1)$$

But the symmetry of the result, (1) shows that in this case, the diameter $y = mx$ bisects all chords parallel to the diameter $y = m_1 x$.

Such a pair of diameters are called Conjugate Diameters.

Hence,

Conjugate Diameters. Def. : Two diameters are said to be conjugate when each bisects all chords parallel to the other.

Two diameters $y = mx$ and $y = m_1 x$ are therefore, conjugate, if

$$mm_1 = -\frac{b^2}{a^2}$$

▶ **282.** *The tangent at the extremity of any diameter is parallel to the chords which it bisects.*

In the figure of Art. 279, let (x', y') be the point P on the ellipse, the tangent at which is parallel to the chord QR, whose equation is

$$y = mx + c \qquad \qquad ...(1)$$

The tangent at the point (x', y') is

$$\frac{xx'}{a^2} + \frac{yy'}{b^2} = 1 \qquad \qquad ...(2)$$

Since equations (1) and (2) are parallel, we have

$$m = -\frac{b^2 x'}{a^2 y'}$$

i.e., the point (x', y') lies on the straight line

$$y = -\frac{b^2}{a^2 m} x .$$

But, by Art. 279, this is the diameter which bisects QR and all chords which are parallel to it.

Cor. : It follows that two conjugate diameters CP and CD are such that each is parallel to the tangent at the extremity of the other. Hence, given either of these, we have a geometrical construction for the other.

➤ **283.** *The tangents at the ends of any chord meet on the diameter which bisects the chord.*

Let the equation to the chord QR (Art. 279) be

$$y = mx + c \qquad \qquad ...(1)$$

Let T be the point of intersection of the tangents at Q and R, and let its coordinates be h and k.

Since, QR is the chord of contact of tangents from T, its equation is, by Art. 273,

$$\frac{xh}{a^2} + \frac{yk}{b^2} = 1 \qquad \qquad ...(2)$$

The equations (1) and (2), therefore represent the same straight line, so that

$$m = -\frac{b^2 h}{a^2 k}$$

i.e., (h, k) lies on the straight line

$$y = -\frac{b^2}{a^2 m} x,$$

which, by Art. 279, is the equation to the diameter bisecting the chord QR. Hence, T lies on the straight line CP.

➤ **284.** *If the eccentric angles of the ends, P and D, of a pair of conjugate diameters be ϕ and ϕ', then ϕ and ϕ' differ by a right angle.*

Since, P is the point $(a \cos \phi, b \sin \phi)$, the equation to CP is

$$y = x \cdot \frac{b}{a} \tan \phi \qquad \qquad ...(1)$$

So, the equation to CD is

$$y = x \cdot \frac{b}{a} \tan \phi' \qquad \qquad ...(2)$$

These diameters are (Art. 281) conjugate if

$$\frac{b^2}{a^2} \tan \phi \tan \phi' = -\frac{b^2}{a^2}$$

i.e., if $\qquad \tan \phi = -\cot \phi' = \tan (\phi' \pm 90°)$

i.e., if $\qquad \phi - \phi' = \pm 90°$

Cor. 1.: The points on the auxiliary circle corresponding to P and D subtend a right angle at the centre.

For if p and d be these points then, by Art. 258, we have

$$\angle\, pCA' = \phi \quad \text{and} \quad \angle\, dCA' = \phi'$$

Hence, $\angle\, pCd = \angle dCA' - \angle pCA' = \phi - \phi' = 90°.$

Cor. 2. : In the figure of Art. 286, if P be the point ϕ, then D is the point $\phi + 90°$ and D' is the point $\phi - 90°$.

➤ **285.** From the previous article it follows that if P be the point $(a \cos \phi, b \sin \phi)$, then D is the point

$$\{ a \cos (90° + \phi) ,\; b \sin (90° + \phi)\}$$

i.e., $(- a \sin \phi,\; b \cos \phi)$

Hence, if PN and DM be the ordinates of P and D, we have

$$\frac{NP}{b} = -\frac{CM}{a}, \quad \text{and} \quad \frac{CN}{a} = \frac{MD}{b}.$$

➤ **286.** *If PCP' and DCD' be a pair of conjugate diameters, then (1) $CP^2 + CD^2$ is constant, and (2) the area of the parallelogram formed by the tangents at the ends of these diameters is constant.*

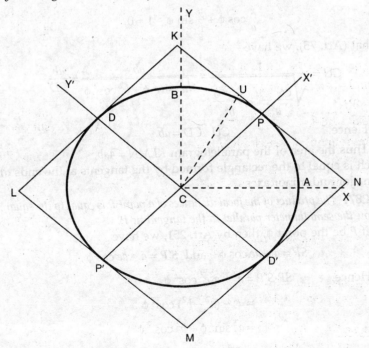

Let P be the point ϕ, so that its coordinates are $a \cos \phi$ and $b \sin \phi$. Then D is the point $90° + \phi$, so that its coordinates are

$$a \cos (90° + \phi) \quad \text{and} \quad b \sin (90° + \phi)$$

i.e., $-a \sin \phi$ and $b \cos \phi$

(1) We therefore, have

$$CP^2 = a^2 \cos^2 \phi + b^2 \sin^2 \phi$$

and $$CD^2 = a^2 \sin^2 \phi + b^2 \cos^2 \phi$$

Hence, $$CP^2 + CD^2 = a^2 + b^2$$

= the sum of the squares of the semi-axes of the ellipse.

(2) Let $KLMN$ be the paralielogram formed by the tangents at P, D, P' and D'.

We have

$$\text{area } KLMN = 4 \cdot \text{area } CPKD$$

$$= 4 \cdot CU \cdot PK = 4\, CU \cdot CD$$

where CU is the perpendicular from C upon the tangent at P.

Now the equation to the tangent at P is

$$\frac{x}{a} \cos \phi + \frac{y}{b} \sin \phi - 1 = 0$$

so that (Art. 75), we have

$$CU = \frac{1}{\sqrt{\dfrac{\cos^2 \phi}{a^2} + \dfrac{\sin^2 \phi}{b^2}}} = \frac{ab}{\sqrt{a^2 \sin^2 \phi + b^2 \cos^2 \phi}} = \frac{ab}{CD}$$

Hence, $$CU \cdot CD = ab$$

Thus the area of the parallelogram $KLMN = 4ab$, which is equal to the rectangle formed by the tangents at the ends of the major and minor axes.

➤ **287.** *The product of the focal distances of a point P is equal to the square on the semidiameter parallel to the tangent at P.*

If P be the point ϕ, then by Art. 251, we have

$$SP = a + ae \cos \phi \quad \text{and} \quad S'P = a - ae \cos \phi$$

Hence, $$SP \cdot S'P = a^2 - a^2 e^2 \cos^2 \phi$$

$$= a^2 - (a^2 - b^2) \cos^2 \phi$$

$$= a^2 \sin^2 \phi + b^2 \cos^2 \phi$$

$$= CD^2$$

➤ **288.**

EXAMPLE *If P and D be the ends of conjugate diameters, find the locus of*
(1) *the middle point of PD*
(2) *the intersection of the tangents at P and D, and*
(3) *the foot of the perpendicular from the centre upon PD.*
P is the point $(a \cos \phi, b \sin \phi)$ *and D is* $(-a \sin \phi, b \cos \phi)$.
(1) If (x, y) be the middle point of *PD*, we have

$$x = \frac{a \cos \phi - a \sin \phi}{2}, \quad \text{and} \quad y = \frac{b \sin \phi + b \cos \phi}{2}$$

If we eliminate ϕ, we shall get the required locus. We obtain

$$\frac{x^2}{a^2} + \frac{y^2}{b^2} = \frac{1}{4} \left[(\cos \phi - \sin \phi)^2 + (\sin \phi + \cos \phi)^2 \right] = \frac{1}{2}$$

The locus is therefore, a concentric and similar ellipse.
[N.B. Two ellipses are similar if the ratio of their axes are the same, so that they have the same eccentricity.]
(2) The tangents are

$$\frac{x}{a} \cos \phi + \frac{y}{b} \sin \phi = 1$$

and

$$-\frac{x}{a} \sin \phi + \frac{y}{b} \cos \phi = 1$$

Both of these equations hold at the intersection of the tangents. If we eliminate ϕ, we shall have the equation of the locus of their intersections.
By squaring and adding, we have

$$\frac{x^2}{a^2} + \frac{y^2}{b^2} = 2$$

so that the locus is another similar and concentric ellipse.
(3) By Art. 259, on putting $\phi' = 90° + \phi$, the equation to *PD* is

$$\frac{x}{a} \cos (45° + \phi) + \frac{y}{b} \sin (45° + \phi) = \cos 45°$$

Let the length of the perpendicular from the centre by p and let it make an angle ω with the axis. Then this line must be equivalent to

$$x \cos \omega + y \sin \omega = p.$$

Comparing the equations, we have

$$\cos (45° + \phi) = \frac{a \cos \omega \cos 45°}{p}$$

and

$$\sin (45° + \phi) = \frac{b \sin \omega \cos 45°}{p}.$$

Hence, by squaring and adding, $2p^2 = a^2 \cos^2 \omega + b^2 \sin^2 \omega$
i.e., the locus required is the curve

$$2r^2 = a^2 \cos^2 \theta + b^2 \sin^2 \theta$$

i.e., $$2(x^2 + y^2)^2 = a^2 x^2 + b^2 y^2$$

➤ **289. Equiconjugate diameters.** Let P and D be extremities of equiconjugate diameters, so that $CP^2 = CD^2$.

If the eccentric angle of P be ϕ, we then have

$$a^2 \cos^2 \phi + b^2 \sin^2 \phi = a^2 \sin^2 \phi + b^2 \cos^2 \phi,$$

giving $$\tan^2 \phi = 1,$$

i.e., $$\phi = 45° \quad \text{or} \quad 135°$$

The equation of CP is then

$$y = x \cdot \frac{b}{a} \tan \phi,$$

i.e., $$y = \pm \frac{b}{a} x \qquad \qquad …(1)$$

and that to CD is $$y = -x \frac{b}{a} \cot \phi,$$

i.e., $$y = \mp \frac{b}{a} x \qquad \qquad …(2)$$

If a rectangle be formed whose sides are the tangents at A, A', B, and B' the lines (1) and (2) are easily seen to be its diagonals.

The directions of the equiconjugates are therefore, along the diagonals of the circumscribing rectangle.

The length of each equiconjugate is, by Art., 286,

$$\sqrt{\frac{a^2 + b^2}{2}}.$$

➤ **290. Supplemental Chords. Def. :** The chords joining any point P on an ellipse to the extremities, R and R', of any diameter of the ellipse are called supplemental chords.

Supplemental chords are parallel to conjugate diameters.

Let P be the point whose eccentric angle is ϕ, and R and R' the points whose eccentric angles are ϕ_1 and $180° + \phi_1$.

The equations to PR and PR' and then (Art. 259)

$$\frac{x}{a} \cos \frac{\phi + \phi_1}{2} + \frac{y}{b} \sin \frac{\phi + \phi_1}{2} = \cos \frac{\phi - \phi_1}{2} \qquad …(1)$$

and $$\frac{x}{a} \cos \frac{\phi + 180° + \phi_1}{2} + \frac{y}{b} \sin \frac{\phi + 180° + \phi_1}{2} = \cos \frac{\phi - 180° - \phi_1}{2},$$

i.e., $$-\frac{x}{a} \sin \frac{\phi + \phi_1}{2} + \frac{y}{b} \cos \frac{\phi + \phi_1}{2} = \sin \frac{\phi - \phi_1}{2} \qquad … (2)$$

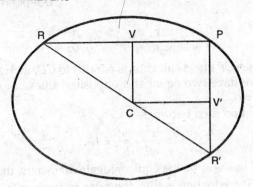

The "m" of the straight line (1) $= -\dfrac{b}{a}\cot\dfrac{\phi+\phi_1}{2}$.

The "m" of the line, (2) $= \dfrac{b}{a}\tan\dfrac{\phi+\phi_1}{2}$.

The product of these "$m's$" $= -\dfrac{b^2}{a^2}$, so that, by Art. 281, the lines PR and PR' are parallel to conjugate diameters.

This proposition may also be easily proved geometrically.

For let V and V' be the middle points of PR and PR'.

Since V and C are respectively the middle points of RP and RR' the line CV is parallel to PR'. Similarly CV' is parallel to RP.

Since CV bisects PR it bisects all chords parallel to PR, i.e., all chords parallel to VC'. So CV' bisects all chords parallel to CV.

Hence, CV and CV' are in the direction of conjugate diameters and therefore, PR' and PR, being parallel to CV and CV' respectively, are parallel to conjugate diameters.

➤ **291.** *To find the equation to an ellipse referred to a pair of conjugate diameters.*

Let the conjugate semi-diameters be CP and CD (Fig. Art. 286), whose lengths are a' and b' respectively.

If we transform the equation to the ellipse referred to its principal axes, to CP and CD as axes of coordinates, then, since the origin is unaltered, it becomes, by Art., 134, of the form

$$Ax^2 + 2Hxy + By^2 = 1 \qquad \ldots(1)$$

Now the point P, $(a', 0)$, lies on (1), so that

$$Aa'^2 = 1 \qquad \ldots(2)$$

So, since D, the point $(0, b')$, lies on (1), we have

$$Bb'^2 = 1$$

Hence, $A = \dfrac{1}{a'^2}$ and $B = \dfrac{1}{b'^2}$.

Also, since CP bisects all chords parallel to CD, therefore, for each value of x we have two equal and opposite values of y. This cannot be unless $H = 0$.

The equation then becomes

$$\frac{x^2}{a'^2} + \frac{y^2}{b'^2} = 1.$$

Cor. : If the axes be the equiconjugate diameters, the equation is $x^2 + y^2 = a'^2$. The equation is thus the same in form as the equation to a circle. In the case of the ellipse however the axes are oblique.

➤ **292.** It will be noted that the equation to the ellipse, when referred to a pair of conjugate diameters, is of the same form as it is when referred to its principal axes. The latter are merely a particular case of a pair of conjugate diameters.

Just as in Art. 262, it may be shewn that the equation to the tangent at the point (x', y') is

$$\frac{xx'}{a'^2} + \frac{yy'}{b'^2} = 1.$$

Similarly, for the equation to the polar.

EXAMPLE *If QVQ' be a double ordinate of the diameter CP, and if the tangent at Q meet CP in T, then $CV.CT = CP^2$.*

If Q be the point (x', y'), the tangent at it is

$$\frac{xx'}{a'^2} + \frac{yy'}{b'^2} = 1.$$

Putting $y = 0$, we have $x = \dfrac{a'^2}{x'}$

i.e. $CT = \dfrac{a'^2}{x'} = \dfrac{CP^2}{CV}$

i.e. $CV . CT = CP^2.$

═══ EXAMPLES XXXIV ═══

1. In the ellipse $\dfrac{x^2}{36} + \dfrac{y^2}{9} = 1$, find the equation to the chord which passes through the point $(2,1)$ and is bisected at that point.

2. Find, with respect to the ellipse $4x^2 + 7y^2 = 8$,

   (i) the polar of the point $\left(-\dfrac{1}{2}, 1\right)$, and

   (ii) the pole of the straight line $12x + 7y + 16 = 0$

3. Tangents are drawn from the point (3, 2) to the ellipse $x^2 + 4y^2 = 9$. Find the equation to their chord of contact and the equation of the straight line joining (3,2) to the middle point of this chord of contact.

4. Write down the equation of the pair of tangents drawn to the ellipse $3x^2 + 2y^2 = 5$ from the point (1, 2), and prove that the angle between them is $\tan^{-1}\dfrac{12\sqrt{5}}{5}$.

5. In the ellipse $\dfrac{x^2}{a^2} + \dfrac{y^2}{b^2} = 1$, write down the equations to the diameters which are conjugate to the diameters whose equations are
$$x - y = 0,\ x + y = 0,\ y = \frac{a}{b}x \text{ and } y = \frac{b}{a}x.$$

6. Shew that the diameters whose equations are $y + 3x = 0$ and $4y - x = 0$, are conjugate diameters of the ellipse $3x^2 + 4y^2 = 5$.

7. If the product of the perpendiculars from the foci upon the polar of P be constant and equal to c^2, prove that the locus of P is the ellipse $b^4x^2(c^2 + a^2e^2) + c^2a^4y^2 = a^4b^4$.

8. Shew that the four lines which join the foci to two points P and Q on an ellipse all touch a circle whose centre is the pole of PQ.

9. If the pole of the normal at P lie on the normal at Q, then shew that the pole of the normal at Q lies on the normal at P.

10. CK is the perpendicular from the centre on the polar of any point P, and PM is the perpendicular from P on the same polar and is produced to meet the major axis in L. Show that (1) $CK.PL = b^2$, and (2) the product of the perpendiculars from the foci on the polar $= CK . LM$.
What do these theorems become when P is on the ellipse?

11. In the previous question, if PN be the ordinate of P and the polar meet the axis in T, shew that $CL = e^2 . CN$ and $CT . CN = a^2$.

12. If tangents TP and TQ be drawn from a point T, whose coordinates are h and k, prove that the area of the triangle TPQ is
$$ab\left(\frac{h^2}{a^2} + \frac{k^2}{b^2} - 1\right)^{3/2} \div \left(\frac{h^2}{a^2} + \frac{k^2}{b^2}\right),$$
and that the area of the quadrilateral $CPTQ$ is
$$ab\left(\frac{h^2}{a^2} + \frac{k^2}{b^2} - 1\right)^{1/2}$$

13. Tangents are drawn to the ellipse from the point
$$\left(\frac{a^2}{\sqrt{a^2 - b^2}},\ \sqrt{a^2 + b^2}\right);$$
prove that they intercept on the ordinate through the nearer focus a distance equal to the major axis.

14. Prove that the angle between the tangents that can be drawn from any point (x_1, y_1) to the ellipse is

$$\operatorname{atan}^{-1} \frac{2ab \sqrt{\dfrac{x_1^2}{a^2} + \dfrac{y_1^2}{b^2} - 1}}{x_1^2 + y_1^2 - a^2 - b^2},$$

15. If T be the point (x_1, y_1), shew that the equation to the straight lines joining it to the foci, S and S', is

$$(x_1 y - x y_1)^2 - a^2 e^2 (y - y_1)^2 = 0.$$

Prove that the bisector of the angle between these lines also bisects the angle between the tangents TP and TQ that can be drawn from T, and hence that

$$\angle STP = \angle S'TQ.$$

16. If two tangents to an ellipse and one of its foci be given, prove that the locus of its centre is a straight line.

17. Prove that the straight lines joining the centre of the intersections of the straight line $y = mx + \sqrt{\dfrac{a^2 m^2 + b^2}{2}}$ with the ellipse are conjugate diameters.

18. Any tangent to an ellipse meets the director circle in p and d; prove that Cp and Cd are in the directions of conjugate diameters of the ellipse.

19. If CP be conjugate to the normal at Q, prove that CQ is conjugate to the normal at P.

20. If a fixed straight line parallel to either axis meet a pair of conjugate diameters in the points K and L, shew that the circle described on KL as diameter passes through two fixed points on the other axis.

21. Prove that a chord which joins the ends of a pair of conjugate diameters of an ellipse always touches a similar ellipse.

22. The eccentric angles of two points P and Q on the ellipse are ϕ_1 and ϕ_2; prove that the area of the parallelogram formed by the tangents at the ends of the diameters through P and Q is

$$4ab \operatorname{cosec} (\phi_1 - \phi_2)$$

and hence that it is least when P and Q are at the end of conjugate diameters.

23. A pair of conjugate diameters is produced to meet the directrix; shew that the orthocentre of the triangle so formed is at the focus.

24. If the tangent at any point P meet in the points L and L'
   (i) two parallel tangents, or (2) two conjugate diameters,
   prove that in each case the rectangle $LP . PL'$ is equal to the square on the semidiameter which is parallel to the tangent at P.

25. A point is such that the perpendicular from the centre on its polar with respect to the ellipse is constant and equal to c; shew that its locus is the ellipse

$$\frac{x^2}{a^4} + \frac{y^2}{b^4} = \frac{1}{c^2}.$$

26. Tangents are drawn from any point on the ellipse $\frac{x^2}{a^2} + \frac{y^2}{b^2} = 1$ to the

circle $x^2 + y^2 = r^2$; prove that the chords of contact are tangents to the ellipse $a^2x^2 + b^2y^2 = r^4$.

If $\frac{1}{r^2} = \frac{1}{a^2} + \frac{1}{b^2}$ prove that the lines joining the centre to the points of

contact with the circle are conjugate diameters of the second ellipse.

27. CP and CD are conjugate diameters of the ellipse; prove that the locus of the orthocentre of the triangle CPD is the curve

$$2(b^2y^2 + a^2x^2)^3 = (a^2 - b^2)(b^2y^2 - a^2x^2)^2.$$

28. If circles be described on two semi-conjugate diameters of the ellipse as diameters, prove that the locus of their second points of intersection is the curve $2(x^2 + y^2)^2 = a^2x^2 + b^2y^2$

➤ **293.** *To prove that, in general, four normals can be drawn from any point to an ellipse, and that the sum of the eccentric angles of their feet is equal to an odd multiple of two right angles.*

The normal at any point, whose eccentric angle is ϕ, is

$$\frac{ax}{\cos\phi} - \frac{by}{\sin\phi} = a^2 - b^2 = a^2e^2.$$

If this normal pass through the point (h, k), we have

$$\frac{ah}{\cos\phi} - \frac{bk}{\sin\phi} = a^2e^2 \qquad \dots(1)$$

For a given point (h, k) this equation gives the eccentric angles of the feet of the normals which pass through (h, k).

Let $\tan\frac{\phi}{2} = t$, so that

$$\cos\phi = \frac{1 - \tan^2\dfrac{\phi}{2}}{1 + \tan^2\dfrac{\phi}{2}} = \frac{1 - t^2}{1 + t^2}$$

and $$\sin\phi = \frac{2\tan\dfrac{\phi}{2}}{1 + \tan^2\dfrac{\phi}{2}} = \frac{2t}{1 + t^2}.$$

Substituting these values in Eq. (1), we have

$$ah\frac{1+t^2}{1-t^2} - bk\frac{1+t^2}{2t} = a^2e^2,$$

i.e. $bkt^4 + 2t^3(ah + a^2e^2) + 2t(ah - a^2e^2) - bk = 0$ ...(2)

Let t_1, t_2, t_3 and t_4 be the roots of this equation, so that, by Art. 2,

$$t_1 + t_2 + t_3 + t_4 = -2\frac{ah + a^2e^2}{bk} \qquad \text{...(3)}$$

$$t_1t_2 + t_1t_3 + t_1t_4 + t_2t_3 + t_2t_4 + t_3t_4 = 0 \qquad \text{...(4)}$$

$$t_2t_3t_4 + t_3t_4t_1 + t_4t_1t_2 + t_1t_2t_3 = -2\frac{ah - a^2e^2}{bk} \qquad \text{...(5)}$$

and $t_1t_2t_3t_4 = -1$ ...(6)

Hence, (Trigonometry, Art. 125), we have

$$\tan\left(\frac{\phi_1}{2} + \frac{\phi_2}{2} + \frac{\phi_3}{2} + \frac{\phi_4}{2}\right) = \frac{s_1 - s_3}{1 - s_2 + s_4} = \frac{s_1 - s_2}{0} = \infty.$$

$\therefore$ $\dfrac{\phi_1 + \phi_2 + \phi_3 + \phi_4}{2} = n\pi + \dfrac{\pi}{2},$

and hence $\phi_1 + \phi_2 + \phi_3 + \phi_4 = (2n + 1)\pi$

= an odd multiple of two right angles.

➤ **294.** We shall conclude the chapter with some examples of loci connected with the ellipse.

EXAMPLE 1 *Find the locus of the intersection of tangents at the ends of chords of an ellipse, which are of constant length 2c.*

Let QR be any such chord, and let the tangents at Q and R meet in a point P, whose coordinates are (h, k).

Since, QR is the polar of P, its equation is

$$\frac{xh}{a^2} + \frac{yk}{b^2} = 1 \qquad \text{... (1)}$$

The abscissae of the points in which this straight line meets the ellipse are given by

$$\left(1 - \frac{xh}{a^2}\right)^2 = \frac{k^2}{b^2}\left(1 - \frac{x^2}{a^2}\right)$$

i.e. $\dfrac{x^2}{a^2}\left(\dfrac{h^2}{a^2} + \dfrac{k^2}{b^2}\right) - \dfrac{2xh}{a^2} + 1 - \dfrac{k^2}{b^2} = 0.$

If x_1 and x_2 be the roots of this equation, *i.e.*, the abscissae of Q and R, we have

$$x_1 + x_2 = \frac{2a^2b^2h}{b^2h^2 + a^2k^2} \quad \text{and} \quad x_1x_2 = \frac{a^4(b^2 - k^2)}{b^2h^2 + a^2k^2}$$

$$\therefore (x_1 - x_2)^2 = (x_1 + x_2)^2 - 4x_1x_2 = \frac{4a^4[b^2h^2 + a^2k^2 - a^2b^2]k^2}{(b^2h^2 + a^2k^2)^2} \qquad \text{...(2)}$$

If y_1 and y_2 be the ordinates of Q and R, we have from equation (1)

$$\frac{x_1h}{a^2} + \frac{y_1k}{b^2} = 1$$

and

$$\frac{x_2h}{a^2} + \frac{y_2k}{b^2} = 1,$$

so that, by subtraction,

$$y_2 - y_1 = \frac{-b^2h}{a^2k}(x_2 - x_1).$$

The condition of the question therefore gives

$$4c^2 = (x_2 - x_1)^2 + (y_2 - y_1)^2 = \left(1 + \frac{b^4h^2}{a^4k^2}\right)(x_2 - x_1)^2$$

$$= \frac{4(a^4k^2 + b^4h^2)(b^2h^2 + a^2k^2 - a^2b^2)}{(b^2h^2 + a^2k^2)^2}, \qquad \text{[by equation (2)]}$$

Hence, the point (h, k) always lies on the curve

$$c^2\left(\frac{x^2}{a^2} + \frac{y^2}{b^2}\right)^2 = \left(\frac{a^2y^2}{b^2} + \frac{b^2x^2}{a^2}\right)\left(\frac{x^2}{a^2} + \frac{y^2}{b^2} - 1\right),$$

which is therefore, the locus of P.

EXAMPLE 2 *Find the locus (1) of the middle points, and (2) of the poles, of normal chords of the ellipse.*

The chord, whose middle point is (h, k), is parallel to the polar of (h, k), and is therefore,

$$(x - h)\frac{h}{a^2} + (y - k)\frac{k}{b^2} = 0 \qquad \text{...(1)}$$

If this be a normal, it must be the same as

$$ax \sec \theta - by \operatorname{cosec} \theta = a^2 - b^2 \qquad \text{...(2)}$$

We therefore, have

$$\frac{a \sec \theta}{\dfrac{h}{a^2}} = \frac{-b \operatorname{cosec} \theta}{\dfrac{k}{b^2}} = \frac{a^2 - b^2}{\dfrac{h^2}{a^2} + \dfrac{k^2}{b^2}}$$

so that

$$\cos \theta = \frac{a^3}{h(a^2 - b^2)}\left(\frac{h^2}{a^2} + \frac{k^2}{b^2}\right),$$

and
$$\sin \theta = -\frac{b^3}{k(a^2 - b^2)}\left(\frac{h^2}{a^2} + \frac{k^2}{b^2}\right)$$

Hence, by the elimination of θ,

$$\left(\frac{a^6}{h^2} + \frac{b^6}{k^2}\right)\left(\frac{h^2}{a^2} + \frac{k^2}{b^2}\right)^2 = (a^2 - b^2)^2.$$

The equation to the required locus is therefore,

$$\left(\frac{x^2}{a^2} + \frac{y^2}{b^2}\right)^2\left(\frac{a^6}{x^2} + \frac{b^6}{y^2}\right) = (a^2 - b^2)^2.$$

Again, if (x_1, y_1) be the pole of the normal chord (2), the latter equation must be equivalent to the equation

$$\frac{xx_1}{a^2} + \frac{yy_1}{b^2} = 1 \qquad \qquad \dots (3)$$

Comparing equations (2) and (3), we have

$$\frac{a^3 \sec \theta}{x_1} = -\frac{b^3 \csc \theta}{y_1} = a^2 - b^2,$$

so that
$$1 = \cos^2\theta + \sin^2\theta = \left(\frac{a^6}{x_1^2} + \frac{b^6}{y_1^2}\right)\frac{1}{(a^2 - b^2)^2}$$

and hence the required locus is

$$\frac{a^6}{x^2} + \frac{b^6}{y^2} = (a^2 - b^2)^2.$$

EXAMPLE 3 *Chords of the ellipse* $\dfrac{x^2}{a^2} + \dfrac{y^2}{b^2} = 1$ *always touch the concentric and coaxal ellipse* $\dfrac{x^2}{\alpha^2} + \dfrac{y^2}{\beta^2} = 1$; *find the locus of their poles.*

Any tangent to the second ellipse is

$$y = mx + \sqrt{\alpha^2 m^2 + \beta^2} \qquad \qquad \dots(1)$$

Let the tangents at the points where it meets the first ellipse meet in (h, k). Then (1) must be the same as the polar of (h, k) with respect to the first ellipse, *i.e.* it is the same as

$$\frac{xh}{a^2} + \frac{yk}{b^2} - 1 = 0 \qquad \qquad \dots(2)$$

Since, equations (1) and (2), coincide, we have

$$\frac{m}{\dfrac{h}{a^2}} = \frac{-1}{\dfrac{k}{b^2}} = \frac{\sqrt{\alpha^2 m^2 + \beta^2}}{-1}$$

Hence, $m = -\dfrac{b^2}{a^2}\dfrac{h}{k}$ and $\sqrt{\alpha^2 m^2 + \beta^2} = \dfrac{b^2}{k}$.

Eliminating m, we have

$$\alpha^2 \frac{b^4}{a^4}\frac{h^2}{k^2} + \beta^2 = \frac{b^4}{k^2}.$$

i.e., the point (h, k) lies on the ellipse

$$\frac{\alpha^2}{a^4}x^2 + \frac{\beta^2}{b^4}y^2 = 1$$

i.e. on a concentric and coaxial ellipse whose semi-axes conic coid respectively.

EXAMPLES XXXV

The tangents drawn from a point P to the ellipse make angles θ_1 and θ_2 with the major axis; find the locus of P when

1. $\theta_1 + \theta_2$ is constant $(= 2\alpha)$. *[Compare Ex. 1, Art. 235.]*
2. $\tan\theta_1 + \tan\theta_2$ is constant $(= c)$.
3. $\tan\theta_1 - \tan\theta_2$ is constant $(= d)$.
4. $\tan^2\theta_1 + \tan^2\theta_2$ is constant $(= \lambda)$.
   Find the locus of the intersection of tangents:
5. Which meet at a given angle α.
6. If the sum of the eccentric angles of their points of contact be equal to a constant angle 2α.
7. If the difference of these eccentric angles be 120°.
8. If the lines joining the points of contact to the centre be perpendicular.
9. If the sum of the ordinates of the points of contact be equal to b.
   Find the locus of the middle points of chords of an ellipse
10. Whose distance from the centre is the constant length c.
11. Which subtend a right angle at the centre.
12. Which pass through the given point (h, k).
13. Whose length is constant $(= 2c)$.
14. Whose poles are on the auxiliary circle.
15. The tangents at the ends of which intersect at the right angles.
16. Prove that the locus of the intersection of normals at the ends of conjugate diameters is the curve

$$2(a^2x^2 + b^2y^2)^3 = (a^2 - b^2)^2(a^2x^2 - b^2y^2)^2.$$

17. Prove that the locus of the intersection of normals at the ends of chords, parallel to the tangent at the point whose eccentric angle is α, is the conic

$$2(ax\sin\alpha + by\cos\alpha)(ax\cos\alpha + by\sin\alpha) = (a^2 - b^2)^2\sin 2\alpha\cos^2 2\alpha.$$

If the chords be parallel to an equiconjugate diameter, the locus is a diameter perpendicular to the other equiconjugate.

18. A parallelogram circumscribes the ellipse and two of its opposite angular points lie on the straight lines $x^2 = h^2$; prove that the locus of the other two is the conic

$$\frac{x^2}{a^2} + \frac{y^2}{b^2}\left(1 - \frac{a^2}{h^2}\right) = 1.$$

19. Circles of constant radius c are drawn to pass through the ends of a variable diameter of the ellipse. Prove that the locus of their centres is the curve

$$(x^2 + y^2)(a^2x^2 + b^2y^2 + a^2b^2) = c^2(a^2x^2 + b^2y^2).$$

20. The polar of a point P with respect to an ellipse touches a fixed circle, whose centre is on the major axis and which passes through the centre of the ellipse. Shew that the locus of P is a parabola, whose latus rectum is a third proportional to the diameter of the circle and the latus rectum of the ellipse.

21. Prove that the locus of the pole, with respect to the ellipse, of any tangent of the auxiliary circles is the curve $\dfrac{x^2}{a^4} + \dfrac{y^2}{b^4} = \dfrac{1}{a^2}$.

22. Shew that the locus of the pole, with respect to the auxiliary circle, of a tangent to the ellipse is a similar concentric ellipse, whose major axis is at right angles to that of the original ellipse.

23. Chords of the ellipse touch the parabola $ay^2 = -2b^2x$; prove that the locus of their poles is the parabola $ay^2 = 2b^2 x$.

24. Prove that the sum of the angles that the four normals drawn from any point to an ellipse make with the axis is equal to the sum of the angles that the two tangents from the same point make with the axis.
[Use the equation of Art. 268.]

25. Triangles are formed by pairs of tangents drawn from any point on the ellipse

$$a^2x^2 + b^2y^2 = (a^2 + b^2)^2 \text{ to the ellipse } \frac{x^2}{a^2} + \frac{y^2}{b^2} = 1,$$

and their chord of contact. Prove that the orthocentre of each such triangle lies on the ellipse.

26. An ellipse is rotated through a right angle in its own plane about its centre, which is fixed; prove that the locus of the point of intersection of a tangent to the ellipse in its original position with the tangent at the same point of the curve in its new position is

$$(x^2 + y^2)(x^2 + y^2 - a^2 - b^2) = 2(a^2 - b^2)xy.$$

27. If Y and Z be the feet of the perpendiculars from the foci upon the tangent at any point P of an ellipse, prove that the tangents at Y and Z to the auxiliary circle meet on the ordinate of P and that the locus of their point of intersection is another ellipse.

28. Prove that the directrices of the two parabolas that can be drawn to have ther foci at any given point P of the ellipse and to pass through its foci meet at an angle which is equal to twice the eccentric angle of P.

29. Chords at right angles are drawn through any point P of the ellipse, and the line joining their extremities meets the normal in the point Q. Prove that Q is the same for all such chords, its coodinates being,

$$\frac{a^3 e^2 \cos \alpha}{a^2 + b^2} \quad \text{and} \quad \frac{-a^2 b e^2 \sin \alpha}{a^2 + b^2}.$$

Prove also that the major axis is the bisector of the angle PCQ, and that the locus of Q for different positions of P is the ellipse

$$\frac{x^2}{a^2} + \frac{y^2}{b^2} = \left(\frac{a^2 - b^2}{a^2 + b^2}\right)^2.$$

13

THE HYPERBOLA

➤ **295.** The hyperbola is a Conic Section in which the eccentricity *e* is greater than unity.

To find the equation to a hyperbola.

Let ZK be the directrix, S the focus, and let SZ be perpendicular to the directrix.

There will be a point A on AZ, such that

$$SA = e \cdot AZ \qquad \qquad ...(1)$$

Since, $e > 1$, there will be another point A', on SZ produced, such that

$$SA' = e \cdot A'Z \qquad \qquad ...(2)$$

Let the length AA' be called $2a$, and let C be the middle point of AA'.

Subtracting (1) from (2), we have

$$2a = AA' = e \cdot A'Z - e \cdot AZ$$
$$= e [CA' + CZ] - e [CA - CZ] = e \cdot 2CZ,$$

i.e., $$CZ = \frac{a}{e} \qquad \qquad ...(3)$$

Adding (1) and (2), we have

$$e (AZ + A'Z) = SA' + SA = 2CS,$$

i.e., $$e \cdot AA' = 2 \cdot CS,$$

and hence $$CS = ae \qquad \qquad ...(4)$$

Let C be the origin, CSX the axis of x, and a straight line CY, through C perpendicular to CX, the axis of y.

Let P be any point on the curve, whose coordinates are x and y, and let PM be the perpendicular upon the directrix, and PN the perpendicular on AA'.

The focus S is the point $(ae, 0)$.

The relation $SP^2 = e^2 \cdot PM^2 = e^2 \cdot ZN^2$ then gives

$$(x - ae)^2 + y^2 = e^2 \left[x - \frac{a}{e} \right]^2,$$

i.e., $$x^2 - 2aex + a^2e^2 + y^2 = e^2x^2 - 2aex + a^2,$$

Hence, $$x^2 (e^2 - 1) - y^2 = a^2 (e^2 - 1),$$

i.e., $$\frac{x^2}{a^2} - \frac{y^2}{a^2 (e^2 - 1)} = 1 \qquad \qquad ...(5)$$

Since, in the case of the hyperbola, $e > 1$, the quantity $a^2 (e^2 - 1)$ is positive. Let it be called b^2, so that the equation (5) becomes

$$\frac{x^2}{a^2} - \frac{y^2}{b^2} = 1 \qquad \qquad ...(6)$$

where $$b^2 = a^2e^2 - a^2 = CS^2 - CA^2 \qquad \qquad ...(7)$$

and therefore, $$CS^2 = a^2 + b^2 \qquad \qquad ...(8)$$

➤ **296.** The equation (6) may be written

$$\frac{y^2}{b^2} = \frac{x^2}{a^2} - 1 = \frac{x^2 - a^2}{a^2} = \frac{(x - a)(x + a)}{a^2},$$

i.e., $$\frac{PN^2}{b^2} = \frac{AN \cdot NA'}{a^2}$$

so that $$PN^2 : AN \cdot NA' :: b^2 : a^2$$

If we put $x = 0$ in equation (6), we have $y^2 = -b^2$, shewing that the curve meets the axis CY in imaginary points.

Def.: The points A and A' are called the vertices of the hyperbola, C is the centre, AA' is the transverse axis of the curve, whilst the line BB' is called the conjugate axis, where B and B' are two points on the axis of y equidistant from C, as in the figure of Art. 315, and such that

$$B'C = CB = b$$

➤ **297.** Since S is the point $(ae, 0)$, the equation referred to the focus as origin is, by Art. 128,

$$\frac{(x + ae)^2}{a^2} - \frac{y^2}{b^2} = 1,$$

i.e.,

$$\frac{x^2}{a^2} + 2\frac{ex}{a} - \frac{y^2}{b^2} + e^2 - 1 = 0.$$

Similarly, the equations, referred to the vertex A and foot of the directrix Z respectively as origins, will be found to be

$$\frac{x^2}{a^2} - \frac{y^2}{b^2} + \frac{2x}{a} = 0$$

and

$$\frac{x^2}{a^2} - \frac{y^2}{b^2} + \frac{2x}{ae} = 1 - \frac{1}{e^2}$$

The equation to the hyperbola, whose focus, directrix, and eccentricity are any given quantities, may be written down as in the case of the ellipse (Art. 249).

➤ **298.** *There exist a second focus and a second directrix to the curve.*
On SC produced take a point S', such that

$$SC = CS' = ae,$$

and another point Z', such that

$$ZC = CZ' = \frac{a}{e}$$

Draw $Z'M'$ perpendicular to AA', and let PM be produced to meet it in M'.

The equation (5) of Art. 295 may be written in the form

$$x^2 + 2aex + a^2e^2 + y^2 = e^2x^2 + 2aex + a^2,$$

i.e.,

$$(x + ae)^2 + y^2 = e^2\left(\frac{a}{e} + x\right)^2,$$

i.e.,

$$S'P^2 = e^2(Z'C + CN)^2 = e^2 \cdot PM'^2$$

Hence, any point P of the curve is such that its distance from S' is e times its distance from $Z'K'$, so that we should have obtained the same curve if we had started with S' as focus, $Z'K'$ as directrix, and the same eccentricity e.

➤ **299.** *The difference of the focal distances of any point on the hyperbola is equal to the transverse axis.*

For (Fig., Art. 295), we have

$$SP = e \cdot PM, \text{ and } S'P = e \cdot PM'$$

Hence, $\quad S'P - SP = e\,(PM' - PM) = e \cdot MM'$

$$= e \cdot ZZ' = 2e \cdot CZ = 2a$$

$$= \text{the transverse axis } AA'$$

Also $\quad SP = e \cdot PM = e \cdot ZN = e \cdot CN - e \cdot CZ = ex' - a,$

and $\quad S'P = e \cdot PM' = e \cdot Z'N = e \cdot CN + e \cdot Z'C = ex' + a$

where x' is the abscissa of the point P referred to the centre as origin.

➤ **300.** *Latus-rectum of the Hyperbola.*

Let LSL' be the latus-rectum, *i.e.*, the double ordinate of the curve drawn through S.

By the definition of the curve, the semi-latus-rectum SL

$$= e \text{ times the distance of } L \text{ from the directrix}$$

$$= e \cdot SZ = e\,(CS - CZ)$$

$$= e \cdot CS - e \cdot CZ = ae^2 - a = \frac{b^2}{a}$$

by equations (3), (4) and (7) of Art. 295.

➤ **301.** *To trace the curve*

$$\frac{x^2}{a^2} - \frac{y^2}{b^2} = 1 \qquad \qquad \ldots(1)$$

The equation may be written in either of the forms

$$y = \pm b\,\sqrt{\frac{x^2}{a^2} - 1} \qquad \qquad \ldots(2)$$

or $\qquad \qquad x = \pm a\,\sqrt{\frac{y^2}{b^2} + 1} \qquad \qquad \ldots(3)$

From (2), it follows that, if $x^2 < a^2$, *i.e.*, if x lie between a and $-a$, then y is impossible. There is therefore, no part of the curve between A and A'.

For all values of $x^2 > a^2$, the equation (2) shews that there are two equal and opposite values of y, so that the curve is symmetrical with respect to the axis of x. Also, as the value of x increases, the corresponding values of y increase, until corresponding to an infinite value of x, we have an infinite value of y.

For all values of y, the equation (3) gives two equal and opposite values to x, so that the curve is symmetrical with respect to the axis of y.

If a number of values in succession be given to x, and the corresponding values of y be determined, we shall obtain a series of points, which will all be found to lie on a curve of the shape given in the figure of Art. 295.

The curve consists of two portions, one of which extends in an infinite direction towards the positive direction of the axis of x, and the other in an infinite direction towards the negative end of this axis.

➤ **302.** *The quantity* $\dfrac{x'^2}{a^2} - \dfrac{y'^2}{b^2} - 1$ *is positive, zero, or negative, according as the point (x', y') lies within, upon, or without, the curve.*

Let Q be the point (x', y'), and let the ordinate QN through Q meet the curve in P, so that, by equation (6) of Art. 295,

$$\frac{x'^2}{a^2} - \frac{PN^2}{b^2} = 1$$

and hence

$$\frac{PN^2}{b^2} = \frac{x'^2}{a^2} - 1$$

If Q be within the curve then y', i.e. QN, is less than PN, so that

$$\frac{y'^2}{b^2} < \frac{PN^2}{b^2}, \quad i.e., \quad < \frac{x'^2}{a^2} - 1.$$

Hence, in this case, $\dfrac{x'^2}{a^2} - \dfrac{y'^2}{b^2} > 0$, *i.e.*, is positive.

Similarly, if Q be without the curve, then $y' > PN$, and

we have $\dfrac{x'^2}{a^2} - \dfrac{y'^2}{b^2} - 1$ negative.

➤ **303.** *To find the length of any central radius drawn in a given direction.*

The equation (6) of Art. 295, when transferred to polar coordinates, becomes

$$r^2 \left(\frac{\cos^2 \theta}{a^2} - \frac{\sin^2 \theta}{b^2} \right) = 1,$$

i.e.,

$$\frac{1}{r^2} = \frac{\cos^2 \theta}{a^2} - \frac{\sin^2 \theta}{b^2} = \frac{\cos^2 \theta}{b^2} \left(\frac{b^2}{a^2} - \tan^2 \theta \right) \qquad \text{...(1)}$$

This is the equation giving the value of any central radius of the curve drawn at an inclination θ to the transverse axis.

So long as $\tan^2 \theta < \dfrac{b^2}{a^2}$, the equation (1) gives two equal and opposite values of r corresponding to any value of θ.

For values of $\tan^2 \theta > \dfrac{b^2}{a^2}$, the corresponding values of $\dfrac{1}{r^2}$ are negative, and the corresponding values of r imaginary. Any radius drawn at a greater inclination than $\tan^{-1} \dfrac{b}{a}$ does not therefore meet the curve in any real points, so that all the curve is included within two straight lines drawn through C and inclined at an angle $\tan^{-1} \dfrac{b}{a}$ to CX.

Writing (1) in the form

$$r^2 = \frac{b^2}{\cos^2 \theta \left(\dfrac{b^2}{a^2} - \tan^2 \theta \right)}$$

ve see that r is least when the denominator is greatest, $i.e.$, when $\theta = 0$. The radius vector CA is therefore, the least.

Also, when $\tan \theta = \pm \dfrac{b}{a}$, the value of r is infinite.

For values of θ between 0 and $\tan^{-1} \dfrac{b}{a}$, the corresponding positive values of r give the portion AR of the curve (Fig., Art. 295) and the corresponding negative values give the portion $A'R'$.

For values of θ between 0 and $-\tan^{-1} \dfrac{b}{a}$, the positive values of R give the portion AR_1, and the negative values give the portion $A'R'_1$

The ellipse and the hyperbola since they both have a centre C, such that all chords of the conic passing through it are bisected at it, are together called **Central Conics**.

► **304.** In the hyperbola any ordinate of the curve does not meet the circle on AA' as diameter in real points. There is, therefore no real eccentric angle as in the case of the ellipse.

When it is desirable to express the coordinates of any point of the curve in terms of one variable, the substitutions

$$x = a \sec \phi \quad \text{and} \quad y = b \tan \phi$$

may be used; for these substitutions clearly satisfy the equation (6) of Art. 295.

The angle ϕ can be easily defined geometrically.

On AA' describe the auxiliary circle, (Fig., Art. 306) and from the foot N of any ordinate NP of the curve draw a tangent NU to this circle, and join CU. Then

$$CU = CN \cos NCU,$$

i.e., $$x = CN = a \sec NCU$$

The angle NCU is therefore, the angle ϕ

Also, $$NU = CU \tan \phi = a \tan \phi,$$

so that $$NP : NU :: b : a.$$

The ordinate of the hyperbola is therefore in a constant ratio to the length of the tangent drawn from its foot to the auxiliary circle.

This angle ϕ is not so important an angle for the hyperbola as the eccentric angle is for the ellipse.

➤ **305.** Since the fundamental equation to the hyperbola only differs from that to the ellipse in having $-b^2$ instead of b^2, it will be found that many propositions for the hyperbola are derived from those for the ellipse by changing the sign of b^2.

Thus, as in Art. 260, the straight line $y = mx + c$ meets the hyperbola in points which are real, coincident, or imaginary, according as

$$c^2 > = < a^2m^2 - b^2$$

As in Art. 262, the equation to the tangent at (x', y') is

$$\frac{xx'}{a^2} - \frac{yy'}{b^2} = 1$$

As in Art. 263, the straight line

$$y = mx + \sqrt{a^2m^2 - b^2}$$

is always a tangent.

The straight line

$$x \cos \alpha + y \sin \alpha = p$$

is a tangent, if $$p^2 = a^2\cos^2\alpha - b^2 \sin^2 \alpha$$

The straight line, $$lx + my = n$$

is a tangent, if $$n^2 = a^2l^2 - b^2m^2 \qquad \text{[Art. 264]}$$

The normal at the point (x', y') is, as in Art. 266,

$$\frac{x - x'}{\dfrac{x'}{a^2}} = \frac{y - y'}{\dfrac{y'}{-b^2}}$$

➤ **306.** With some modifications the properties of Arts. 269 and 270 are true for the hyperbola also, if the corresponding figure be drawn.

In the case of the hyperbola the tangent bisects the interior, and the normal the exterior, angle between the focal distances SP and $S'P$.

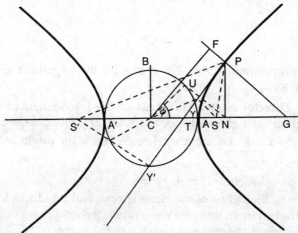

It follows that, if an ellipse and a hyperbola have the same foci S and S', they cut at right angles at any common point P. For the tangents in the two cases are respectively the internal and external bisectors of the angle SPS', and are therefore at right angles.

➤ **307.** The equation to the straight lines joining the points $(a \sec \phi, b \tan \phi)$ and $(a \sec \phi', b \tan \phi')$ can be shewn to be

$$\frac{x}{a} \cos \frac{\phi' - \phi}{2} - \frac{y}{b} \sin \frac{\phi + \phi'}{2} = \cos \frac{\phi + \phi'}{2}$$

Hence, by putting $\phi' = \phi$, it follows that the tangent at the point $(a \sec \phi, b \tan \phi)$ is

$$\frac{x}{a} - \frac{y}{b} \sin \phi = \cos \phi$$

It could easily be shewn that the equation to the normal is

$$ax \sin \phi + by = (a^2 + b^2) \tan \phi$$

➤ **308.** The proposition of Art. 272 is true also for the hyperbola. As in Art. 273, the chord of contact of tangents from (x_1, y_1) is

$$\frac{xx_1}{a^2} - \frac{yy_1}{b^2} = 1$$

As in Art. 274, the polar of any point (x_1, y_1) is

$$\frac{xx_1}{a^2} - \frac{yy_1}{b^2} = 1$$

As in Arts. 279 and 281, the locus of the middle points of chords, which are parallel to the diameter $y = mx$, is the diameter $y = m_1x$, where

$$mm_1 = \frac{b^2}{a^2}$$

The proposition of Art. 278 is true for the hyperbola also, if we replace b^2 by $-b^2$.

➤ **309. Director circle.** The locus of the intersection of tangents which are at right angles is, as in Art. 271, found to be the circle $x^2 + y^2 = a^2 - b^2$, i.e. a circle whose centre is the origin and whose radius is $\sqrt{a^2 - b^2}$.

If $b^2 < a^2$, this circle is real.

If $b^2 = a^2$, the radius of the circle is zero, and it reduces to a point circle at the origin. In this case the centre is the only point from which tangents at right angles can be drawn to the curve.

If $b^2 > a^2$, the radius of the circle is imaginary, so that there is no such circle, and so no tangents at right angles can be drawn to the curve.

➤ **310. Equilateral, or Rectangular, Hyperbola.**

The particular kind of hyperbola in which the lengths of the transverse and conjugate axes are equal is called an equilateral, or rectangular, hyperbola. The reason for the name "rectangular" will be seen in Art. 318.

Since, in this case, $b = a$, the equation to the equilateral hyperbola, referred to its centre and axes, is $x^2 - y^2 = a^2$.

The eccentricity of the rectangular hyperbola is $\sqrt{2}$.

For, by Art. 295, we have, in this case,

$$e^2 = \frac{a^2 + b^2}{a^2} = \frac{2a^2}{a^2} = 2,$$

so that $\qquad e = \sqrt{2}$

➤ **311.**

EXAMPLE *The perpendiculars from the centre upon the tangent and normal at any point of the hyperbola $\dfrac{x^2}{a^2} - \dfrac{y^2}{b^2} = 1$ meet them in Q and R. Find the loci of Q and R.*

As in Art. 308, the straight line

$$x \cos \alpha + y \sin \alpha = p$$

is a tangent, if $\qquad p^2 = a^2 \cos^2 \alpha - b^2 \sin^2 \alpha.$

But p and α are the polar coordinates of Q, the foot of the perpendicular on this straight line from C.

The polar equation to the locus of Q is therefore,

$$r^2 = a^2 \cos^2 \theta - b^2 \sin^2 \theta,$$

i.e., in Cartesian coordinates,

$$(x^2 + y^2)^2 = a^2 x^2 - b^2 y^2$$

If the hyperbola be rectangular, we have $a = b$, and the polar equation is

$$r^2 = a^2 (\cos^2 \theta - \sin^2 \theta) = a^2 \cos 2\theta.$$

Again, by Art. 307, any normal is

$$ax \sin \phi + by = (a^2 + b^2) \tan \phi \qquad \ldots(1)$$

The equation to the perpendicular on it from the origin is

$$bx - ay \sin \phi = 0 \qquad \ldots(2)$$

If we eliminate ϕ, we shall have the locus of R.

From (2), we have $\qquad \sin \phi = \dfrac{bx}{ay}$

and then $\qquad \tan \phi = \dfrac{\sin \phi}{\sqrt{1 - \sin^2 \phi}} = \dfrac{bx}{\sqrt{a^2 y^2 - b^2 x^2}}$

Substituting in (1), the locus is

$$(x^2 + y^2)^2 (a^2 y^2 - b^2 x^2) = (a^2 + b^2)^2 x^2 y^2$$

EXAMPLES XXXVI

Find the equation to the hyperbola, referred to its axes as axes of coordinates

1. whose transverse and conjugate axes are respectively 3 and 4.
2. whose conjugate axis is 5 and the distance between whose foci is 13.
3. whose conjugate axis is 7 and which passes through the point $(3, -2)$,
4. the distance between whose foci is 16 and whose eccentricity is $\sqrt{2}$.
5. In the hyperbola $4x^2 - 9y^2 = 36$, find the axes, the coordinates of the foci, the eccentricity, and the latus rectum.
6. Find the equation to the hyperbola of given transverse axis whose vertex bisects the distance between the centre and the focus.

7. Find the equation to the hyperbola, whose eccentricity is $\frac{5}{4}$, whose focus is $(a, 0)$, and whose directrix is $4x - 3y = a$.

Find also the coordinates of the centre and the equation to the other directrix.

8. Find the points common to the hyperbola $25x^2 - 9y^2 = 225$ and the straight line $25x + 12y - 45 = 0$.

9. Find the equation of the tangent to the hyperbola $4x^2 - 9y^2 = 1$ which is parallel to the line $4y = 5x + 7$.

10. Prove that a circle can be drawn through the foci of a hyperbola and the points in which any tangent meets the tangents at the vertices.

11. An ellipse and a hyperbola have the same principal axes. Shew that the polar of any point on either curve with respect to the other touches the first curve

12. In both an ellipse and a hyperbola, prove that the focal distance of any point and the perpendicular from the centre upon the tangent at it meet on a circle whose centre is the focus and whose radius is the semi-transverse axis.

13. Prove that the straight lines $\frac{x}{a} - \frac{y}{b} = m$ and $\frac{x}{a} + \frac{y}{b} = \frac{1}{m}$ always meet on the hyperbola.

14. Find the equation to, and the length of, the common tangent to the two hyperbolas $\frac{x^2}{a^2} - \frac{y^2}{b^2} = 1$ and $\frac{y^2}{a^2} - \frac{x^2}{b^2} = 1$.

15. In the hyperbola $16x^2 - 9y^2 = 144$, find the equation to the diameter which is conjugate to the diameter whose equation is $x = 2y$.

16. Find the equation to the chord of the hyperbola
$$25x^2 - 16y^2 = 400$$
which is bisected at the point $(5, 3)$.

17. In a rectangular hyperbola, prove that
$$SP \cdot S'P = CP^2$$

18. the distance of any point from the centre varies inversely as the perpendicular from the centre upon its polar.

19. iuf the normal at P meet the axes in G and g, then $PG = Pg = PC$.

20. the angle subtended by any chord at the centre is the supplement of the angle between the tangents at the ends of the chord.

21. the angles subtended at its vertices by any chord which is parallel to its conjugate axis are supplementary.

22. The normal to the hyperbola $\frac{x^2}{a^2} - \frac{y^2}{b^2} = 1$ meets the axes in M and N, and lines MP and NP are drawn at right angles to the axes; prove that the locus of P is the hyperbola
$$a^2x^2 - b^2y^2 = (a^2 + b^2)^2$$

23. If one axis of a varying central conic be fixed in magnitude and position, prove that the locus of the point of contact of a tangent drawn to it from a fixed point on the other axis is a parabola.

24. If the ordinate MP of a hyperbola be produced to Q, so that MQ is equal to either of the focal distances of P, prove that the locus of Q is one or other of a pair of parallel straight lines.

25. Shew that the locus of the centre of a circle which touches externally two given circles is a hyperbola.

26. On a level plain the crack of the rifle and the thud of the ball striking the target are heard at the same instant; prove that the locus of the hearer is a hyperbola.

27. Given the base of a triangle and the ratio of the tangents of half the base angles, prove that the vertex moves on a hyperbola whose foci are the extremities of the base.

28. Prove that the locus of the poles of normal chords with respect to the hyperbola $\dfrac{x^2}{a^2} - \dfrac{y^2}{b^2} = 1$ is the curve

$$y^2 a^6 - x^2 b^6 = (a^2 + b^2)^2 x^2 y^2$$

29. Find the locus of the pole of a chord of the hyperbola which subtends a right angle at (1) the centre, (2) the vertex, and (3) the focus of the curve.

30. Shew that the locus of poles with respect to the parabola $y^2 = 4ax$ of tangents to the hyperbola $x^2 - y^2 = a^2$ is the ellipse $4x^2 + y^2 = 4a^2$.

31. Prove that the locus of the pole with respect to the hyperbola $\dfrac{x^2}{a^2} - \dfrac{y^2}{b^2} = 1$ of any tangent to the circle, whose diameter is the line joining the foci, is the ellipse $\dfrac{x^2}{a^4} + \dfrac{y^2}{b^4} = \dfrac{1}{a^2 + b^2}$.

32. Prove that the locus of the intersection of tangents to a hyperbola, which meet at a constant angle β, is the curve

$$(x^2 + y^2 + b^2 - a^2)^2 = 4 \cot^2 \beta \, (a^2 y^2 - b^2 x^2 + a^2 b^2)$$

33. From points on the circle $x^2 + y^2 = a^2$ tangents are drawn to the hyperbola $x^2 - y^2 = a^2$; prove that the locus of the middle points of the chords of contact is the curve

$$(x^2 - y^2)^2 = a^2 (x^2 + y^2)$$

34. Chords of a hyperbola are drawn, all passing through the fixed point (h, k); prove that the locus of their middle points is a hyperbola whose centre is the point $\left(\dfrac{h}{2}, \dfrac{k}{2} \right)$, and which is similar to either the hyperbola or its conjugate.

➤ **312. Asymptote. Def.** An asymptote is a straight line, which meets the conic in two points both of which are situated at an infinite distance, but which is itself not altogether at infinity.

➤ **313.** *To find the asymptotes of the hyperbola*

$$\frac{x^2}{a^2} - \frac{y^2}{b^2} = 1$$

As in Art. 260, the straight line

$$y = mx + c \qquad \qquad \text{...(1)}$$

meets the hyperbola in points, whose abscissae are given by the equation

$$x^2 (b^2 - a^2 m^2) - 2a^2 mcx - a^2 (c^2 + b^2) = 0 \qquad \text{...(2)}$$

If the straight line (1) be an asymptote, both roots of (2) must be infinite.

Hence, the coefficients of x^2 and x in it must both be zero.

We therefore, have

$$b^2 - a^2 m^2 = 0 \quad \text{and} \quad a^2 mc = 0$$

Hence, \qquad\qquad $m = \pm \dfrac{b}{a}$ \quad and \quad $c = 0$

Substituting these values in (1), we have, as the required equation,

$$y = \pm \frac{b}{a} x$$

There are therefore two asymptotes both passing through the centre and equally inclined to the axis of x, the inclination being

$$\tan^{-1} \frac{b}{a}$$

The equation to the asymptotes, written as one equation, is:

$$\frac{x^2}{a^2} - \frac{y^2}{b^2} = 0$$

Cor. : For all values of c one root of equation (2) is infinite if $m = \pm \dfrac{b}{a}$. Hence, any straight line, which is parallel to an asymptote, meets the curve in one point at infinity and in one finite point.

➤ **314.** That the asymptote passes through two coincident points at infinity, i.e. touches the curve at infinity, may be seen by finding the equations to the tangents to the curve which pass through any point $\left(x_1, \dfrac{b}{a} x_1 \right)$ on the asymptote $y = \dfrac{b}{a} x$.

As in Art. 305, the equation to either tangent through this point is

$$y = mx + \sqrt{a^2 m^2 - b^2}$$

where

$$\frac{b}{a} x_1 = mx_1 + \sqrt{a^2 m^2 - b^2},$$

i.e., on clearing of surds,

$$m^2 (x_1^2 - a^2) - 2m\frac{b}{a} x_1^2 + (x_1^2 + a^2) \frac{b^2}{a^2} = 0$$

One root of this equation is $m = \dfrac{b}{a}$, so that one tangent through the

given point is $y = \dfrac{b}{a} x$, i.e. the asymptote itself.

➤ **315.** *Geometrical construction for the asymptotes.*

Let $A'A$ be the transverse axis, and along the conjugate axis measure off CB and CB', each equal to b. Through B and B' draw parallels to the transverse axis and through A and A' parallels to the conjugate axis, and let these meet respectively in K_1, K_2, K_3, and K_4, as in the figure.

Clearly the equations of $K_1 C K_3$ and $K_2 C K_4$ are

$$y = \frac{b}{a} x \quad \text{and} \quad y = -\frac{b}{a} x,$$

and these are therefore the equations of the asymptotes.

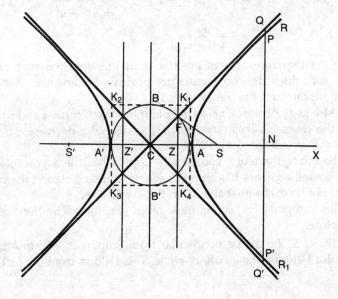

➤ **316.** Let any double ordinate PNP' of the hyperbola be produced both ways to meet the asymptotes in Q and Q', and let the abscissa CN be x'.

Since P lies on the curve, we have, by Art. 302,

$$NP = \frac{b}{a}\sqrt{x'^2 - a^2}$$

Since, Q is on the asymptote whose equation is $y = \frac{b}{a}x$,

We have $NQ = \frac{b}{a}x'$

Hence, $PQ = NQ - NP = \frac{b}{a}(x' - \sqrt{x'^2 - a^2})$,

and $P'Q = \frac{b}{a}(x' + \sqrt{x'^2 - a^2})$

Therefore, $PQ \cdot P'Q = \frac{b^2}{a^2}\{x'^2 - (x'^2 - a^2)\} = b^2$.

Hence, if from any point on an asymptote a straight line be drawn perpendicular to the transverse axis, the product of the segments of this line, intercepted between the point and the curve, is always equal to the square on the semi-conjugate axis.

Again, $PQ = \frac{b}{a}(x' - \sqrt{x'^2 - a^2}) = \frac{b}{a}\dfrac{a^2}{x' + \sqrt{x'^2 - a^2}}$

$$= \frac{ab}{x' + \sqrt{x'^2 - a^2}}$$

PQ is therefore always positive, and therefore the part of the curve, for which the coordinates are positive, is altogether between the asymptote and the transverse axis.

Also as x' increases, i.e. as the point P is taken further and further from the centre C, it is clear that PQ continually decreases; finally, when x' is infinitely great, PQ is infinitely small.

The curve therefore, continually approaches the asymptote but never actually reaches it, although, at a very great distance, the curve would not be distinguishable from the asymptote.

This property is sometimes taken as the definition of an asymptote.

➤ **317.** If SF be the perpendicular from S upon an asymptote, the point F lies on the auxiliary circle. This follows from the fact that

the asymptote is a tangent, whose point of contact happens to lie at infinity, or it may be proved directly.
For

$$CF = CS \cos FCS = CS \cdot \frac{CA}{CK} = \sqrt{a^2 + b^2} \cdot \frac{a}{\sqrt{a^2 + b^2}} = a$$

Also, Z being the foot of the directrix, we have

$$CA^2 = CS \cdot CZ, \qquad \text{(At. 295)}$$

and hence $\quad CF^2 = CS \cdot CZ, \quad i.e., \quad CS : CF :: CF : CZ.$

By geometry, it follows that $\angle CZF = \angle CFS =$ a right angle, and hence that F lies on the directrix.

Hence, the perpendiculars from the foci on either asymptote meet it in the same points as the corresponding directrix, and the common points of intersection lie on the auxiliary circle.

➤ **318. Equilateral or Rectangular Hyperbola :** In this curve (Art. 310) the quantities a and b are equal. The equations to the asymptotes are therefore $y = \pm x$, i.e. they are inclined at angles $\pm 45°$ to the axis of x, and hence they are at right angles. Hence, the hyperbola is generally called a **rectangular** hyperbola.

➤ **319. Conjugate Hyperbola :** The hyperbola which has BB' as its transverse axis, and AA' as its conjugate axis, is said to be the conjugate hyperbola of the hyperbola whose transverse and conjugate axes are respectively AA' and BB',
Thus the hyperbola

$$\frac{y^2}{b^2} - \frac{x^2}{a^2} = 1 \qquad \qquad \dots(1)$$

is conjugate to the hyperbola

$$\frac{x^2}{a^2} - \frac{y^2}{b^2} = 1 \qquad \qquad \dots(2)$$

Just as in Art. 313, the equation to the asymptotes of (1) is,

$$\frac{y^2}{b^2} - \frac{x^2}{a^2} = 0$$

which, by the same article, is the equation to the asymptotes of (2).

Thus, a hyperbola and its conjugate have the same asymptotes.
The conjugate hyperbola is the dotted curve in the figure of Art. 323.

➤ **320.** *Intersections of a hyperbola with a pair of conjugate diameters.*
The straight line $y = m_1 x$ intersects the hyperbola

$$\frac{x^2}{a^2} - \frac{y^2}{b^2} = 1$$

in points whose abscissae are given by

$$x^2\left[\frac{1}{a^2} - \frac{m_1^2}{b^2}\right] = 1$$

i.e., by the equation $\quad x^2 = \dfrac{a^2b^2}{b^2 - a^2m_1^2}$

The points are therefore real or imaginary, according as

$$a^2m_1^2 \text{ is } < \text{ or } > b^2,$$

i.e., according as

$$m_1 \text{ is numerically } < \text{ or } > \frac{b}{a} \qquad \qquad \ldots(1)$$

i.e., according as the inclination of the straight line to the axis of x is less or greater than the inclination of the asymptotes.

Now, by Art. 308, the straight lines $y = m_1x$ and $y = m_2x$ are conjugate diameters if

$$m_1 m = \frac{b^2}{a^2} \qquad \qquad \ldots(2)$$

Hence, one of the quantities m_1 and m_2 must be less than $\dfrac{b}{a}$ and the other greater than $\dfrac{b}{a}$

Let m_1 be $< \dfrac{b}{a}$, so that, by (1), the straight line $y = m_1x$ meets the hyperbola in real points.

Then, by (2), m_2 must be $> \dfrac{b}{a}$, so that, by (1), the straight line $y = m_2x$ will meet the hyperbola in imaginary points.

It follows therefore, that only one of a pair of conjugate diameters meets a hyperbola in real points.

➤ **321.** *If a pair of diameters be conjugate with respect to a hyperbola, they will be conjugate with respect to its conjugate hyperbola.*

For the straight lines $y = m_1x$ and $y = m_2x$ are conjugate with respect to the hyperbola

$$\frac{x^2}{a^2} - \frac{y^2}{b^2} = 1 \qquad \qquad \ldots(1)$$

if $$m_1 m_2 = \frac{b^2}{a^2} \qquad \qquad \text{...(2)}$$

Now, the equation to the conjugate hyperbola only differs from (1) in having $-a^2$ instead of a^2 and $-b^2$ instead of b^2, so that the above pair of straight lines will be conjugate with respect to it, if

$$m_1 m_2 = \frac{-b^2}{-a^2} = \frac{b^2}{a^2} \qquad \qquad \text{...(3)}$$

But the relation (3) is the same as (2)

Hence, the proposition

➤ **322.** *If a pair of diameters be conjugate with respect to a hyperbola, one of them meets the hyperbola in real points and the other meets the conjugate hyperbola in real points.*

Let the diameters be $y = m_1 x$ and $y = m_2 x$, so that

$$m_1 m_2 = \frac{b^2}{a^2}$$

As in Art. 320 let $m_1 < \frac{b}{a}$, and hence, $m_2 > \frac{b}{a}$, so that the straight line $y = m_1 x$ meets the hyperbola in real points.

Also, the straight line $y = m_2 x$ meets the conjugate hyperbola $\frac{y^2}{b^2} - \frac{x^2}{a^2} = 1$ in points whose abscissae are given by the equation,

$$x^2 \left(\frac{m_2^2}{b^2} - \frac{1}{a^2} \right) = 1, \quad i.e., \quad \text{by } x^2 = \frac{a^2 b^2}{m_2^2 a^2 - b^2}.$$

Since, $m_2 > \frac{b}{a}$, these abscissae are real.

Hence, the proposition.

➤ **323.** *If a pair of conjugate diameters meet the hyperbola and its conjugate in P and D, then* (1) $CP^2 - CD^2 = a^2 - b^2$, *and* (2) *the tangents at P, D and the other ends of the diameters passing through them form a parallelogram whose vertices lie on the asymptotes and whose area is constant.*

Let P be any point on the hyperbola $\frac{x^2}{a^2} - \frac{y^2}{b^2} = 1$ whose coordinates are $(a \sec \phi, b \tan \phi)$.

The equation to the diameter CP is therefore,

$$y = \frac{b \tan \phi}{a \sec \phi} x = x \cdot \frac{b}{a} \sin \phi$$

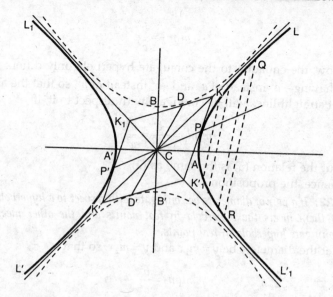

By Art. 308, the equation to the straight line, which is conjugate to CP, is

$$y = x\,\frac{b}{a\sin\phi}$$

This straight line meets the conjugate hyperbola

$$\frac{y^2}{b^2} - \frac{x^2}{a^2} = 1$$

in the points $(a\tan\phi,\ b\sec\phi)$, and $(-a\tan\phi,\ -b\sec\phi)$ so that D is the point $(a\tan\phi,\ b\sec\phi)$.

We therefore, have

$$CP^2 = a^2\sec^2\phi + b^2\tan^2\phi,$$

and
$$CD^2 = a^2\tan^2\phi + b^2\sec^2\phi$$

Hence,
$$CP^2 - CD^2 = (a^2 - b^2)(\sec^2\phi - \tan^2\phi) = a^2 - b^2$$

Again, the tangents at P and D to the hyperbola and the conjugate hyperbola are easily seen to be

$$\frac{x}{a} - \frac{y}{b}\sin\phi = \cos\phi \qquad \dots(1)$$

and
$$\frac{y}{b} - \frac{x}{a}\sin\phi = \cos\phi \qquad \dots(2)$$

These meet at the point

$$\frac{x}{a} = \frac{y}{b} = \frac{\cos \phi}{1 - \sin \phi}$$

This point lies on the asymptote CL

Similarly, the intersection of the tangents at P and D' lies on CL_1', that of tangents at D' and P' on CL', and those at D and P' on CL_1

If tangents be therefore drawn at the points where a pair of conjugate diameters meet a hyperbola and its conjugate, they form a parallelogram whose angular points are on the asymptotes

Again, the perpendicular from C on the straight line (1)

$$= \frac{\cos \phi}{\sqrt{\dfrac{1}{a^2} + \dfrac{1}{b^2} \sin^2 \phi}} = \frac{ab \cos \phi}{\sqrt{b^2 + a^2 \sin^2 \phi}}$$

$$= \frac{ab}{\sqrt{b^2 \sec^2 \phi + a^2 \tan^2 \phi}} = \frac{ab}{CD} = \frac{ab}{PK}$$

so that $PK \times$ perpendicular from C on $PK = ab$,

i.e., area of the parallelogram $CPKD = ab$

Also, the areas of the parallelograms $CPKD, CDK_1P', CP'K'D'$, and $CD'K_1'P$ are all equal.

The area $KK_1K'K_1'$ therefore $= 4ab$

Cor. : $PK = CD = D'C = K_1'P$, so that the portion of a tangent to a hyperbola intercepted between the asymptotes is bisected at the point of contact.

➤ **324.** *Relation between the equation to the hyperbola, the equation to its asymptotes, and the equation to the conjugate hyperbola.*

The equations to the hyperbola, the asymptotes, and the conjugate hyperbola are respectively

$$\frac{x^2}{a^2} - \frac{y^2}{b^2} = 1 \qquad\qquad \dots(1)$$

$$\frac{x^2}{a^2} - \frac{y^2}{b^2} = 0 \qquad\qquad \dots(2)$$

and $$\frac{x^2}{a^2} - \frac{y^2}{b^2} = -1 \qquad\qquad \dots(3)$$

We notice that the equation (2) differs from equation (1) by a constant, and that the equation (3) differs from (2) by exactly the same quantity that (2) differs from (1).

If now we transform the equations in any way we please—by changing the origin and directions of the axes—by the most general substitutions of Art. 132 and by multiplying the equations by any—the same—constant, we shall alter the left-hand members of (1), (2), and (3) in exactly the same way, and the right-hand constants in the equations will still be constants, and differ in the same way as before.

Hence, whatever be the form of the equation to a hyperbola, the equation to the asymptotes only differs from it by a constant, and the equation to the conjugate hyperbola differs from that to the asymptotes by the same constant.

➤ **325.** As an example of the foregoing article, let it be required to find the asymptotes of the hyperbola

$$3x^2 - 5xy - 2y^2 + 5x + 11y - 8 = 0 \qquad \text{...(1)}$$

Since, the equation to the asymptotes only differs from it by a constant, it must be of the form

$$3x^2 - 5xy - 2y^2 + 5x + 11y + c = 0 \qquad \text{...(2)}$$

Since, (2) represents the asymptotes it must represent two straight lines. The condition for this is (Art. 116)

$$3(-2)c + 2 \cdot \frac{5}{2} \cdot \frac{11}{2}\left(-\frac{5}{3}\right) - 3\left(\frac{11}{2}\right)^2 - (-2)\left(\frac{5}{2}\right)^2 - c\left(-\frac{5}{2}\right)^2 = 0,$$

i.e.,
$$c = -12$$

The equation to the asymptotes is therefore,

$$3x^2 - 5xy - 2y^2 + 5x + 11y - 12 = 0,$$

and the equation to the conjugate hyperbola is

$$3x^2 - 5xy - 2y^2 + 5x + 11y - 16 = 0$$

➤ **326.** An another example we see that the equation to any hyperbola whose asymptotes are the straight lines

$$Ax + By + C = 0 \quad \text{and} \quad A_1x + B_1y + C_1 = 0,$$

is
$$(Ax + By + C)(A_1x + B_1y + C_1) = \lambda^2 \qquad \text{...(1)}$$

where λ is any constant.

For (1), only differs by a constant from the equation to the asymptotes, which is

$$(Ax + By + C)(A_1x + B_1y + C_1) = 0 \qquad \text{...(2)}$$

If in (1), we substitute $-\lambda^2$ for λ^2 we shall have the equation to its conjugate hyperbola.

If follows that any equation of the form

$$(Ax + By + C)(A_1x + B_1y + C_1) = \lambda^2$$

represents a hyperbola whose asymptotes are

$$Ax + By + C = 0 \quad \text{and} \quad A_1x + B_1y + C_1 = 0$$

Thus the equation $x(x+y) = a^2$ represents a hyperbola whose asymptotes are $x = 0$ and $x + y = 0$.

Again, the equation $x^2 + 2xy \cot 2\alpha - y^2 = a^2$,

i.e., $(x \cot \alpha - y)(x \tan \alpha + y) = a^2$

represents a hyperbola whose asymptotes are

$$x \cot \alpha - y = 0, \quad \text{and} \quad x \tan \alpha + y = 0$$

➤ **327.** It would follow from the preceding articles that the equation to any hyperbola whose asymptotes are $x = 0$ and $y = 0$ is $xy = \text{const.}$

The constant could be easily determined in terms of the semi-transverse and semi-conjugate axes.

In Art. 328, we shall obtain this equation by direct transformation from the equation referred to the principal axes.

EXAMPLES XXXVII

1. Through the positive vertex of the hyperbola a tangent is drawn; where does it meet the conjugate hyperbola?
2. If e and e' be the eccentricities of a hyperbola and its conjugate, prove that $\dfrac{1}{e^2} + \dfrac{1}{e'^2} = 1$
3. Prove that chords of a hyperbola, which touch the conjugate hyperbola, are bisected at the point of contact.
4. Shew that the chord, which joins the points in which a pair of conjugate diameters meets the hyperbola and its conjugate, is parallel to one asymptote and is bisected by the other.
5. Tangents are drawn to a hyperbola from any point on one of the branches of the conjugate hyperbola; shew that their chord of contact will touch the other branch of the conjugate hyperbola.
6. A straight line is drawn parallel to the conjugate axis of a hyperbola to meet it and the conjugate hyperbola in the points P and Q; shew that the tangents at P and Q meet on the curve

$$\frac{y^4}{b^4}\left(\frac{y^2}{b^2} - \frac{x^2}{a^2}\right) = \frac{4x^2}{a^2}$$

and that the normals meet on the axis of x.
7. From a point G on the transverse axis GL is drawn perpendicular to the asymptote, and GP a normal to the curve at P. Prove that LP is parallel to the conjugate axis.
8. Find the asymptotes of the curve $2x^2 + 5xy + 2y^2 + 4x + 5y = 0$, and

find the general equation of all hyperbolas having the same asymptotes.

9. Find the equation to the hyperbola, whose asymptotes are the straight lines $x + 2y + 3 = 0$, and $3x + 4y + 5 = 0$, and which passes through the point $(1, -1)$.

Write down also the equation to the conjugate hyperbola.

10. In a rectangular hyperbola, prove that CP and CD are equal, and are inclined to the axis at angles which are complementary.

11. C is the centre of the hyperbola $\dfrac{x^2}{a^2} - \dfrac{y^2}{b^2} = 1$ and the tangent at any point P meets the asymptotes in the points Q and R. Prove that the equation to the locus of the centre of the circle circumscribing the triangle CQR is $4(a^2x^2 - b^2y^2) = (a^2 + b^2)^2$.

12. A series of hyperbolas is drawn having a common transverse axis of length $2a$. Prove that the locus of a point P on each hyperbola. such that its distance from the transverse axis is equal to its distance from an asymptote, is the curve $(x^2 - y^2)^2 = 4x^2(x^2 - a^2)$.

➤ **328.** *To find the equation to a hyperbola referred to its asymptotes.*

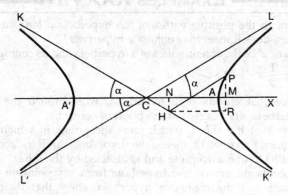

Let P be any point on the hyperbola, whose equation referred to its axes is

$$\frac{x^2}{a^2} - \frac{y^2}{b^2} = 1 \qquad \qquad …(1)$$

Draw PH parallel to one asymptote CL to meet the other CK' in H, and let CH and HP be h and k respectively. Then h and k are the coordinates of P referred to the asymptotes.

Let α be the semi-angle between the asymptotes, so that by Art. 313, $\tan \alpha = \dfrac{b}{a}$

and hence,
$$\frac{\sin \alpha}{b} = \frac{\cos \alpha}{a} = \frac{1}{\sqrt{a^2 + b^2}}$$

Draw HN perpendicular to the transverse axis, and HR parallel to the transverse axis, to meet the ordinate PM of the point P in R.

Then, since PH and HR are parallel respectively to CL and CM, we have

$$\angle PHR = \angle LCM = \alpha.$$

Hence,
$$CM = CN + HR = CH \cos \alpha + HP \cos \alpha$$
$$= (h + k) \frac{a}{\sqrt{a^2 + b^2}}$$

and
$$MP = RP - HN = HP \sin \alpha - CH \sin \alpha$$
$$= (k - h) \frac{b}{\sqrt{a^2 + b^2}}$$

Therefore, since CM and MP satisfy the equation (1), we have
$$\frac{(h + k)^2}{a^2 + b^2} - \frac{(k - h)^2}{a^2 + b^2} = 1, \ \ i.e., \ \ \ hk = \frac{a^2 + b^2}{4}$$

Hence, since (h, k) is any point on the hyperbola, the required equation is

$$xy = \frac{a^2 + b^2}{4}$$

This is often written in the form $xy = c^2$, where $4c^2$ equals the sum of the squares of the semiaxes of the hyperbola.

Similarly, the equation to the conjugate hyperbola, is, when referred to the asymptotes,

$$xy = -\frac{a^2 + b^2}{4}$$

▶ **329.** *To find the equation to the tangent at any point of the hyperbola* $xy = c^2$.

Let (x', y') be any point P on the hyperbola, and (x'', y'') a point Q on it, so that we have

$$x'y' = c^2 \hspace{4cm} \text{...(1)}$$

and
$$x''y'' = c^2 \hspace{4cm} \text{...(2)}$$

The equation to the line PQ is then

$$y - y' = \frac{y'' - y'}{x'' - x'} (x - x') \hspace{2.5cm} \text{...(3)}$$

But, by (1) and (2), we have

$$\frac{y'' - y'}{x'' - x'} = \frac{\dfrac{c^2}{x''} - \dfrac{c^2}{x'}}{x'' - x'} = \frac{c^2}{x'x''} \frac{x' - x''}{x'' - x'} = -\frac{c^2}{x'x''}$$

Hence, the equation (3) becomes

$$y - y' = -\frac{c^2}{x'x''}(x - x') \qquad \qquad ...(4)$$

Let now the point Q be taken indefinitely near to P, so that $x'' = x'$ ultimately, and therefore, by Art. 149, PQ becomes the tangent at P.

Then (4), becomes

$$y - y' = -\frac{c^2}{x'^2}(x - x') = -\frac{y'}{x'}(x - x'), \text{ by (1)}$$

The required equation is therefore,

$$xy' + x'y = 2x'y' = 2c^2 \qquad \qquad ...(5)$$

The equation (5) may also be written in the form

$$\frac{x}{x'} + \frac{y}{y'} = 2 \qquad \qquad ...(6)$$

➤ **330.** *The tangent at any point of a hyperbola cuts off a triangle of constant area from the asymptotes, and the portion of it intercepted between the asymptotes is bisected at the point of contact.*

Take the asymptotes as axes and let the equation to the hyperbola be $xy = c^2$.

The tangent at any point P is $\dfrac{x}{x'} + \dfrac{y}{y'} = 2$

This meets the axes in the points $(2x', 0)$ and $(0, 2y')$.

If these points be L and L', and the centre be C, we have

$$CL = 2x' \quad \text{and} \quad CL' = 2y'$$

If 2α be the angle between the asymptotes, the area of the triangle

$$LCL' = \frac{1}{2} CL \cdot CL' \sin 2\alpha = 2x'y' \sin 2\alpha = \frac{a^2 + b^2}{2} \cdot 2 \sin \alpha \cos \alpha = ab$$

(Art. 328)

Also, since L is the point $(2x', 0)$ and L' is $(0, 2y')$, the middle point of LL' is (x', y'), *i.e.,* the point of contact P.

➤ **331.** As in Art. 274, the polar of any point (x_1, y_1) with respect to the curve can be shown to be

$$xy_1 + x_1y = 2c^2$$

Since, in general, the point (x_1, y_1) does not lie on the curve the equation to the polar cannot be put into the form (6) of Art. 329.

➤ **332.** The equation to the normal at the point (x', y') is $y - y' = m(x - x')$, where m is chosen so that this line is perpendicular to the tangent

$$y = -\frac{y'}{x'}x + \frac{2c^2}{x'}$$

If ω be the angle between the asymptotes we then obtain, by Art. 93,

$$m = \frac{x' - y'\cos\omega}{y' - x'\cos\omega}$$

so that the required equation to the normal is

$$y(y' - x'\cos\omega) - x(x' - y'\cos\omega) = y'^2 - x'^2$$

$$\left[\text{Also } \cos\omega = \cos 2\alpha = \cos^2\alpha - \sin^2\alpha = \frac{a^2 - b^2}{a^2 + b^2}\right]$$

If the hyperbola be rectangular, then $\omega = 90°$, and the equation to the normal becomes $xx' - yy' = x'^2 - y'^2$.

➤ **333. Equation referred to the asymptotes.**
One Variable.
The equation $xy = c^2$ is clearly satisfied by the substitution $x = ct$ and $y = \frac{c}{t}$.

Hence, for all values of t, the point whose coordinates are $\left(ct, \frac{c}{t}\right)$ lies on the curve, and it may be called the point "t"

The tangent at the point "t" is by Art. 329,

$$\frac{x}{t} + yt = 2c$$

Also the normal is, by the last article,

$$y(1 - t^2\cos\omega) - x(t^2 - \cos\omega) = \frac{c}{t}(1 - t^4),$$

or when the hyperbola is rectangular,

$$y - xt^2 = \frac{c}{t}(1 - t^4)$$

The equations to the tangents at the points "t_1" and "t_2" are

$$\frac{x}{t_1} + yt_1 = 2c \quad \text{and} \quad \frac{x}{t_2} + yt_2 = 2c,$$

and hence the tangents meet at the point

$$\left(\frac{2ct_1t_2}{t_1 + t_2}, \frac{2c}{t_1 + t_2} \right)$$

The line joining "t_1" and "t_2" which is the polar of this point is therefore, by Art. 331

$$x + yt_1t_2 = c\,(t_1 + t_2)$$

This form also follows by writing down the equation to the straight line joining the points

$$\left(ct_1, \frac{c}{t_1} \right) \text{and} \left(ct_2, \frac{c}{t_2} \right)$$

➤ **334.**

EXAMPLE 1   *If a rectangular hyperbola circumscribe a triangle, it also passes through the orthocentre of the triangle.*

Let the equation to the curve referred to its asymptotes be

$$xy = c^2 \qquad \qquad \text{...(1)}$$

Let the angular points of the triangle be P, Q, and R, and let their coordinates be

$$\left(ct_1, \frac{c}{t_1} \right), \left(ct_2, \frac{c}{t_2} \right) \text{ and } \left(ct_3, \frac{c}{t_3} \right)$$

respectively.

As in the last article, the equation to QR is

$$x + yt_2t_3 = c\,(t_2 + t_3)$$

The equation to the straight line, through P perpendicular to QR, is therefore,

$$y - \frac{c}{t_1} = t_2t_3\,[x - ct_1]$$

i.e.,

$$y + ct_1t_2t_3 = t_2t_3\left[x + \frac{c}{t_1t_2t_3} \right] \qquad \text{...(2)}$$

Similarly, the equation to the straight line through Q perpendicular to RP is

$$y + ct_1t_2t_3 = t_3t_1\left[x + \frac{c}{t_1t_2t_3} \right] \qquad \text{...(4)}$$

The common point of (2) and (3) is clearly

$$\left(-\frac{c}{t_1 t_2 t_3}, -ct_1 t_2 t_3\right) \qquad \ldots(4)$$

and this is therefore, the orthocentre.

But the coordinates (4) satisfy (1). Hence the proposition.

Also, if $\left(ct_4, \dfrac{c}{t_4}\right)$ be the orthocentre of the points "t_1", "t_2" and "t_3" we have $t_1 t_2 t_3 t_4 = -1$.

EXAMPLE 2 *If a circle and the rectangular hyperbola $xy = c^2$ meet in the four points "t_1," "t_2," "t_3" and "t_4", prove that*

(1) $t_1 t_2 t_3 t_4 = 1$,

(2) *the centre of mean position of the four points bisects the distance between the centres of the two curves,*

and (3) *the centre of the circle through the points "t_1," "t_2," "t_3," is*

$$\left\{\frac{c}{2}\left(t_1 + t_2 + t_3 + \frac{1}{t_1 t_2 t_3}\right), \frac{c}{2}\left(\frac{1}{t_1} + \frac{1}{t_2} + \frac{1}{t_3} + t_1 t_2 t_3\right)\right\}$$

Let the equation to the circle be

$$x^2 + y^2 - 2gx - 2fy + k = 0$$

so that its centre is the point (g, f).

Any point on the hyperbola is $\left(ct, \dfrac{c}{t}\right)$. If this lie on the circle, we have

$$c^2 t^2 + \frac{c^2}{t^2} - 2gct - 2f\frac{c}{t} + k = 0,$$

so that

$$t^4 - 2\frac{g}{c}t^3 + \frac{k}{c^2}t^2 - \frac{2f}{c}t + 1 = 0 \qquad \ldots(1)$$

If $t_1, t_2, t_3,$ and t_4 be roots of this equation, we have, by Art. 2,

$$t_1 t_2 t_3 t_4 = 1 \qquad \ldots(2)$$

$$t_1 + t_2 + t_3 + t_4 = \frac{2g}{c} \qquad \ldots(3)$$

and

$$t_2 t_3 t_4 + t_3 t_4 t_1 + t_4 t_1 t_2 + t_1 t_2 t_3 = \frac{2f}{c} \qquad \ldots(4)$$

Dividing (4) by (2), we have

$$\frac{1}{t_1} + \frac{1}{t_2} + \frac{1}{t_3} + \frac{1}{t_4} = \frac{2f}{c} \qquad \ldots(5)$$

The centre of the mean position of the four points,

i.e., the point $\left\{\dfrac{c}{4}(t_1 + t_2 + t_3 + t_4), \dfrac{c}{4}\left(\dfrac{1}{t_1} + \dfrac{1}{t_2} + \dfrac{1}{t_3} + \dfrac{1}{t_4}\right)\right\},$

is therefore the point $\left(\dfrac{g}{2}, \dfrac{f}{4}\right)$, and this is the middle point of the line joining $(0, 0)$ and (g, f).

Also, since $t_4 = \dfrac{1}{t_1 t_2 t_3}$, we have

$$g = \frac{c}{2}\left(t_1 + t_2 + t_3 + \frac{1}{t_1\, t_2\, t_3}\right) \quad \text{and} \quad f = \frac{c}{2}\left(\frac{1}{t_1} + \frac{1}{t_2} + \frac{1}{t_3} + t_1 t_2 t_3\right)$$

Again, since $t_1 t_2 t_3 t_4 = 1$, we have product of the abscissae of the four points = product of their ordinates = c^4.

EXAMPLES XXXVIII

1. Prove that the foci of the hyperbola $xy = \dfrac{a^2 + b^2}{4}$ are given by

$$x = y = \pm\frac{a^2 + b^2}{2a}$$

2. Shew that two concentric rectangular hyperbolas, whose axes meet at an angle of 45°, cut orthogonally.

3. A straight line always passes through a fixed point; prove that the locus of the middle point of the portion of it, which is intercepted between two given straight lines, is a hyperbola whose asymptotes are parallel to the given lines.

4. If the ordinate NP at any point P of an ellipse be produced to Q, so that NQ is equal to the subtangent at P, prove that the locus of Q is a hyperbola.

5. From a point P perpendiculars PM and PN are drawn to two straight lines OM and ON. If the area $OMPN$ be constant, prove that the locus of P is a hyperbola.

6. A variable line has its ends on two lines given in position and passes through a given point; prove that the locus of a point which divides it in any given ratio is a hyperbola.

7. The coordinates of a point are $a \tan(\theta + \alpha)$ and $b \tan(\theta + \beta)$, where θ is variable; prove that the locus of the point is a hyperbola.

8. A series of circles touch a given straight line at a given point. Prove that the locus of the pole of a given straight line with regard to these circles is a hyperbola whose asymptotes are respectively a parallel to the first given straight line and a perpendicular to the second.

9. If a right-angled triangle be inscribed in a rectangular hyperbola, prove that the tangent at the right angle is the perpendicular upon the hypothenuse.

10. In a rectangular hyperbola, prove that all straight lines, which subtend a right angle at a point P on the curve, are parallel to the normal at P.

11. Chords of a rectangular hyperbola are at right angles, and they subtend a right angle at a fixed point O; prove that they intersect on the polar of O.

12. Prove that any chord of a rectangular hyperbola subtends angles which are equal or supplementary (1) at the ends of a perpendicular chord and (2) at the ends of any diameter.

13. In a rectangular hyperbola, shew that the angle between a chord PQ and the tangent at P is equal to the angle which PQ subtends at the other end of the diameter through P.

14. Shew that the normal to the rectangular hyperbola $xy = c^2$ at the point "t" meets the curve again at a point "t'" such that
$$t^3 t' = -1$$

15. If P_1, P_2 and P_3 be three points on the rectangular hyperbola $xy = c^2$, whose abscissae are $x_1, x_2,$ and x_3, prove that the area of the triangle $P_1 P_2 P_3$ is
$$\frac{c^2}{2} \frac{(x_2 - x_3)(x_3 - x_1)(x_1 - x_2)}{x_1 x_2 x_3}$$
and that the tangents at these points form a triangle whose area is.
$$2c^2 \frac{(x_2 - x_3)(x_3 - x_1)(x_1 - x_2)}{(x_2 + x_3)(x_3 + x_1)(x_1 + x_2)}$$

16. Find the coordinates of the points of contact of common tangents to the two hyperbolas
$$x^2 - y^2 = 3a^2 \quad \text{and} \quad xy = 2a^2$$

17. The transverse axis of a rectangular hyperbola is $2c$ and the asymptotes are the axes of coordinates; shew that the equation of the chord which is bisected at the point $(2c, 3c)$ is $3x + 2y = 12c$.

18. Prove that the portions of any line which are intercepted between the asymptotes and the curve are equal.

19. Shew that the straight lines drawn from a variable point on the curve to any two fixed points on it intercept a constant distance on either asymptote.

20. Shew that the equation to the director circle of the conic $xy = c^2$ is
$$x^2 + 2xy \cos \omega + y^2 = 4c^2 \cos \omega$$

21. Prove that the asymptotes of the hyperbola $xy = hx + ky$ are $x = k$ and $y = h$.

22. Shew that the straight line $y = mx + 2c\sqrt{-m}$ always touches the hyperbola $xy = c^2$, and that its point of contact is $\left(\dfrac{c}{\sqrt{-m}}, c\sqrt{-m} \right)$.

23. Prove that the locus of the foot of the perpendicular let fall from the

centre upon chords of the rectangular hyperbola $xy = c^2$ which subtend half a right angle at the origin is the curve

$$r^4 - 2c^2 r^2 \sin 2\theta = c^4$$

24. A tangent to the parabola $x^2 = 4ay$ meets the hyperbola $xy = k^2$ in two points P and Q. Prove that the middle point of PQ lies on a parabola.

25. If a hyperbola be rectangular, and its equation be $xy = c^2$, prove that the locus of the middle points of chords of constant length $2d$ is

$$(x^2 + y^2)(xy - c^2) = d^2 xy$$

26. Shew that the pole of any tangent to the rectangular hyperbola $xy = c^2$, with respect to the circle $x^2 + y^2 = a^2$, lies on a concentric and similarly placed rectangular hyperbola.

27. Prove that the locus of the poles of all normal chords of the rectangular hyperbola $xy = c^2$ is the curve

$$(x^2 - y^2)^2 + 4c^2 xy = 0$$

28. Prove that triangles can be inscribed in the hyperbola $xy = c^2$, whose sides touch the parabola $y^2 = 4ax$.

29. A point moves on the given straight line $y = mx$; prove that the locus of the foot of the perpendicular let fall from the point upon its polar with respect to the ellipse $\dfrac{x^2}{a^2} + \dfrac{y^2}{b^2} = 1$ is a rectangular hyperbola, one of whose asymptotes is the diameter of the ellipse which is conjugate to the given straight line.

30. If from a fixed point on a rectangular hyperbola, perpendiculars are let fall on any two conjugate diameters, the straight line joining the feet of these perpendiculars has a constant direction.

31. A quadrilateral circumscribes a hyperbola; prove that the straight line joining the middle points of its diagonals passes through the centre of the curve.

32. A, B, C and D are the points of intersection of a circle and a rectangular hyperbola. If AB pass through the centre of the hyperbola, prove that CD passes through the centre of the circle.

33. If a circle and a rectangular hyperbola meet in four points $P, Q, R,$ and S, show that the orthocentres of the triangles $QRS, RSP, SPQ,$ and PQR also lie on a circle.

Prove also that the tangents to the hyperbola at R and S meet in a point which lies on the diameter of the hyperbola which is at right angles to PQ.

34. A series of hyperbolas is drawn, having for asymptotes the principal axes of an ellipse; shew that the common chords of the hyperbolas and the ellipse are all parallel to one of the conjugate diameters of the ellipse.

35. A circle, passing through the centre of a rectangular hyperbola, cuts the curve in the points A, B, C and D; prove that the circumcircle of the triangle formed by the tangents at A, B, and C goes through the centre of the hyperbola, and has its centre at the point of the hyperbola which is diametrically opposite to D.

36. Given five points on a circle of radius a; prove that the centres of the rectangular hyperbolas, each passing through four of these points, all lie on a circle of radius $\dfrac{a}{2}$.

37. If a rectangular hyperbola circumscribe a triangle, shew that it meets the circle circumscribing the triangle in a fourth point, which is at the other end of the diameter of the hyperbola which passes through the orthocentre of the triangle.

Hence, prove that the locus of the centre of a rectangular hyperbolas which circumscribes a triangle is the nine-point circle of the triangle.

14

POLAR EQUATION OF A CONIC SECTION, ITS FOCUS BEING THE POLE

➤ **335.** Let S be the focus, A the vertex, and ZM the directrix; draw SZ perpendicular to ZM.

Let ZS be chosen as the positive direction of the initial line, and produce it to X.

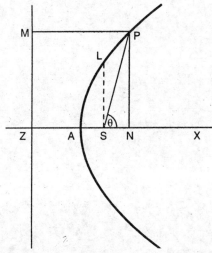

Take any point P on the curve, and let its polar coordinates be r and θ, so that we have

$$SP = r \quad \text{and} \quad \angle XSP = \theta$$

Draw PN perpendicular to the initial line, and PM perpendicular to the directrix.

Let SL be the semi-latus-rectum, and let $SL = l$.

Since $SL = e \cdot SZ$, we have

$$SZ = \frac{l}{e}$$

Hence, $r = SP = e \cdot PM = e \cdot ZN$

$$= e\,(ZS + SN)$$

$$= e\left(\frac{l}{e} + SP \cdot \cos\theta\right) = l + e \cdot r \cdot \cos\theta$$

Therefore, $r = \dfrac{l}{1 - e\cos\theta}$ ...(1)

This, being the relation holding between the polar coordinates of any point on the curve, is by Art. 42, the required polar equation.

Cor. : If SZ be taken as the positive direction of the initial line and the vectorial angle measured clockwise, the equation to the curve is

$$r = \frac{l}{1 + e\cos\theta}$$

➤ **336.** If the conic be a parabola, we have $e = 1$, and the equation is

$$r = \frac{l}{1 - \cos\theta} = \frac{l}{2\sin^2\dfrac{\theta}{2}} = \frac{l}{2}\,\mathrm{cosec}^2\frac{\theta}{2}$$

If the initial line, instead of being the axis, be such that the axis is inclined at an angle γ to it, then, in the previous article, instead of θ we must substitute $\theta - \gamma$.

The equation in this case is then

$$\frac{l}{r} = 1 - e\cos(\theta - \gamma)$$

➤ **337.** *To trace the curve* $\dfrac{l}{r} = 1 - e\cos\theta.$

Case I. $e = 1$, so that the equation is $\dfrac{l}{r} = 1 - \cos\theta.$

When θ is zero, we have $\dfrac{l}{r} = 0$, so that r is infinite. As θ increases from $0°$ to $90°$ $\cos\theta$ decreases from 1 to 0, and hence $\dfrac{l}{r}$ increases from 0 to 1, *i.e.*, r decreases from infinity to l.

As θ increases from $90°$ to $180°$, $\cos\theta$ decreases from 0 to -1, and hence, $\dfrac{l}{r}$ increases from 1 to 2, *i.e.*, r decreases from l to $\dfrac{1}{2}l$.

Similarly, as θ changes from $180°$ to $270°$, r increases from $\dfrac{l}{2}$ to l, and, as θ changes from $270°$ to $360°$, r increases from l to ∞.

The curve is thus the parabola $\infty FPLAL'P'F' \infty$ of Art. 197.

Case II : $e < 1$. When θ is zero, we have $\dfrac{l}{r} = 1 - e$, *i.e.*, $r = \dfrac{l}{1-e}$. This gives the point A' in the figure of Art. 247.

As θ increases from $0°$ to $90°$, $\cos\theta$ decreases from 1 to 0, and therefore, $1 - e\cos\theta$ increases from $1 - e$ to 1, *i.e.*, $\dfrac{l}{r}$ increases from $1 - e$ to 1, *i.e.*, r decreases from $\dfrac{l}{1-e}$ to l. We thus obtain the portion $A'PBL$.

As θ increases from $90°$ to $180°$, $\cos\theta$ decreases from 0 to -1, and therefore, $1 - e\cos\theta$ increases from 1 to $1 + e$, *i.e.*, $\dfrac{l}{r}$ increases from 1 to $1 + e$, *i.e.*, r decreases from l to $\dfrac{l}{1+e}$.

We thus obtain the portion LA of the curve, where

$$SA = \frac{l}{1+e}$$

Similarly, as θ increases from $180°$ to $270°$ and then to $360°$, we have the porti AL' and $L'B'P'A'$.

Since $\cos\theta = \cos(-\theta) = \cos(360° - \theta)$, the curve is symmetrical about the line SA'.

Case III. : $e > 1$. When θ is zero, $1 - e\cos\theta$ is equal to $1 - e$, i.e. $-(e-1)$, and is therefore, a negative quantity, since $e > 1$. This zero value of θ gives $r = -l \div (e-1)$.

We thus have the point A' in the figure of Art. 295.

Let θ increase from $0°$ to $\cos^{-1}\left(\dfrac{1}{e}\right)$. Thus $1 - e\cos\theta$ increases algebraically from $-(e-1)$ to -0,

i.e., $\dfrac{l}{r}$ increases algebraically from $-(e-1)$ to -0

i.e., r decreases algebraically from $-\dfrac{l}{e-1}$ to $-\infty$.

For these values of θ the radius vector is therefore, active and increases in numerical length from $\dfrac{l}{e-1}$ to ∞.

We thus have the portion $A'P_1'R' \infty$ of the curve. For this portion r is negative.

If θ be very slightly greater than $\cos^{-1}\dfrac{1}{e}$, then $\cos\theta$ is slightly less than $\dfrac{1}{e}$, so that $1 - e \cos \theta$ is small and positive, and therefore, r is very great and is positive. Hence, as θ increases through the angle $\cos^{-1} \dfrac{1}{e}$, the value of r changes from $-\infty$ to $+\infty$.

As θ increases from $\cos^{-1} \dfrac{1}{e}$ to π, $1 - e \cos \theta$ increases from 0 to $1 + e$ and hence r decreases from ∞ to $\dfrac{l}{1+e}$.

Now, $\dfrac{l}{1+e}$ is $< \dfrac{l}{e-1}$. Hence, the point A, which corresponds to $\theta = \pi$, is such that $SA < SA'$.

For values of θ between $\cos^{-1} \dfrac{1}{e}$ and π we therefore, have the portion, ∞RPA, of the curve. For this portion r is positive.

As θ increases from π to $2\pi - \cos^{-1} \dfrac{1}{e}$, $e \cos \theta$ increases from $-e$ to 1, so that $1 - e \cos \theta$ decreases from $1 + e$ to 0, and therefore, r increases from $\dfrac{l}{1+e}$ to ∞. Corresponding to these values of θ we have the portion $AL'R_1 \infty$ of the curve, for which r is positive.

Finally, as θ increases from $2\pi - \cos^{-1} \dfrac{1}{e}$ to 2π, $e \cos \theta$ increases from 1 to e, so that $1 - e \cos \theta$ decreases algebraically from 0 to $1 - e$, i.e., $\dfrac{l}{r}$ is negative and increases numerically from 0 to $e - 1$, and therefore, r is negative and decreases from ∞ to $\dfrac{l}{e-1}$. Corresponding to these values of θ we have the portion, $\infty R_1' A'$, of the curve. For this portion r is negative.

r is therefore, always positive for the right-hand branch of the curve and negative for the left-hand branch.

It will be noted that the curve is described in the order

$$A'P_1'R' \infty \infty RPAL'R_1 \infty \infty R_1'A'.$$

➤ **338.** In Case III. of the last article, let any straight line be drawn through S to meet the nearer branch in p, and the further branch in q.

The vectorial angle of p is XSp, and we have

$$Sp = \frac{l}{1 - \cos XSp}$$

The vectorial angle of q is not XSq but the angle that qS produced makes with SX, *i.e.*, it is $XSq \mp \pi$. Also for the point q the radius vector is negative so that the relation (1) of Art. 335 gives, for the point q,

$$-Sq = \frac{l}{1 - e\cos(XSq \mp \pi)} = \frac{l}{1 + e\cos XSq},$$

i.e.,
$$Sq = -\frac{l}{1 + e\cos XSq}$$

This is the relation connecting the distance, Sq, of any point on the further branch of the hyperbola with the angle XSq that it makes with the initial line.

➤ **339.** *Equation to the directrices.*

Considering the figure of Art. 295, the numerical values of the distances SZ and SZ' are $\dfrac{l}{e}$ and $\dfrac{l}{e} + 2CZ$,

i.e.,
$$\frac{l}{e} \quad \text{and} \quad \frac{l}{e} + 2\frac{l}{e(e^2 - 1)}$$

since
$$CZ = \frac{a}{e} = \frac{l}{e(e^2 - 1)} \qquad \text{[Art. 300]}$$

The equations to the two directrices are therefore,

$$r\cos\theta = -\frac{l}{e}$$

and
$$r\cos\theta = -\left[\frac{l}{e} + \frac{2l}{e(e^2 - 1)}\right] = -\frac{l}{e}\frac{e^2 + 1}{e^2 - 1}$$

The same equations would be found to hold in the case of the ellipse.

➤ **340.** *Equation to the asymptotes.*

The perpendicular distance from S upon an asymptote (Fig., Art. 315)

$$= CS\sin ACK_1 = ae \cdot \frac{b}{\sqrt{a^2 + b^2}} = b$$

Also the asymptote CQ makes an angle $\cos^{-1}\dfrac{1}{e}$ with the axis. The perpendicular on it from S therefore, makes an angle $\dfrac{\pi}{2} + \cos^{-1}\dfrac{1}{e}$.

Hence, by Art. 88, the polar equation to the asymptote CQ is

$$b = r\cos\left[\theta - \frac{\pi}{2} - \cos^{-1}\frac{1}{e}\right] = r\sin\left[\theta - \cos^{-1}\frac{1}{e}\right]$$

The polar equation to the other asymptote is similarly,

$$b = r \cos\left[\theta - \left(\frac{3\pi}{2} - \cos^{-1}\frac{1}{e}\right)\right] = -r \sin\left(\theta + \cos^{-1}\frac{1}{e}\right)$$

➤ **341.**

EXAMPLE 1 *In any conic, prove that*
    (1) *the sum of the reciprocals of the segments of any focal chord is constant,*
and
    (2) *the sum of the reciprocals of two perpendicular focal chords is constant.*

Let PSP' be any focal chord, and let the vectorial angle of P be α, so that the vectorial angle of P' is $\pi + \alpha$.

(1) By equation (1) of Art. 335, we have

$$\frac{l}{SP} = 1 - e\cos\alpha,$$

and
$$\frac{l}{SP'} = 1 - e\cos(\pi + \alpha) = 1 + e\cos\alpha$$

Hence,
$$\frac{l}{SP} + \frac{l}{SP'} = 2$$

so that
$$\frac{1}{SP} + \frac{1}{SP'} = \frac{2}{l}$$

The semi-latus-rectum is therefore, the harmonic mean between the segments of any focal chord.

(2) Let QSQ' be the focal chord perpendicular to PSP', so that the vectorial angles of Q and Q' are $\frac{\pi}{2} + \alpha$ and $\frac{3\pi}{2} + \alpha$. We then have

$$\frac{l}{SQ} = 1 - e\cos\left(\frac{\pi}{2} + \alpha\right) = 1 + e\sin\alpha,$$

and
$$\frac{l}{SQ'} = 1 - e\cos\left(\frac{3\pi}{2} + \alpha\right) = 1 + e\cos\left(\frac{\pi}{2} + \alpha\right) = 1 - e\sin\alpha,$$

Hence, $PP' = SP + SP' = \dfrac{l}{1 - e\cos\alpha} + \dfrac{l}{1 + e\cos\alpha} = \dfrac{2l}{1 - e^2\cos^2\alpha}$

and $\quad QQ' = SQ + SQ' = \dfrac{l}{1 + e\sin\alpha} + \dfrac{l}{1 - e\sin\alpha} = \dfrac{2l}{1 - e^2\sin^2\alpha}$

Therefore,

$$\frac{1}{PP'} + \frac{1}{QQ'} = \frac{1 - e^2\cos^2\alpha}{2l} + \frac{1 - e^2\sin^2\alpha}{2l} = \frac{2 - e^2}{2l},$$

and is therefore, the same for all such pairs of chords.

EXAMPLE 2 *Prove that the locus of the middle points of focal chords of a conic section is a conic section.*

Let PSQ be any chord, the angle PSX being θ, so that

$$SP = \frac{l}{1 - e \cos \theta}$$

and
$$SQ = \frac{l}{1 - e \cos (\pi + \theta)} = \frac{l}{1 + e \cos \theta}$$

Let R be the middle point of PQ, and let its polar coordinates be r and θ.

Then
$$r = SP - RP = SP - \frac{SP + SQ}{2} = \frac{SP - SQ}{2}$$

$$= \frac{1}{2} l \left[\frac{1}{1 - e \cos \theta} - \frac{1}{1 + e \cos \theta} \right] = l \frac{e \cos \theta}{1 - e^2 \cos^2 \theta}$$

i.e.,
$$r^2 - e^2 r^2 \cos^2 \theta = le \cdot r \cos \theta$$

Transforming to Cartesian coordinates this equation becomes
$$x^2 + y^2 - e^2 x^2 = lex \qquad \ldots(1)$$

If the original conic be a parabola, we have $e = 1$, and equation (1) becomes $y^2 = lx$, so that the locus is a parabola whose vertex is S and latus-rectum l.

If e be not equal to unity, equation (1) may be written in the form
$$(1 - e^2) \left[x - \frac{1}{2} \frac{le}{1 - e^2} \right]^2 + y^2 = \frac{l^2 e^2}{4(1 - e^2)}$$

and therefore, represents an ellipse or a hyperbola according as the original conic is an ellipse or a hyperbola.

➤ **342.** *To find the polar equation of the tangent at any point P of the conic section* $\frac{l}{r} = 1 - e \cos \theta$.

Let P be the point (r_1, α), and let Q be another point on the curve, whose coordinates are (r_2, β), so that we have
$$\frac{l}{r_1} = 1 - e \cos \alpha \qquad \ldots(1)$$

and
$$\frac{l}{r_2} = 1 - e \cos \beta \qquad \ldots(2)$$

By Art. 89, the polar equation of the line PQ is
$$\frac{\sin (\beta - \alpha)}{r} = \frac{\sin (\theta - \alpha)}{r_2} + \frac{\sin (\beta - \theta)}{r_1},$$

By means of equations (1) and (2) this equation becomes
$$\frac{l}{r} \sin (\beta - \alpha) = \sin (\theta - \alpha) \{1 - e \cos \beta\} + \sin (\beta - \theta) \{1 - e \cos \alpha\}$$

$$= \{ \sin (\theta - \alpha) + \sin (\beta - \theta) \}$$

$$- e \{ \sin (\theta - \alpha) \cos \beta + \sin (\beta - \theta) \cos \alpha \}$$

$$= 2 \sin \frac{\beta - \alpha}{2} \cos \frac{2\theta - \alpha - \beta}{2}$$

$$-e \{(\sin \theta \cos \alpha - \cos \theta \sin \alpha) \cos \beta$$
$$+ (\sin \beta \cos \theta - \cos \beta \sin \theta) \cos \alpha\}$$

$$= 2 \sin \frac{\beta - \alpha}{2} \cos \left(\theta - \frac{\alpha + \beta}{2}\right) - e \cos \theta \sin (\beta - \alpha)$$

i.e., $$\frac{l}{r} = \sec \frac{\beta - \alpha}{2} \cos \left(\theta - \frac{\alpha + \beta}{2}\right) - e \cos \theta \qquad \ldots(3)$$

This is the equation to the straight line joining two points, P and Q, on the curve whose vectorial angles, α and β, are given.

To obtain the equation of the tangent at P we take Q indefinitely close to P, *i.e.*, we put $\beta = \alpha$, and the equation (3) then becomes

$$\frac{l}{r} = \cos (\theta - \alpha) - e \cos \theta \qquad \ldots(4)$$

This is the required equation to the tangent at the point α.

➤ **343.** If we assume a suitable form for the equation to the joining chord we can more easily obtain the required equation.

Let the required equation be

$$\frac{l}{r} = L \cos (\theta - \gamma) - e \cos \theta \qquad \ldots(1)$$

[On transformation to Cartesian coordinates this equation is easily seen to represent a straight line; also since it contains two arbitrary constants, L and γ, it can be made to pass through any two points]

If it pass through the point (r_1, α), we have

$$1 - e \cos \alpha = \frac{l}{r_1} = L \cos (\alpha - \gamma) - e \cos \alpha,$$

i.e., $$L \cos (\alpha - \gamma) = 1 \qquad \ldots(2)$$

Similarly, if it passes through the point (r_2, β) on the curve, we have

$$L \cos (\beta - \gamma) = 1 \qquad \ldots(3)$$

Solving these, we have, [since α and β are not equal]

$$\alpha - \gamma = - (\beta - \gamma), \quad \textit{i.e.,} \quad \gamma = \frac{\alpha + \beta}{2}$$

Substituting this value in (3), we obtain $L = \sec \dfrac{\alpha - \beta}{2}$

This equation (1) is then,

$$\frac{l}{r} = \sec \frac{\alpha - \beta}{2} \cos \left(\theta - \frac{\alpha + \beta}{2}\right) - e \cos \theta$$

As in the last article, the equation to the tangent at the point α is then

$$\frac{l}{r} = \cos(\theta - \alpha) - e\cos\theta$$

➤ **344.** *To find the polar equation of the polar of any point (r_1, θ_1) with respect to the conic section $\dfrac{l}{r} = 1 - e\cos\theta$*

Let the tangents at the points whose vectorial angles are α and β meet in the point (r_1, θ_1).

The coordinates r_1 and θ_1 must therefore, satisfy equation (4) of Art. 342, so that

$$\frac{l}{r_1} = \cos(\theta_1 - \alpha) - e\cos\theta_1 \qquad \dots(1)$$

Similarly,

$$\frac{l}{r_1} = \cos(\theta_1 - \beta) - e\cos\theta_1 \qquad \dots(2)$$

Subtracting (2) from (1), we have

$$\cos(\theta_1 - \alpha) = \cos(\theta_1 - \beta)$$

and therefore,

$$\theta_1 - \alpha = -(\theta_1 - \beta) \quad \text{[since } \alpha \text{ and } \beta \text{ are not equal]}$$

i.e.,

$$\frac{\alpha + \beta}{2} = \theta_1 \qquad \dots(3)$$

Substituting this value in (1), we have

$$\frac{l}{r_1} = \cos\left\{\frac{\alpha + \beta}{2} - \alpha\right\} - e\cos\theta_1$$

i.e.,

$$\cos\frac{\beta - \alpha}{2} = \frac{l}{r_1} + e\cos\theta_1 \qquad \dots(4)$$

Also, by equation (3) of Art. 342, the equation of the line joining the points α and β is

$$\frac{l}{r} + e\cos\theta = \sec\frac{\beta - \alpha}{2}\cos\left(\theta - \frac{\alpha + \beta}{2}\right)$$

i.e.,

$$\left(\frac{l}{r} + e\cos\theta\right)\cos\frac{\beta - \alpha}{2} = \cos\left(\theta - \frac{\alpha + \beta}{2}\right)$$

i.e.

$$\left(\frac{l}{r} + e\cos\theta\right)\left(\frac{l}{r_1} + e\cos\theta_1\right) = \cos(\theta - \theta_1) \qquad \dots(5)$$

This therefore is the required polar equation to the polar of the point (r_1, θ_1).

➤ **345.** *To find the equation to the **normal** at the point whose vectorial angle is* α.

The equation to the tangent at the point α is

$$\frac{l}{r} = \cos(\theta - \alpha) - e \cos \theta,$$

i.e., in Cartesian coordinates,

$$x(\cos \alpha - e) + y \sin \alpha = l \qquad \ldots(1)$$

Let the equation to the normal be

$$A \cos \theta + B \sin \theta = \frac{l}{r} \qquad \ldots(2)$$

i.e.,

$$Ax + By = l \qquad \ldots(3)$$

Since (1) and (3) are perpendicular, we have

$$A(\cos \alpha - e) + B \sin \alpha = 0 \qquad \ldots(4)$$

Since, (2) goes through the point $\left(\dfrac{l}{1 - e \cos \alpha}, \alpha \right)$ we have

$$A \cos \alpha + B \sin \alpha = 1 - e \cos \alpha \qquad \ldots(5)$$

Solving (4) and (5), we have

$$A = \frac{1 - e \cos \alpha}{e} \quad \text{and} \quad B = \frac{(1 - e \cos \alpha)(e - \cos \alpha)}{e \sin \alpha}$$

The equation (2) then becomes

$$\sin \alpha \cos \theta + (e - \cos \alpha) \sin \theta = \frac{le \sin \alpha}{r(1 - e \cos \alpha)}$$

i.e.,

$$\sin(\theta - \alpha) - e \sin \theta = -\frac{e \sin \alpha}{1 - e \cos \alpha} \cdot \frac{l}{r}$$

➤ **346.** If the axis of the conic be inclined at an angle γ to the initial line, so that the equation to the conic is

$$\frac{l}{r} = 1 - e \cos(\theta - \gamma),$$

the equation to the tangent at the point α is obtained by substituting $\alpha - \gamma$ and $\theta - \gamma$ for α and θ in the equation of Art. 342.

The tangent is therefore,

$$\frac{l}{r} = \cos(\theta - \alpha) - e \cos(\theta - \gamma)$$

The equation of the line joining the two points α and β is, by the same article,

$$\frac{l}{r} = \sec\frac{\beta - \alpha}{2}\cos\left(\theta - \frac{\alpha + \beta}{2}\right) - e\cos(\theta - \gamma)$$

The equation to the polar of the point (r_1, θ_1) is, by Art. 344,

$$\left\{\frac{l}{r} + e\cos(\theta - \gamma)\right\}\left\{\frac{l}{r_1} + e\cos(\theta_1 - \gamma)\right\} = \cos(\theta - \theta_1)$$

Also the equation to the normal at the point α

$$r\{e\sin(\theta - \gamma) + \sin(\alpha - \theta)\} = \frac{el\sin(\alpha - \gamma)}{1 - e\cos(\alpha - \gamma)}$$

➤ **347.**

EXAMPLE 1 *If the tangents at any two points P and Q of a conic meet in a point T, and if the straight line PQ meet the directrix corresponding to S in a point K, then the angle KST is a right angle.*

If the vectorial angles of P and Q be α and β respectively, the equation to PQ is, by equation (3) of Art. 342

$$\frac{l}{r} = \sec\frac{\beta - \alpha}{2}\cos\left(\theta - \frac{\alpha + \beta}{2}\right) - e\cos\theta \qquad \ldots(1)$$

Also the equation to the directrix is, by Art. 339,

$$\frac{l}{r} = -e\cos\theta \qquad \ldots(2)$$

If we solve the equations (1) and (2), we shall obtain the polar coordinates of K.

But, by subtracting (2) from (1), we have

$$0 = \sec\frac{\beta - \alpha}{2}\cos\left(\theta - \frac{\alpha + \beta}{2}\right), \quad i.e., \quad \theta - \frac{\alpha + \beta}{2} = \frac{\pi}{2}$$

i.e.,
$$\angle KSX = \frac{\pi}{2} + \frac{\alpha + \beta}{2}$$

so that SK bisects the exterior angle between SP and SQ.

Also, by equation (3) of Art. 344, we have the vectorial angle of T equal to $\frac{\alpha + \beta}{2}$, *i.e.,* $\angle TSX = \frac{\alpha + \beta}{2}$

Hence,
$$\angle KST = \angle KSX - \angle TSX = \frac{\pi}{2}$$

EXAMPLE 2 *S is the focus and P and Q two points on a conic such that the angle PSQ is constant and equal to 2δ; prove that*

(1) *the locus of the intersection of tangents at P and Q is a conic section whose focus is S,*

and (2) *the line PQ always touches a conic whose focus is S.*

(1) Let the vectorial angles of P and Q be respectively $\gamma + \delta$ and $\gamma - \delta$ where γ is variable.

By equation (4) of Art. 342, the tangents at P and Q are therefore,

$$\frac{l}{r} = \cos(\theta - \gamma - \delta) - e\cos\theta \qquad \ldots(1)$$

and $$\frac{l}{r} = \cos (\theta - \gamma + \delta) - e \cos \theta \qquad \ldots(2)$$

If, between these two equations, we eliminate the variable quantity γ, we shall have the locus of the point of intersection of the two tangents.

Subtracting (2) from (1), we have

$$\cos (\theta - \gamma - \delta) = \cos (\theta - \gamma + \delta)$$

Hence, (since δ is not zero) we have $\gamma = \theta$

Substituting for γ in (1), we have

$$\frac{l}{r} = \cos \delta - e \cos \theta,$$

i.e., $$\frac{l \sec \delta}{r} = 1 - e \sec \delta \cos \theta$$

Hence, the required locus is a conic whose focus is S, whose latus rectum is $2l \sec \delta$, and whose eccentricity is $e \sec \delta$.

It is therefore, an ellipse, parabola, or hyperbola, according as $e \sec \delta$ is $< = > 1$, *i.e.,* according as $\cos \delta > = < e$.

(2) The equation to PQ is, by equation (3) of Art. 342,

$$\frac{l}{r} = \sec \delta \cos (\theta - \gamma) - e \cos \theta$$

i.e., $$\frac{l \cos \delta}{r} = \cos (\theta - \gamma) - e \cos \delta \cos \theta \qquad \ldots(3)$$

Comparing this with equation (4) of Art. 342, we see that it always touches a conic whose latus rectum is $2l \cos \delta$ and whose eccentricity is $e \cos \delta$.

Also the directrix is in each case the same as that of the original conic. For both $\dfrac{l \sec \delta}{e \sec \delta}$ and $\dfrac{l \cos \delta}{e \cos \delta}$ are equal to $\dfrac{l}{e}$

EXAMPLE 3   *A circle passes through the focus S of a conic and meets it in four points whose distances from S are $r_1, r_2, r_3,$ and r_4. Prove that*

(1) $r_1 r_2 r_3 r_4 = \dfrac{d^2 l^2}{e^2}$, *where $2l$ and e are the latus rectum and eccentricity of the conic, and d is the diameter of the circle,*

and (2) $$\frac{1}{r_1} + \frac{1}{r_2} + \frac{1}{r_3} + \frac{1}{r_4} = \frac{2}{l}$$

Take the focus as pole, and the axis of the conic as initial line, so that its equation is

$$\frac{l}{r} = 1 - e \cos \theta \qquad \ldots(1)$$

If the diameter of the circle, which passes through S be inclined at an angle γ to the axis, its equation is, by Art. 172,

$$r = d \cos (\theta - \gamma) \qquad \ldots(2)$$

If, between (1) and (2), we eliminate θ, we shall have an equation in r, whose roots are $r_1, r_2, r_3,$ and r_4.

From (1) we have $\cos\theta = \dfrac{r-l}{er}$, and hence $\sin\theta = \sqrt{1 - \left(\dfrac{r-l}{er}\right)^2}$,

and then (2) gives

$$r = d\cos\gamma\cos\theta + d\sin\gamma\sin\theta,$$

i.e., $\{er^2 - d\cos\gamma(r-l)\}^2 = d^2\sin^2\gamma[e^2r^2 - (r-l)^2],$

i.e., $e^2r^4 - 2ed\cos\gamma\cdot r^3 + r^2(d^2 + 2eld\cos\gamma - e^2d^2\sin^2\gamma) - 2ld^2r + d^2l^2 = 0$

Hence, by Art. 2, we have

$$r_1 r_2 r_3 r_4 = \frac{d^2 l^2}{e^2} \qquad \qquad \ldots(3)$$

and

$$r_2 r_3 r_4 + r_3 r_4 r_1 + r_4 r_1 r_2 + r_1 r_2 r_3 = \frac{2ld^2}{e^2} \qquad \qquad \ldots(4)$$

Dividing (4) by (3), we have

$$\frac{1}{r_1} + \frac{1}{r_2} + \frac{1}{r_3} + \frac{1}{r_4} = \frac{2}{l}$$

EXAMPLES XXXIX

1. In a parabola, prove that the length of a focal chord which is inclined at 30° to the axis is four times the length of the latus-rectum.

   The tangents at two points, P and Q, of a conic meet in T, and S is the focus; prove that

2. if the conic be a parabola, then $ST^2 = SP \cdot SQ$.

3. if the conic be central, then $\dfrac{1}{SP \cdot SQ} - \dfrac{1}{ST^2} = \dfrac{1}{b^2}\sin^2\dfrac{PSQ}{2}$, where b is the semi-minor axis.

4. The vectorial angle of T is the semi-sum of the vectorial angles of P and Q.

   Hence, by reference to Art. 338, prove that, if P and Q be on different branches of a hyperbola, then ST bisects the supplement of the angle PSQ, and that in other cases, whatever be the conic, ST bisects the angle PSQ.

5. A straight line drawn through the common focus S of a number of conics meets them in the points $P_1, P_2 \ldots$; on it is taken a point Q such that the reciprocal of SQ is equal to the sum of the reciprocals of $SP_1, SP_2 \ldots$, Prove that the locus of Q is a conic section whose focus is S, and shew that the reciprocal of its latus rectum is equal to the sum of the reciprocals of the latera recta of the given conics.

6. Prove that perpendicular focal chords of a rectangular hyperbola are equal.

7. PSP' and QSQ' are two perpendicular focal chords of a conic; prove that $\dfrac{1}{PS \cdot SP'} + \dfrac{1}{QS \cdot SQ'}$ is constant.

8. Shew that the length of any focal chord of a conic is a third proportional to the transverse axis and the diameter parallel to the chord.

9. If a straight line drawn through the focus S of a hyperbola, parallel to an asymptote, meet the curve in P, prove that SP is one quarter of the latus rectum.

10. Prove that the equations $\dfrac{l}{r} = 1 - e \cos \theta$ and $\dfrac{l}{r} = -e \cos \theta - 1$ represent the same conic.

11. Two conics have a common focus; prove that two of their common chords pass through the intersection of their directrices.

12. P is any point on a conic, whose focus is S, and a straight line is drawn through S at a given angle with SP to meet the tangent at P in T; prove that the locus of T is a conic whose focus and directrix are the same as those of the original conic.

13. If a chord of a conic section subtend a constant angle 2α at the focus, prove that the locus of the point where it meets the internal bisector of the angle 2α is the conic section

$$\frac{l \cos \alpha}{r} = 1 - e \cos \alpha \cos \theta$$

14. Two conic sections have a common focus about which one of them is turned; prove that the common chord is always a tangent to another conic, having the same focus, and whose eccentricity is the ratio of the eccentricities of the given conics.

15. Two ellipses have a common focus; two radii vectores, one to each ellipse, are drawn from the focus at right angles to one another and tangents are drawn at their extremities; prove that these tangents meet on a fixed conic, and find when it is a parabola.

16. Prove that the sum of the distances from the focus of the points in which a conic is intersected by any circle, whose centre is at a fixed point on the transverse axis, is constant.

17. Shew that the equation to the circle circumscribing the triangle formed by the three tangents to the parabola $r = \dfrac{2a}{1 - \cos \theta}$ drawn at the points whose vectorial angles are α, β, and γ, is

$$r = a \operatorname{cosec} \frac{\alpha}{2} \operatorname{cosec} \frac{\beta}{2} \operatorname{cosec} \frac{\gamma}{2} \sin \left(\frac{\alpha + \beta + \gamma}{2} - \theta \right)$$

and hence that it always passes through the focus.

18. If tangents be drawn to the same parabola at points whose vectorial angles are α, β, γ, and δ, shew that the centres of the circles circumscribing the four triangles formed by these four lines all lie on the circle whose equation is

$$r = -\frac{a}{2} \operatorname{cosec} \frac{\alpha}{2} \operatorname{cosec} \frac{\beta}{2} \operatorname{cosec} \frac{\gamma}{2} \operatorname{cosec} \frac{\delta}{2} \cos \left[\theta - \frac{\alpha + \beta + \gamma + \delta}{2} \right]$$

19. The circle circumscribing the triangle formed by three tangents to a parabola is drawn; prove that the tangent to it at the focus makes

with the axis an angle equal to the sum of the angles made with the axis by the three tangents.

20. Shew that the equation to the circle, which passes through the focus and touches the curve $\dfrac{l}{r} = 1 - e \cos \theta$ at the point $\theta = \alpha$, is

$$r(1 - e \cos \alpha)^2 = l \cos(\theta - \alpha) - el \cos(\theta - 2\alpha)$$

21. A given circle, whose centre is on the axis of a parabola, passes through the focus S and is cut in four points A, B, C, and D by any conic, of given latus-rectum, having S as focus and a tangent to the parabola for directrix; prove that the sum of the distances of the points A, B, C and D from S is constant.

22. Prove that the locus of the vertices of all parabolas that can be drawn touching a given circle of radius a and having a fixed point on the circumference as focus is $r = 2a \cos^3 \dfrac{\theta}{3}$, the fixed point being the pole and the diameter through it the initial line.

23. Two conic sections have the same focus and directrix. Shew that any tangent from the outer curve to the inner one subtends a constant angle at the focus.

24. Two equal ellipses, of eccentricity e, are placed with their axes at right angles and they have one focus S in common; if PQ be a common tangent, shew that the angle PSQ is equal to $2 \sin^{-1} \dfrac{e}{\sqrt{2}}$.

25. Prove that the two conics $\dfrac{l_1}{r} = 1 - e_1 \cos \theta$ and $\dfrac{l_2}{r} = 1 - e_2 \cos(\theta - \alpha)$ will touch one another, if

$$l_1^2(1 - e_2^2) + l_2^2(1 - e_1^2) = 2l_1 l_2 (1 - e_1 e_2 \cos \alpha)$$

26. An ellipse and a hyperbola have the same focus S and intersect in four real points, two on each branch of the hyperbola; if r_1 and r_2 be the distances from S of the two points of intersection on the nearer branch, and r_3 and r_4 be those of the two points on the further branch, and if l and l' be the semi-latera-recta of the two conics, prove that

$$(l + l')\left(\frac{1}{r_1} + \frac{1}{r_2}\right) + (l - l')\left(\frac{1}{r_3} + \frac{1}{r_4}\right) = 4$$

[Make use of Art. 333.]

27. If the normals at three points of the parabola $r = a \operatorname{cosec}^2 \dfrac{\theta}{2}$, whose vectorial angles are α, β, and γ, meet in a point whose vectorial angle is δ, prove that $2\delta = \alpha + \beta + \gamma - \pi$.

15

GENERAL EQUATION OF THE SECOND DEGREE. TRACING OF CURVES.

➤ **348. Particular cases of conic sections :** The general definition of a Conic Section in Art. 196 was that it is the locus of a point P which moves so that its distance from a given point S is in a constant ratio to its perpendicular distance PM from a given straight line ZK.

When S does not lie on the straight line ZK, we have found that the locus is an ellipse, a parabola, or a hyperbola according as the eccentricity e is $< =$ or > 1.

The Circle is a sub-case of the Ellipse. For the equation of Art. 139 is the same as the equation (6) of Art. 247 when $b^2 = a^2$, i.e., when $e = 0$. In this case $CS = 0$, and $SZ = \dfrac{a}{e} - ae = \infty$ The circle is therefore, a Conic Section, whose eccentricity is zero, and whose directrix is at an infinite distance.

Next, let S lie on the straight line ZK, so that S and Z coincide.

In this case, since,

$$SP = e \cdot PM,$$

We have $\sin PSM = \dfrac{PM}{SP} = \dfrac{1}{e}$

If $e > 1$, then P lies on one or other of the two straight lines SU and SU' inclined to KK' at an angle $\sin^{-1}\left(\dfrac{1}{e}\right)$.

If $e = 1$, then PSM is a right angle, and the locus becomes two coincident straight lines coinciding with SX.

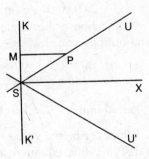

If $e < 1$, the $\angle PSM$ is imaginary, and the locus consists of two imaginary straight lines.

If, again, both KK' and S be at infinity and S be on KK', the lines SU and SU' of the previous figure will be two straight lines meeting at infinity, i.e., will be two parallel straight lines.

Finally, it may happen that the axes of an ellipse may both be zero, so that it reduces to a point.

Under the head of a conic section we must therefore include:

(1) An Ellipse (including a circle and a point)

(2) A Parabola

(3) A Hyperbola

(4) Two straight lines, real or imaginary, intersecting, coincident, or parallel.

➤ **349.** *To shew that the general equation of the second degree*

$$ax^2 + 2hxy + by^2 + 2gx + 2fy + c = 0 \qquad \text{...(1)}$$

always represents a conic section.

Let the axes of coordinates be turned through an angle θ, so that, as in Art. 129, we substitute for x and y the quantities $x \cos \theta - y \sin \theta$ and $x \sin \theta + y \cos \theta$ respectively. The equation (1) then becomes

$$a (x \cos \theta - y \sin \theta)^2 + 2h (x \cos \theta - y \sin \theta)(x \sin \theta + y \cos \theta)$$
$$+ b (x \sin \theta + y \cos \theta)^2 + 2g (x \cos \theta - y \sin \theta)$$
$$+ 2f (x \sin \theta + y \cos \theta) + c = 0$$

i.e., $x^2 (a \cos^2 \theta + 2h \cos \theta \sin \theta + b \sin^2 \theta)$
$$+ 2xy \{ h (\cos^2 \theta - \sin^2 \theta) - (a - b) \cos \theta \sin \theta \}$$
$$+ y^2 (a \sin^2 \theta - 2h \cos \theta \sin \theta + b \cos^2 \theta) + 2x (g \cos \theta + f \sin \theta)$$
$$+ 2y (f \cos \theta - g \sin \theta) + c = 0 \qquad \text{...(2)}$$

Now, choose the angle θ so that the coefficient of xy in this equation may vanish,

i.e., so that $h (\cos^2 \theta - \sin^2 \theta) = (a - b) \sin \theta \cos \theta$,

i.e., $2h \cos 2\theta = (a - b) \sin 2\theta$,

i.e., so that $\tan 2\theta = \dfrac{2h}{a - b}$

Whatever be the values of a, b, and h, there is always a value of θ satisfying this equation and such that it lies between $-45°$ and $+45°$. The values of $\sin \theta$ and $\cos \theta$ are therefore known.

On substituting their values in equation (2), let it become

$$Ax^2 + By^2 + 2Gx + 2Fy + c = 0 \qquad \text{... (3)}$$

First, let neither A nor B be zero.

The equation (3) may then be written in the form

$$A\left(x+\frac{G}{A}\right)^2 + B\left(y+\frac{F}{B}\right)^2 = \frac{G^2}{A}+\frac{F^2}{B}-c.$$

Transform the origin to the point $\left(-\dfrac{G}{A},\ -\dfrac{F}{B}\right)$

The equation becomes

$$Ax^2 + By^2 = \frac{G^2}{A}+\frac{F^2}{B}-c = K \text{ (say)} \qquad \qquad \text{...(4)}$$

i.e.,

$$\frac{x^2}{\dfrac{K}{A}}+\frac{y^2}{\dfrac{K}{B}} = 1 \qquad \qquad \text{...(5)}$$

If $\dfrac{K}{A}$ and $\dfrac{K}{B}$ be both positive, the equation represents an ellipse (Art. 247)

If $\dfrac{K}{A}$ and $\dfrac{K}{B}$ be one positive and the other negative, it represents a hyperbola (Art. 295). If they be both negative, the locus is an imaginary ellipse.

If K be zero, then equation (4) represents two straight lines, which are real or imaginary according as A and B have opposite or the same signs.

Secondly, let either A or B be zero, and let it be A. Then equation (3) can be written in the form

$$B\left(y+\frac{F}{B}\right)^2 + 2G\left[x+\frac{c}{2G}-\frac{F^2}{2BG}\right] = 0.$$

Transform the origin to the point whose coordinates are

$$\left(-\frac{c}{2G}+\frac{F^2}{2BG},\ -\frac{F}{B}\right)$$

This equation then becomes

$$By^2 + 2Gx = 0$$

i.e.,

$$y^2 = -\frac{2G}{B}x$$

which represents a parabola. (Art. 197)

If, in addition to A being zero, we also have G zero, the equation (3) becomes,

$$By^2 + 2Fy + c = 0$$

i.e.,
$$y + \frac{F}{B} = \pm \sqrt{\frac{F^2}{B^2} - \frac{c}{B}}$$

and this represents two parallel straight lines, real or imaginary.

Thus, in every case the general equation represents one of the conic sections enumerated in Art. 348.

➤ **350. Centre of a Conic Section : Def.:** The centre of a conic section is a point such that all chords of the conic which pass through it are bisected there.

When the equation to the conic is in the form
$$ax^2 + 2hxy + by^2 + c = 0 \qquad \dots (1)$$
the origin is the centre.

For let (x', y') be any point on (1), so that we have
$$ax'^2 + 2hx'y' + by'^2 + c = 0 \qquad \dots (2)$$
This equation may be written in the form
$$a(-x')^2 + 2h(-x')(-y') + b(-y')^2 + c = 0$$
and hence shews that the point $(-x', -y')$ also lies on (1).

But the points (x', y') and $(-x', -y')$ lie on the same straight line through the origin, and are at equal distances from the origin.

The chord of the conic which passes through the origin and any point (x', y') of the curve is therefore, bisected at origin.

The origin is therefore, the centre.

➤ **351.** When the equation to the conic is given in the form
$$ax^2 + 2hxy + by^2 + 2gx + 2fy + c = 0 \qquad \dots (1)$$
the origin is the centre only when both f and g are zero.

For, if the origin be the centre, then corresponding to *each* point (x', y') on (1), there must be also a point $(-x', -y')$ lying on the curve.

Hence, we must have
$$ax'^2 + 2hx'y' + by'^2 + 2gx' + 2fy' + c = 0 \qquad \dots (2)$$
and
$$ax'^2 + 2hx'y' + by'^2 - 2gx' - 2fy' + c = 0 \qquad \dots (3)$$
Subtracting (3) from (2), we have
$$gx' + fy' = 0$$

This relation is to be true for *all* the points (x', y') which lie on the curve (1). But this can only be the case when $g = 0$ and $f = 0$.

➤ **352.** *To obtain the coordinates of the centre of the conic given by the general equation, and to obtain the equation to the curve referred to axes through the centre parallel to the original axes.*

Transform the origin to the point $(\bar{x}, \bar{y})$, so that for x and y we have to substitute $x + \bar{x}$ and $y + \bar{y}$. The equation then becomes

$$a(x + \bar{x})^2 + 2h(x + \bar{x})(y + \bar{y}) + b(y + \bar{y})^2 + 2g(x + \bar{x}) + 2f(y + \bar{y}) + c = 0,$$

i.e.,

$$ax^2 + 2hxy + by^2 + 2x(a\bar{x} + h\bar{y} + g) + 2y(h\bar{x} + b\bar{y} + f)$$
$$+ a\bar{x}^2 + 2h\bar{x}\,\bar{y} + b\bar{y}^2 + 2g\bar{x} + 2f\bar{y} + c = 0 \qquad \ldots(2)$$

If the point $(\bar{x}, \bar{y})$ be the centre of the conic section, the coefficients of x and y in the equation (2) must vanish, so that we have

$$a\bar{x} + h\bar{y} + g = 0 \qquad \ldots(3)$$

and

$$h\bar{x} + b\bar{y} + f = 0 \qquad \ldots(4)$$

Solving equations (3) and (4), we have, in general,

$$\bar{x} = \frac{fh - bg}{ab - h^2} \quad \text{and} \quad \bar{y} = \frac{gh - af}{ab - h^2} \qquad \ldots(5)$$

With these values the constant term in equation (2)

$$= a\bar{x}^2 + 2h\bar{x}\,\bar{y} + b\bar{y}^2 + 2g\bar{x} + 2f\bar{y} + c$$
$$= \bar{x}(a\bar{x} + h\bar{y} + g) + \bar{y}(h\bar{x} + b\bar{y} + f) + g\bar{x} + f\bar{y} + c$$
$$= g\bar{x} + f\bar{y} + c \qquad \ldots(6)$$

by equations (3) and (4),

$$= \frac{abc + 2fgh - af^2 - bg^2 - ch^2}{ab - h^2}, \qquad \text{by equations (5)}$$

$$= \frac{\Delta}{ab - h^2}$$

where Δ is the discriminant of the given general equation (Art. 118). The equation (2) can therefore, be written in the form

$$ax^2 + 2hxy + by^2 + \frac{\Delta}{ab - h^2} = 0.$$

This is the required equation referred to the new axes through the centre.

EXAMPLE *Find the centre of the conic section*

$$2x^2 - 5xy - 3y^2 - x - 4y + 6 = 0$$

and its equation when transformed to the centre.

The centre is given by the equations $2\bar{x} - \frac{5}{2}\bar{y} - \frac{1}{2} = 0,$

and $-\frac{5}{2}\bar{x} - 3\bar{y} - 2 = 0$, so that $\bar{x} = \frac{-2}{7}$ and $\bar{y} = -\frac{3}{7}.$

The equation referred to the centre is then

$$2x^2 - 5xy - 3y^2 + c' = 0$$

where $\qquad c' = -\frac{1}{2} \cdot \overline{x} - 2 \cdot \overline{y} + 6 = \frac{1}{7} + \frac{6}{7} + 6 = 7 \qquad$ (Art. 352)

The required equation is thus

$$2x^2 - 5xy - 3y^2 + 7 = 0.$$

➤ **353.** Sometimes the equations (3) and (4) of the last article do not give suitable values for $\overline{x}$ and $\overline{y}$.

For, if $ab - h^2$ be zero, the values of $\overline{x}$ and $\overline{y}$ in (5) are both infinite. When $ab - h^2$ is zero, the conic section is a parabola. [Art. 239.]

The centre of a parabola is therefore, at infinity.

Again, if $\dfrac{a}{h} = \dfrac{h}{b} = \dfrac{g}{f}$, the result (5) of the last article is of the form

$\dfrac{0}{0}$ and the equations (3) and (4) reduce to the same equation, *viz.*,

$$a\overline{x} + h\overline{y} + g = 0.$$

We then have only one equation to determine the centre, and there is therefore an inifinite number of centres all lying on the straight line

$$ax + hy + g = 0$$

In this case the conic section consists of a pair of parallel straight lines, both parallel to the line of centres.

➤ **354.** The student who is acquainted with the Differential Calculus will observe, from equations (3) and (4) of Art. 352, that the coordinates of the centre satisfy the equations that are obtained by differentiating, with regard to x and y, the original equation of the conic section.

It will also be observed that the coefficients of $\overline{x}, \overline{y}$, and unity in the equations (3), (4), and (6) of Art. 352 are the quantities (in the order in which they occur) which make up the determinant of Art. 118.

This determinant being easy to write down, the student may thence recollect the equations for the centre and the value of c.

The reason why this relation holds will appear from the next article.

➤ **355.**

EXAMPLE *Find the condition that the general equation of the second degree may represent two straight lines.*

The centre $(\overline{x}, \overline{y})$ of the conic is given by

$$a\overline{x} + h\overline{y} + g = 0 \qquad \qquad \text{...(1)}$$

and $\qquad\qquad h\overline{x} + b\overline{y} + f = 0 \qquad\qquad$ ...(2)

Also, if it be transformed to the centre as origin, the equation becomes

$$ax^2 + 2hxy + by^2 + c' = 0 \qquad\qquad ...(3)$$

where $\qquad\qquad c' = g\overline{x} + f\overline{y} + c$

Now the equation (3) represents two straight lines if c' be zero,

i.e., if $\qquad\qquad g\overline{x} + f\overline{y} + c = 0 \qquad\qquad$ ...(4)

The equation therefore, represents two straight lines if the relations (1), (2), and (4) be simultaneously true.

Eliminating the quantities $\overline{x}$ and $\overline{y}$ from these equations, we have, by Art. 12,

$$\begin{vmatrix} a, & h, & g \\ h, & b, & f \\ g, & f, & c \end{vmatrix} = 0$$

This is the condition found in Art. 118.

➤ **356.** *To find the equations to the asymptotes of the conic section given by the general equation of the second degree.*

Let the equation be

$$ax^2 + 2hxy + by^2 + 2gx + 2fy + c = 0 \qquad\qquad ...(1)$$

Since, the equation to the asymptotes has been shewn to differ from the equation to the curve only in its constant term, the required equation must be

$$ax^2 + 2hxy + by^2 + 2gx + 2fy + c + \lambda = 0 \qquad\qquad ...(2)$$

Also (2) is to be a pair of straight lines.

Hence, $\quad ab(c + \lambda) + 2fgh - af^2 - bg^2 - (c + \lambda)h^2 = 0.$ (Art. 116)

Therefore, $\qquad \lambda = -\dfrac{abc + 2fgh - af^2 - bg^2 - ch^2}{ab - h^2} = -\dfrac{\Delta}{ab - h^2}$

The required equation to the asymptotes is therefore,

$$ax^2 + 2hxy + by^2 + 2gx + 2fy + c - \frac{\Delta}{ab - h^2} = 0 \qquad\qquad ...(2)$$

Cor.: Since, the equation to the hyperbola, which is conjugate to a given hyperbola, differs as much from the equation to the common asymptotes as the original equation does, it follows that the equation to the hyperbola, which is conjugate to the hyperbola (1), is

$$ax^2 + 2hxy + by^2 + 2gx + 2fy + c - 2\frac{\Delta}{ab - h^2} = 0$$

➤ **357.** *To determine by an examination of the general equation what kind of conic section it represents?*

[On applying the method of Art. 313 to the ellipse and parabola, it would be found that the asymptotes of the ellipse are imaginary, and that a parabola only has one asymptote, which is at an infinite distance and parallel to its axis.]

The straight lines $\quad ax^2 + 2hxy + by^2 = 0 \quad\qquad$ ...(1)

are parallel to the lines (2) of the last article, and hence, represent straight lines parallel to the asymptotes.

Now the equation (1) represents real, coincident, or imaginary straight lines according as h^2 is $> =$ or $< ab$, *i.e.*,, the asymptotes are real, coincident, or imaginary, according as $h^2 > =$ or $< ab$, *i.e.*, the conic section is a hyperbola, parabola, or ellipse, according as $h^2 > =$ or $< ab$.

Again, the lines (1) are at right angles, *i.e.*, the curve is a rectangular hyperbola, if $a + b = 0$.

Also, by Art. 143, the general equation represents a circle if $a = b$, and $h = 0$.

Finally, by Art. 116, the equation represents a pair of straight lines if $\Delta = 0$; also these straight lines are parallel if the terms of the second degree form a perfect square, *i.e.*, if

$$h^2 = ab$$

➤ **358.** The results for the general equation

$$ax^2 + 2hxy + by^2 + 2gx + 2fy + c = 0$$

are collected in the following table, the axes of coordinates being rectangular.

Curve	Condition
Ellipse	$h^2 < ab$
Parabola	$h^2 = ab$
Hyperbola	$h^2 > ab$
Circle	$a = b$ and $h = 0$
Rectangular hyperbola	$a + b = 0$
Two straight lines, real or imaginary	$\Delta = 0$ *i.e.*, $abc + 2fgh - af^2 - bg^2 - ch^2 = 0$
Two parallel straight lines	$\Delta = 0$ and $h^2 = ab$

If the axes of coordinates be oblique, the lines (1) of Art. 356 are right angles if $a + b - 2h \cos \omega = 0$ (Art. 93); so that the conic section is a rectangular hyperbola if $a + b - 2h \cos \omega = 0$.

Also, by Art. 175, the conic section is a circle if $b = a$ and

$$h = a \cos \omega$$

The conditions for the other cases in the previous article are the same for both oblique and rectangular axes.

EXAMPLES XL

What conics do the following equations represent? When possible, find their centres, and also their equations referred to the centre

1. $12x^2 - 23xy + 10y^2 - 25x + 26y = 14$
2. $13x^2 - 18xy + 37y^2 + 2x + 14y - 2 = 0$
3. $y^2 - 2\sqrt{3}\, xy + 3x^2 + 6x - 4y + 5 = 0$
4. $2x^2 - 72xy + 23y^2 - 4x - 28y - 48 = 0$
5. $6x^2 - 5xy - 6y^2 + 14x + 5y + 4 = 0$
6. $3x^2 - 8xy - 3y^2 + 10x - 13y + 8 = 0$

Find the asymptotes of the following hyperbolas and also the equations to their conjugate hyperbolas.

7. $8x^2 + 10xy - 3y^2 - 2x + 4y = 2$
8. $y^2 - xy - 2x^2 - 5y + x - 6 = 0$
9. $55x^2 - 120xy + 20y^2 + 64x - 48y = 0$
10. $19x^2 + 24xy + y^2 - 22x - 6y = 0$
11. If $(\bar{x}, \bar{y})$ be the centre of the conic section

$$f(x, y) \equiv ax^2 + 2hxy + by^2 + 2gx + 2fy + c = 0,$$

prove that the equation to the asymptotes is $f(x, y) = f(\bar{x}, \bar{y})$

If t be a variable quantity, find the locus of the point (x, y) when

12. $x = a\left(t + \dfrac{1}{t}\right)$ and $y = a\left(t - \dfrac{1}{t}\right)$

13. $x = at + bt^2$ and $y = bt + at^2$
14. $x = 1 + t + t^2$ and $y = 1 - t + t^2$

If θ be a variable angle, find the locus of the point (x, y) when

15. $x = a \tan(\theta + \alpha)$ and $y = b \tan(\theta + \beta)$
16. $x = a \cos(\theta + \alpha)$ and $y = b \cos(\theta + \beta)$.

What are represented by the equations

17. $(x - y)^2 + (x - a)^2 = 0$
18. $xy + a^2 = a(x + y)$
19. $x^3 - y^3 = (y - a)(x^2 - y^2)$
20. $x^3 + y^3 - xy(x + y) + a^2(y - x) = 0$

21. $(x^2 - a^2)^2 - y^4 = 0$

22. $x^3 + y^3 + (x + y)(xy - ax - ay) = 0$

23. $x^2 + xy + y^2 = 0$

24. $(r \cos \theta - a)(r - a \cos \theta) = 0$

25. $r \sin^2 \theta = 2a \cos \theta$

26. $r + \dfrac{1}{r} = 3 \cos \theta + \sin \theta$

27. $\dfrac{1}{r} = 1 + \cos \theta + \sqrt{3} \sin \theta.$

28. $r(4 - 3 \sin^2 \theta) = 8a \cos \theta$

➤ **359.** *To trace the parabola given by the general equation of the second degree*

$$ax^2 + 2hxy + by^2 + 2gx + 2fy + c = 0 \qquad \dots(1)$$

and to find its latus rectum.

First Method : Since, the curve is a parabola we have $h^2 = ab$, so that the terms of the second degree form a perfect square.

But then $a = \alpha^2$ and $b = \beta^2$, so that $h = \alpha\beta$, and the equation (1) becomes

$$(\alpha x + \beta y)^2 + 2gx + 2fy + c = 0 \qquad \dots(2)$$

Let the direction of the axes be changed so that the straight line $\alpha x + \beta y = 0$, i.e., $y = -\dfrac{\alpha}{\beta} x$, may be the new axis of X.

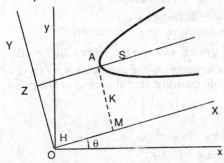

We have therefore, to turn the axes through an angle θ such that $\tan \theta = -\dfrac{\alpha}{\beta}$, and therefore,

$$\sin \theta = -\frac{\alpha}{\sqrt{\alpha^2 + \beta^2}} \quad \text{and} \quad \cos \theta = \frac{\beta}{\sqrt{\alpha^2 + \beta^2}}$$

For x we have to substitute

$$X \cos \theta - Y \sin \theta, \quad i.e., \quad \frac{\beta X + \alpha Y}{\sqrt{\alpha^2 + \beta^2}}$$

and for y the quantity

$$X \sin \theta + Y \cos \theta, \quad i.e., \quad \frac{-\alpha X + \beta Y}{\sqrt{\alpha^2 + \beta^2}} \qquad \text{(Art. 129)}$$

For $\alpha x + \beta y$ we therefore, substitute $Y \sqrt{(\alpha^2 + \beta^2)}$

The equation (2) then becomes

$$Y^2 (\alpha^2 + \beta^2) + \frac{2}{\sqrt{\alpha^2 + \beta^2}} [g (\beta X + \alpha Y) + f (\beta Y - \alpha X)] + c = 0,$$

i.e., $\quad Y^2 + 2Y \dfrac{\alpha g + \beta f}{(\alpha^2 + \beta^2)^{3/2}} = 2X \dfrac{\alpha f - \beta g}{(\alpha^2 + \beta^2)^{3/2}} - \dfrac{c}{\alpha^2 + \beta^2}$

i.e., $\qquad\qquad (Y - K)^2 = 2 \dfrac{\alpha f - \beta g}{(\alpha^2 + \beta^2)^{3/2}} [X - H] \qquad$ ...(3)

where $\qquad\qquad\qquad K = -\dfrac{\alpha g + \beta f}{(\alpha^2 + \beta^2)^{3/2}} \qquad$ ...(4)

and $\qquad -2 \dfrac{\alpha f - \beta g}{(\alpha^2 + \beta^2)^{3/2}} \times H = K^2 - \dfrac{c}{\alpha^2 + \beta^2}$

i.e., $\qquad H = \dfrac{\sqrt{\alpha^2 + \beta^2}}{2 (\alpha f - \beta g)} \left[c - \dfrac{(\alpha g + \beta f)^2}{(\alpha^2 + \beta^2)^2} \right] \qquad$ ...(5)

The equation (3) represents a parabola whose latus rectum is

$2 \dfrac{\alpha f - \beta g}{(\alpha^2 + \beta^2)^{3/2}}$ whose axis is parallel to the new axis of X, and whose

vertex referred to the new axes is the point (H, K).

➤ **360.** *Equation of the axis, and coordinates of the vertex, referred to the original axes.*

Since, the axis of the curve is parallel to the new axis of X, it makes an angle θ with the old axis of x, and hence, the perpendicular on it from the origin makes an angle $90° + \theta$.

Also the length of this perpendicular is K.

The equation to the axis of the parabola is therefore,

$$x \cos (90° + \theta) + y \sin (90° + \theta) = K$$

i.e., $\qquad\qquad - x \sin \theta + y \cos \theta = K$

i.e., $\qquad \alpha x + \beta y = K \sqrt{\alpha^2 + \beta^2} = -\dfrac{\alpha g + \beta f}{\alpha^2 + \beta^2} \qquad$ ...(6)

Again, the vertex is the point in which the axis (6) meets the curve (2).

We have therefore, to solve (6) and (2), *i.e.,* (6) and

$$\frac{(\alpha g + \beta f)^2}{(\alpha^2 + \beta^2)^2} + 2gx + 2fy + c = 0 \qquad \text{...(7)}$$

The solution of (6) and (7) therefore, gives the required coordinates of the vertex.

➤ **361.** It was proved in Art. 224 that if PV be a diameter of the parabola and QV the ordinate to it drawn through any point Q of the curve, so that QV is parallel to the tangent at P, and if θ be the angle between the diameter PV and the tangent at P, then

$$QV^2 = 4\alpha \csc^2 \theta \cdot PV \qquad \ldots(1)$$

If QL be perpendicular to PV and QL' be perpendicular to the tangent at P, we have

$$QL = QV \sin \theta, \text{ and } QL' = PV \sin \theta,$$

so that (1) is $\qquad QL^2 = 4\alpha \csc \theta \cdot QL'$

Hence, the square of the perpendicular distance of any point Q on the parabola from any diameter varies as the perpendicular distance of Q from the tangent at the end of the diameter.

Hence, if $Ax + By + C = 0$ be the equation of any diameter and $A'x + B'y + C' = 0$ be the equation of the tangent at its end, the equation to the parabola is

$$(Ax + By + C)^2 = \lambda (A'x + B'y + C') \qquad \ldots(2)$$

where λ is some constant.

Conversely, if the equation to a parabola can be reduced to the form (2), then

$$Ax + By + C = 0 \qquad \ldots(3)$$

is a diameter of the parabola and the axis of the parabola is parallel to (3).

We shall apply this property in the following article.

➤ **362.** *To trace the parabola given by the general equation of the second degree*

$$ax^2 + 2hxy + by^2 + 2gx + 2fy + c = 0 \qquad \ldots(1)$$

Second Method. Since the curve is a parabola, the terms of the second degree must form a perfect square and $h^2 = ab$.

Put then $a = \alpha^2$ and $b = \beta^2$, so that $h = \alpha\beta$, and the equation (1) becomes

$$(\alpha x + \beta y)^2 = - (2gx + 2fy + c) \qquad \ldots(2)$$

As in the last article the straight line $\alpha x + \beta y = 0$ is a diameter, and the axis of the parabola is therefore, parallel to it, and so its equation is of the form

$$\alpha x + \beta y + \lambda = 0 \qquad \ldots(3)$$

The equation (2) may therefore, be written

$$(\alpha x + \beta y + \lambda)^2 = - (2gx + 2fy + c) + \lambda^2 + 2\lambda (\alpha x + \beta y)$$
$$= 2x (\lambda\alpha - g) + 2y (\beta\lambda - f) + \lambda^2 - c \qquad \ldots(4)$$

Choose λ so that the straight lines

$$\alpha x + \beta y + \lambda = 0 \qquad \qquad \text{...(5)}$$

and

$$2x(\lambda\alpha - g) + 2y(\beta\lambda - f) + \lambda^2 - c = 0 \qquad \text{...(6)}$$

are at right angles, *i.e.*, so that

$$\alpha(\lambda\alpha - g) + \beta(\beta\lambda - f) = 0,$$

i.e., so that

$$\lambda = \frac{\beta f + \alpha g}{\alpha^2 + \beta^2} \qquad \qquad \text{...(7)}$$

The lines (5) and (6) are now, by the last article, a diameter and a tangent at its extremity; also, since they are at right angles, they must be the axis and the tangent at the vertex.

The equation (4) may now, by equation (7), be written

$$\{\alpha x + \beta y + \lambda\}^2 = \frac{2(\alpha f - \beta g)}{\alpha^2 + \beta^2}[\beta x - \alpha y + \mu],$$

where

$$\mu = \frac{\alpha^2 + \beta^2}{2(\alpha f - \beta g)}(\lambda^2 - c)$$

i.e.,

$$\left\{\frac{\alpha x + \beta y + \lambda}{\sqrt{\alpha^2 + \beta^2}}\right\}^2 = \frac{2(\alpha f - \beta g)}{(\alpha^2 + \beta^2)^{3/2}} \cdot \frac{\beta x - \alpha y + \mu}{\sqrt{\alpha^2 + \beta^2}}$$

i.e.

$$PN^2 = \frac{2(\alpha f - \beta g)}{(\alpha^2 + \beta^2)^{3/2}} \cdot AN$$

where PN is the perpendicular from any point P of the curve on the axis, and A is the vertex.

Hence, the axis and tangent at the vertex are the lines (5) and (6), where λ has the value (7), and the latus rectum

$$= 2\frac{\alpha f - \beta g}{(\alpha^2 + \beta^2)^{3/2}}$$

➤ **363.**

EXAMPLE *Trace the parabola*

$$9x^2 - 24xy + 16y^2 - 18x - 101y + 19 = 0$$

The equation is

$$(3x - 4y)^2 - 18x - 101y + 19 = 0 \qquad \text{...(1)}$$

First Method: Take $3x - 4y = 0$ as the new axis of x, *i.e.*, turn the axes through an angle θ, where $\tan\theta = \dfrac{3}{4}$, and therefore, $\sin\theta = \dfrac{3}{5}$ and $\cos\theta = \dfrac{4}{5}$.

For x we therefore, substitute $X \cos \theta - Y \sin \theta$, *i.e.*, $\dfrac{4X - 3Y}{5}$; for y we

put $X \sin \theta + Y \cos \theta$, *i.e.*, $\dfrac{3X + 4Y}{5}$, and hence for $3x - 4y$ the quantity

$-5Y$.

The equation (1), therefore, becomes

$$25Y^2 - \frac{1}{5}[72X - 54Y] - \frac{1}{5}[303X + 404Y] + 19 = 0$$

i.e., $25Y^2 - 75X - 70Y + 19 = 0$ ...(2)

This is the equation to the curve referred to the axes OX and OY.
But, (2) can be written in the form

$$Y^2 - \frac{14Y}{5} = 3X - \frac{19}{25}$$

i.e., $$\left(Y - \frac{7}{5}\right)^2 = 3X - \frac{19}{25} + \frac{49}{25} = 3\left(X + \frac{2}{5}\right)$$

Take a point A whose coordinates referred to OX and OY are $-\dfrac{2}{5}$ and

$\dfrac{7}{5}$ and draw AL and AM parallel to OX and OY respectively.

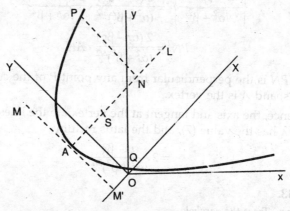

Referred to AL and AM the equation to the parabola is $Y^2 = 3X$. It is
therefore, a parabola, whose vertex is A, whose latus rectum is 3, and
whose axis is AL.

Second Method : The equation (1), can be written,

$$(3x - 4y + \lambda)^2 = (6\lambda + 18)x + y(101 - 8\lambda) + \lambda^2 - 19 \qquad ...(3)$$

Choose λ so that the straight lines

$$3x - 4y + \lambda = 0$$

and $(6\lambda + 18)x + y(101 - 8\lambda) + \lambda^2 - 19 = 0$
may be at right angles.

Hence, λ is given by

$$3(6\lambda + 18) - 4(101 - 8\lambda) = 0 \qquad \text{(Art. 69)}$$

and therefore, $\lambda = 7$

The equation (3) therefore, becomes

$$(3x - 4y + 7)^2 = 15\,(4x + 3y + 2)$$

i.e., $\qquad \left(\dfrac{3x - 4y + 7}{\sqrt{25}}\right)^2 = 3 \cdot \dfrac{4x + 3y + 2}{\sqrt{25}} \qquad$ ...(4)

Let AL be the straight line

$$3x - 4y + 7 = 0 \qquad \text{...(5)}$$

and AM the straight line $\qquad 4x + 3y + 2 = 0 \qquad$ ...(6)

These are at right angles.

If P be any point on the parabola and PN be perpendicular to AL, the equation (4) gives $PN^2 = 3 \cdot AN$.

Hence, as in the first method, we have the parabola.

The vertex is found by solving equations (5) and (6) and is therefore, the point $(-\dfrac{29}{25}, \dfrac{22}{25})$.

In drawing curves it is often advisable, as a verification, to find whether they cut the original axes of coordinates.

Thus, the points in which the given parabola cuts the axis of x are found by putting $y = 0$ in the original equation. The resulting equation is $9x^2 - 18x + 19 = 0$, which has imaginary roots.

The parabola does not therefore, meet Ox.

Similarly it meets Oy in points given by $16y^2 - 101y + 19 = 0$, the roots of which are nearly $6\dfrac{1}{8}$ and $\dfrac{3}{16}$.

The values of OQ and OQ' should therefore, be nearly $\dfrac{3}{16}$ and $6\dfrac{1}{8}$.

➤ **364.** *To find the direction and magnitude of the axes of the central conic section*

$$ax^2 + 2hxy + by^2 = 1 \qquad \text{...(1)}$$

First Method : We know that, when the equation to a central conic section has no term containing xy and the axes are rectangular, the axes of coordinates are the axes of the curve.

Now in Art. 349 we shewed that, to get rid of the term involving xy, we must turn the axes through an angle θ given by

$$\tan 2\theta = \frac{2h}{a - b} \qquad \text{...(2)}$$

The axes of the curve are therefore, inclined to the axes of coordinates at an angle θ given by (2).

Now (2) can be written

$$\frac{2 \tan \theta}{1 - \tan^2 \theta} = \frac{2h}{a - b} = \frac{1}{\lambda} \text{ (say),}$$

$\therefore$ $\tan^2 \theta + 2 \lambda \tan \theta - 1 = 0$ ...(3)

This, being a quadratic equation, gives two values for θ, which differ by a right angle, since the product of the two values of $\tan \theta$ is $- 1$. Let these values be θ_1 and θ_2, which are therefore, the inclinations of the required axes of the curve to the axis of x.

Again, in polar coordinates, equation (1) may be written

$$r^2(a \cos^2 \theta + 2h \cos \theta \sin \theta + b \sin^2 \theta) = 1 = \cos^2 \theta + \sin^2 \theta,$$

i.e., $r^2 = \dfrac{\cos^2 \theta + \sin^2 \theta}{a \cos^2 \theta + 2h \cos \theta \sin \theta + b \sin^2 \theta} = \dfrac{1 + \tan^2 \theta}{a + 2h \tan \theta + b \tan^2 \theta}$ ...(4)

If in (4) we substitute either value of $\tan \theta$ derived from (3) we obtain the length of the corresponding semi-axis.

The directions and magnitudes of the axes are therefore, both found.

Second Method : The directions of the axes of the conic are, as in the first method, given by

$$\tan 2\theta = \frac{2h}{a - b}$$

When referred to the axes of the conic section as the axes of coordinates, let the equation become

$$\frac{x^2}{\alpha^2} + \frac{y^2}{\beta^2} = 1 \qquad \qquad ...(5)$$

Since the equation (1) has become equation (5) by a change of axes without a change of origin, we have, by Art. 135,

$$\frac{1}{\alpha^2} + \frac{1}{\beta^2} = a + b \qquad \qquad ...(6)$$

and $\dfrac{1}{\alpha^2 \beta^2} = ab - h^2$ ...(7)

These two equations easily determine the semi-axes α and β. [For if from the square of (6) we subtract four times equation (7) we have $\left(\dfrac{1}{\alpha^2} - \dfrac{1}{\beta^2}\right)^2$, and hence $\dfrac{1}{\alpha^2} - \dfrac{1}{\beta^2}$; hence by (6) we get $\dfrac{1}{\alpha^2}$ and $\dfrac{1}{\beta^2}$.]

The difficulty of this method lies in the fact that we cannot always easily determine to which direction for an axis the value α belongs and to which the value β.

If the original axes be inclined at an angle ω, the equations (6) and (7) are, by Art. 137,

$$\frac{1}{\alpha^2} + \frac{1}{\beta^2} = \frac{a + b - 2h \cos \omega}{\sin^2 \omega},$$

and

$$\frac{1}{\alpha^2 \beta^2} = \frac{ab - h^2}{\sin^2 \omega}$$

Cor. 1. : The reciprocals of the squares of the semi-axes are, by (6) and (7), the roots of the equation

$$Z^2 - (a + b) Z + ab - h^2 = 0$$

Cor. 2. : It is shewn in most treatises on Geometrical Conics that the area of an ellipse is $\pi\alpha\beta$, which by equation (7) $= \dfrac{\pi}{\sqrt{ab - h^2}}$.

➤ **365.**

EXAMPLE 1 *Trace the curve*

$$14x^2 - 4xy + 11y^2 - 44x - 58y + 71 = 0 \qquad \ldots(1)$$

Since, $(-2)^2 - 14 \cdot 11$ is negative, the curve is an ellipse, [Art. 358.] By Art. 352 the centre $(\bar{x}, \bar{y})$ of the curve is given by the equations

$$14\bar{x} - 2\bar{y} - 22 = 0 \quad \text{and} \quad -2\bar{x} + 11\bar{y} - 29 = 0$$

Hence, $\bar{x} = 2$, and $\bar{y} = 3$.

The equation referred to parallel axes through the centre is

therefore, $14x^2 - 4xy + 11y^2 + c' = 0$

where $c' = -22\bar{x} - 29\bar{y} + 71 = -60$

so that the equation is

$$14x^2 - 4xy + 11y^2 = 60 \qquad \ldots(2)$$

The directions of the axes are given by

$$\tan 2\theta = \frac{2h}{a - b} = \frac{-4}{14 - 11} = -\frac{4}{3}$$

so that $\dfrac{2 \tan \theta}{1 - \tan^2 \theta} = -\dfrac{4}{3}$

and hence, $2 \tan^2 \theta - 3 \tan \theta - 2 = 0$

Therefore, $\tan \theta_1 = 2$ and $\tan \theta_2 = -\dfrac{1}{2}$

Referred to polar coordinates the equation (2) is

$$r^2 (14 \cos^2 \theta - 4 \cos \theta \sin \theta + 11 \sin^2 \theta) = 60 (\cos^2 \theta + \sin^2 \theta)$$

i.e., $r^2 = 60 \dfrac{1 + \tan^2 \theta}{14 - 4 \tan \theta + 11 \tan^2 \theta}$

When $\qquad \tan \theta_1 = 2, \ r_1^2 = 60 \times \dfrac{1+4}{14-8+44} = 6,$

When $\qquad \tan \theta_2 = -\dfrac{1}{2}, \ r_2^2 = 60 \times \dfrac{1+\dfrac{1}{4}}{14+2+\dfrac{11}{4}} = 4$

The lengths of the semi-axes are therefore $\sqrt{6}$ and 2.

Hence, to draw the curve, take the point C, whose coordinates are (2, 3).

Through it draw $A'CA$ inclined at an angle $\tan^{-1} 2$ to the axis of x and mark off

$$A'C = CA = \sqrt{6}$$

Draw BCB' at right angles to ACA' and take $B'C = CB = 2$.

The required ellipse has AA' and BB' as its axes.

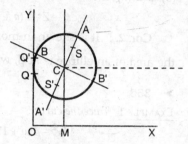

It would be found, as a verification, that the curve does not meet the original axis of x, and that it meets the axis of y at distances from the origin equal to, about 2 and $3\dfrac{1}{2}$ respectively.

EXAMPLE 2 *Trace the curve*

$$x^2 - 3xy + y^2 + 10x - 10y + 21 = 0 \qquad \ldots(1)$$

Since, $\left(\dfrac{-3}{2}\right)^2 - 1 \cdot 1$ is positive, the curve is a hyperbola. [Art. 358]

The centre $(\bar{x}, \bar{y})$ is given by

$$\bar{x} - \dfrac{3}{2}\bar{y} + 5 = 0$$

and $\qquad\qquad \dfrac{-3}{2}\bar{x} + \bar{y} - 5 = 0$

so that $\qquad\qquad \bar{x} = -2, \quad \text{and} \quad \bar{y} = 2$

The equation to the curve, referred to parallel axes through the centre, is then

$$x^2 - 3xy + y^2 + 5(-2) - 5 \times 2 + 21 = 0$$

i.e., $\qquad\qquad x^2 - 3xy + y^2 = -1 \qquad \ldots(2)$

The direction of the axes is given by

$$\tan 2\theta = \dfrac{2h}{a-b} = \dfrac{-3}{1-1} = \infty$$

so that $\qquad\qquad 2\theta = 90° \quad \text{or} \quad 270°,$

and hence $\qquad\qquad \theta_1 = 45° \quad \text{and} \quad \theta_2 = 135°.$

The equation (2) in polar coordinates is

$$r^2 (\cos^2 \theta - 3 \cos \theta \sin \theta + \sin^2 \theta) = - (\sin^2 \theta + \cos^2 \theta),$$

i.e.,

$$r^2 = - \frac{1 + \tan^2 \theta}{1 - 3 \tan \theta + \tan^2 \theta}$$

When $\theta_1 = 45°$, $r_1^2 = - \dfrac{2}{1 - 3 + 1} = 2$, so that $r_1 = \sqrt{2}$

When $\theta_2 = 135°$, $r_2^2 = - \dfrac{2}{1 + 3 + 1} = \dfrac{-2}{5}$, so that $r_2 = \sqrt{\dfrac{-2}{5}}$.

To construct the curve take the point C whose coordinates are -2 and 2. Through C draw a straight line ACA' inclined at $45°$ to the axis of x and mark off $A'C = CA = \sqrt{2}$.

Also through A, draw a straight line KAK' perpendicular to CA and take $AK = K'A = \sqrt{\dfrac{2}{5}}$. By Art. 315, CK and CK' are then the asymptotes.

The curve is therefore, a hyperbola whose centre is C whose transverse axis is $A'A$, and whose asymptotes are CK and CK'.

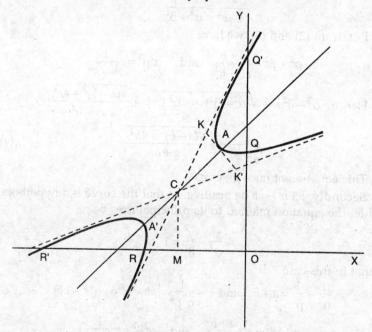

On putting $x = 0$ it will be found that the curve meets the axis of y where $y = 3$ or 7, and, on putting $y = 0$, that it meets the axis of x, where $x = -3$ or -7

Hence $OQ = 3$ $OQ' = 7$, $OR = 3$, and $OR' = 7$

➤ **366.** *To find the eccentricity of the central conic section*

$$ax^2 + 2hxy + by^2 = 1 \qquad \ldots(1)$$

First, let $h^2 - ab$ be negative, so that the curve is an ellipse, and let the equation to the ellipse, referred to its axes, be

$$\frac{x^2}{\alpha^2} + \frac{y^2}{\beta^2} = 1$$

By the theory of Invariants (Art. 135) we have

$$\frac{1}{\alpha^2} + \frac{1}{\beta^2} = a + b \qquad \ldots(2)$$

and

$$\frac{1}{\alpha^2\beta^2} = ab - h^2 \qquad \ldots(3)$$

Also, if e be the eccentricity, we have, if α be $> \beta$,

$$e^2 = \frac{\alpha^2 - \beta^2}{\alpha^2}$$

$$\therefore \quad \frac{e^2}{2 - e^2} = \frac{\alpha^2 - \beta^2}{\alpha^2 + \beta^2}$$

But, from (2) and (3), we have

$$\alpha^2 + \beta^2 = \frac{a + b}{ab - h^2} \quad \text{and} \quad \alpha^2\beta^2 = \frac{1}{ab - h^2}$$

Hence, $\alpha^2 - \beta^2 = + \sqrt{(\alpha^2 + \beta^2)^2 - 4\alpha^2\beta^2} = + \dfrac{\sqrt{(a - b)^2 + 4h^2}}{ab - h^2}$

$$\therefore \quad \frac{e^2}{2 - e^2} = + \frac{\sqrt{(a - b)^2 + 4h^2}}{a + b} \qquad \ldots(4)$$

This equation at once gives e^2.

Secondly, let $h^2 - ab$ be positive, so that the curve is a hyperbola, and let the equation referred to its principal axes be

$$\frac{x^2}{\alpha^2} - \frac{y^2}{\beta^2} = 1$$

so that in this case

$$\frac{1}{\alpha^2} - \frac{1}{\beta^2} = a + b \quad \text{and} \quad -\frac{1}{\alpha^2\beta^2} = ab - h^2 = -(h^2 - ab)$$

Hence, $\quad \alpha^2 - \beta^2 = -\dfrac{a + b}{h^2 - ab} \quad$ and $\quad \alpha^2\beta^2 = \dfrac{1}{h^2 - ab}$

so that $\quad \alpha^2 + \beta^2 = + \sqrt{(\alpha^2 - \beta^2)^2 + 4\alpha^2\beta^2} = + \dfrac{\sqrt{(a - b)^2 + 4h^2}}{h^2 - ab}$

In this case, if e be the eccentricity, we have

$$e^2 = \frac{\alpha^2 + \beta^2}{\alpha^2}$$

i.e., $\dfrac{e^2}{2 - e^2} = \dfrac{\alpha^2 + \beta^2}{\alpha^2 - \beta^2} = -\dfrac{\sqrt{(a-b)^2 + 4h^2}}{a + b}$ ...(5)

This equation gives e^2.

In each case we see that e is a root of the equation

$$\left(\frac{e^2}{2 - e^2}\right)^2 = \frac{(a-b)^2 + 4h^2}{(a+b)^2}$$

i.e., of the equation,

$$e^4 (ab - h^2) + \left\{(a-b)^2 + 4h^2\right\} (e^2 - 1) = 0$$

➤ **367.** *To obtain the foci of the central conic*

$$ax^2 + 2hxy + by^2 = 1$$

Let the direction of the axes of the conic be obtained as in Art. 364, and let θ_1 be the inclination of the major axis in the case of the ellipse, and the transverse axis in the case of the hyperbola, to the axis of x.

Let r_1^2 be the square of the radius corresponding to θ_1, and let r_2^2 be the square of the radius corresponding to the perpendicular direction. [In the case of the hyperbola r_2^2 will be a negative quantity.]

The distance of the focus from the centre is $\sqrt{r_1^2 - r_2^2}$ (Art. 247 and 295). One focus will therefore, be the point

$$(\sqrt{r_1^2 - r_2^2} \cos \theta_1, \ \sqrt{r_1^2 - r_2^2} \sin \theta_1),$$

and the other will be

$$(-\sqrt{r_1^2 - r_2^2} \cos \theta_1, \ -\sqrt{r_1^2 - r_2^2} \sin \theta_1)$$

<u>EXAMPLE</u> *Find the foci of the ellipse traced in Art. 365.*

Here, $\tan \theta_1 = 2$, so that $\sin \theta_1 = \dfrac{2}{\sqrt{5}}$ and $\cos \theta_1 = \dfrac{1}{\sqrt{5}}$

Also $r_1^2 = 6$, and $r_2^2 = 4$, so that $\sqrt{r_1^2 - r_2^2} = \sqrt{2}$

The coordinates of the foci referred to axes through C are therefore

$$\left(\frac{\sqrt{2}}{\sqrt{5}}, \frac{2\sqrt{2}}{\sqrt{5}}\right) \text{ and } \left(-\frac{\sqrt{2}}{\sqrt{5}}, -\frac{2\sqrt{2}}{\sqrt{5}}\right)$$

Their coordinates referred to the original axes OX and OY are

$$\left(\bar{x} \pm \frac{\sqrt{2}}{\sqrt{5}}, \bar{y} \pm \frac{2\sqrt{2}}{\sqrt{5}}\right), \quad \textit{i.e.} \quad \left(2 \pm \frac{\sqrt{2}}{\sqrt{5}}, 3 \pm \frac{2\sqrt{2}}{\sqrt{5}}\right)$$

➤ **368.** The method of obtaining the coordinates of the focus of a parabola given by the general equation may be exemplified by taking the example of Art. 363.

Here it was shewn that the latus rectum is equal to 3, so that, if S be the focus, AS is $\frac{3}{4}$.

It was also shewn that the coordinates of A referred to OX and OY are $-\frac{2}{5}$ and $\frac{7}{5}$.

The coordinates of S referred to the same axes are

$$-\frac{2}{5}+\frac{3}{4} \quad \text{and} \quad \frac{7}{5}, \quad i.e., \quad \frac{7}{20} \quad \text{and} \quad \frac{7}{5}$$

Its coordinates referred to the original axes are therefore,

$$\frac{7}{20}\cos\theta - \frac{7}{5}\sin\theta \quad \text{and} \quad \frac{7}{20}\sin\theta + \frac{7}{5}\cos\theta$$

i.e.,

$$\frac{7}{20}\frac{4}{5} - \frac{7}{5}\frac{3}{5} \quad \text{and} \quad \frac{7}{20}\frac{3}{5} + \frac{7}{5}\frac{4}{5}$$

i.e.,

$$-\frac{14}{25} \quad \text{and} \quad \frac{133}{100}$$

In Art. 393 equations will be found to give the foci of any conic section directly, so that the conic need not first be traced.

➤ **369.**

EXAMPLE 1 *Trace the curve*

$$3(3x-2y+4)^2 + 2(2x+3y-5)^2 = 39 \qquad \text{...(1)}$$

The equation may be written

$$3\left(\frac{3x-2y+4}{\sqrt{13}}\right)^2 + 2\left(\frac{2x+3y-5}{\sqrt{13}}\right)^2 = 3 \qquad \text{...(2)}$$

Now, the straight lines $3x-2y+4=0$ and $2x+3y-5=0$ are at right angles. Let them be CM and CN, intersecting in C which is the point $(-\frac{2}{13}, \frac{23}{13})$.

If P be any point on the curve and PM and PN the perpendiculars upon these lines, the lengths of PM and PN are

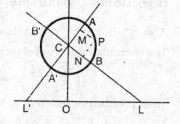

$$\frac{3x-2y+4}{\sqrt{13}} \quad \text{and} \quad \frac{2x+3y-5}{\sqrt{13}}$$

Hence equation (2) states that

$$3PM^2 + 2PN^2 = 3$$

i.e..,
$$\frac{PM^2}{1} + \frac{PN^2}{\frac{3}{2}} = 1$$

The locus of P is therefore, an ellipse whose semi-axes measured along CM and CN are $\sqrt{\frac{3}{2}}$ and 1 respectively.

EXAMPLE 2 *What is represented by the equation*

$$(x^2 - a^2)^2 + (y^2 - a^2)^2 = a^4 ?$$

The equation may be written in the form

$$x^4 + y^4 - 2a^2(x^2 + y^2) + a^4 = 0$$

i.e.,
$$(x^2 + y^2)^2 - 2a^2(x^2 + y^2) + a^4 = 2x^2y^2$$

i.e.,
$$(x^2 + y^2 - a^2)^2 - (\sqrt{2}\,xy)^2 = 0$$

i.e. $(x^2 + \sqrt{2}\,xy + y^2 - a^2)(x^2 - \sqrt{2}\,xy + y^2 - a^2) = 0$

The locus therefore, consists of the two ellipses

$$x^2 + \sqrt{2}\,xy + y^2 - a^2 = 0 \quad \text{and} \quad x^2 - \sqrt{2}\,xy + y^2 = a^2 = 0.$$

These ellipses are equal and their semi-axes would be found to be

$$a\sqrt{2 + \sqrt{2}} \quad \text{and} \quad a\sqrt{2 - \sqrt{2}}$$

The major axis of the first is inclined at an angle of 135° to the axis of x, and that of the second at an angle of 45°.

EXAMPLES XLI

Trace the parabolas:

1. $(x - 4y)^2 = 51y$
2. $(x - y)^2 = x + y + 1$
3. $(5x - 12y)^2 = 2ax + 29ay + a^2$
4. $(4x + 3y + 15)^2 = 5(3x - 4y)$
5. $16x^2 + 24xy + 9y^2 - 5x - 10y + 1 = 0$
6. $9x^2 + 24xy + 16y^2 - 4y - x + 7 = 0$
7. $144x^2 - 120xy + 25y^2 + 619x - 272y + 663 = 0$ and find its focus.
8. $16x^2 - 24xy + 9y^2 + 32x + 86y - 39 = 0$
9. $4x^2 - 4xy + y^2 - 12x + 6y + 9 = 0$
    Find the position and magnitude of the axes of the conics
10. $12x^2 - 12xy + 7y^2 = 48$
11. $3x^2 + 2xy + 3y^2 = 8$

12. $x^2 - xy - 6y^2 = 6$

Trace the following central conics.

13. $x^2 - 2xy \cos 2\alpha + y^2 = 2a^2$

14. $x^2 - 2xy \operatorname{cosec} 2\alpha + y^2 = a^2$

15. $xy = a(x + y)$

16. $xy - y^2 = a^2$

17. $y^2 - 2xy + 2x^2 + 2x - 2y = 0$

18. $x^2 + xy + y^2 + x + y = 1$

19. $2x^2 + 3xy - 2y^2 - 7x + y - 2 = 0$

20. $40x^2 + 36xy + 25y^2 - 196x - 122y + 205 = 0$

21. $9x^2 - 32xy + 9y^2 + 60x + 10y = 64\frac{1}{2}$

22. $x^2 - xy + 2y^2 - 2ax - 6ay + 7a^2 = 0$

23. $10x^2 - 48xy - 10y^2 + 38x + 44y - 5\frac{1}{2} = 0$

24. $4x^2 + 27xy + 35y^2 - 14x - 31y - 6 = 0$

25. $(3x - 4y + a)(4x + 3y + a) = a^2$

26. $3(2x - 3y + 4)^2 + 2(3x + 2y - 5)^2 = 78$

27. $2(3x - 4y + 5)^2 - 3(4x + 3y - 10)^2 = 150$

Find the products of the semi-axes of the conics

28. $y^2 - 4xy + 5x^2 = 2$

29. $4(3x + 4y - 7)^2 + 3(4x - 3y + 9)^2 = 3$

30. $11x^2 + 16xy - y^2 - 70x - 40y + 82 = 0$

Find the foci and the eccentricity of the conics

31. $x^2 - 3xy + 4ax = 2a^2$

32. $4xy - 3x^2 - 2ay = 0$

33. $5x^2 + 6xy + 5y^2 + 12x + 4y + 6 = 0$

34. $x^2 + 4xy + y^2 - 2x + 2y - 6 = 0$

35. Shew that the latus rectum of the parabola

$$(a^2 + b^2)(x^2 + y^2) = (bx + ay - ab)^2$$

is
$$2ab \div \sqrt{a^2 + b^2}$$

36. Prove that the lengths of the semi-axes of the conic

$$ax^2 + 2hxy + ay^2 = d$$

are
$$\sqrt{\frac{d}{a+h}} \quad \text{and} \quad \sqrt{\frac{d}{a-h}}$$

respectively, and that their equation is $x^2 - y^2 = 0$

37. Prove that the squares of the semi-axes of the conic

$$ax^2 + 2hxy + by^2 + 2gx + 2fy + c = 0$$

are $\qquad -2\Delta \div \left\{ (ab - h^2)\,(a + b \pm \sqrt{(a-b)^2 + 4h^2}) \right\}$

where Δ is the discriminant.

38. If λ be a variable parameter, prove that the locus of the vertices of the hyperbolas given by the equation $x^2 - y^2 + \lambda xy = a^2$ is the curve $(x^2 + y^2)^2 = a^2(x^2 - y^2)$.

39. If the point $(at_1^2, 2at_1)$ on the parabola $y^2 = 4ax$ be called the point t_1, prove that the axis of the second parabola through the four points t_1, t_2, t_3, and t_4 makes with the axis of the first an angle

$$\cot^{-1}\left(\frac{t_1 + t_2 + t_3 + t_4}{4}\right)$$

Prove also that if two parabolas meet in four points the distances of the centroid of the four points from the axes are proportional to the latera recta.

40. If the product of the semi-axes of the conic $x^2 + 2xy + 17y^2 = 8$ be unity, shew that the axes of coordinates are inclined at an angle

$$\sin^{-1}\frac{1}{2}.$$

41. Sketch the curve $6x^2 - 7xy - 5y^2 - 4x + 11y = 2$, the axes being inclined at an angle of $30°$.

42. Prove that the eccentricity of the conic given by the general equation satisfies the relation

$$\frac{e^4}{1 - e^2} + 4 = \frac{(a + b - 2h \cos \omega)^2}{(ab - h^2)\sin^2 \omega},$$

where ω is the angle between the axes.

43. The axes being changed in any way, without any change of origin, prove that in the general equation of the second degree the quantities $c,\; \dfrac{f^2 + g^2 - 2fg \cos \omega}{\sin^2 \omega},\; \dfrac{af^2 + bg^2 - 2fgh}{\sin^2 \omega}$, and $\dfrac{\Delta}{\sin^2 \omega}$ are invariants, in addition to the quantities in Art. 137.

[On making the most general substitutions of Art. 132 it is clear that c is unaltered; proceed as in Art. 137, but introduce the condition that the resulting expressions are equal to the product of two linear quantities (Art. 116); the results will then follow.]

16

THE GENERAL CONIC

➤ **370.** In the present chapter we shall consider properties of conic sections which are given by the general equation of the second degree, *viz.*

$$ax^2 + 2hxy + by^2 + 2gx + 2fy + c = 0 \qquad \ldots(1)$$

For brevity, the left-hand side of this equation is often called $\phi(x, y)$, so that the general equation to a conic is

$$\phi(x, y) = 0.$$

Similarly, $\phi(x', y')$ denotes the value of the left-hand side of (1) when x' and y' are substituted for x and y.

The equation (1) is often also written in the form $S = 0$.

➤ **371.** On dividing by c, the equation (1) contains five independent constants $\dfrac{a}{c}, \dfrac{h}{c}, \dfrac{b}{c}, \dfrac{g}{c}$ and $\dfrac{f}{c}$.

To determine these five constants, we shall therefore require five conditions. Conversely, if five independent conditions be given, the constants can be determined. Only one conic, or at any rate, only a finite number of conics, can be drawn to satisfy five independent conditions.

➤ **372.** *To find the equation to the tangent at any point (x', y') of the conic section*

$$\phi(x, y) \equiv ax^2 + 2hxy + by^2 + 2gx + 2fy + c = 0 \qquad \ldots(1)$$

Let (x'', y'') be any other point on the conic.

The equation to the straight line joining this point to (x', y') is

$$y - y' = \frac{y'' - y'}{x'' - x'}(x - x') \qquad \ldots(2)$$

Since both (x', y') and (x'', y'') lie on (1), we have

$$ax'^2 + 2hx'y' + by'^2 + 2gx' + 2fy' + c = 0 \qquad \ldots(3)$$

and $\qquad ax''^2 + 2hx''y'' + by''^2 + 2gx'' + 2fy'' + c = 0 \qquad \ldots(4)$

Hence, by subtraction, we have

$$a (x'^2 - x''^2) + 2h (x'y' - x'' y'') + b (y'^2 - y''^2)$$
$$+ 2g (x' - x'') + 2f(y' - y'') = 0 \qquad ...(5)$$

But $\quad 2(x'y' - x''y'') = (x' + x'') (y' - y'') + (x' - x'') (y' + y'')$

so that (5) can be written in the form

$$(x' - x'') [a (x' + x'') + h (y' + y'') + 2g]$$
$$+ (y' - y'') [h (x' + x'') + b (y' + y'') + 2f] = 0$$

i.e., $\qquad \dfrac{y'' - y'}{x'' - x'} = -\dfrac{a (x' + x'') + h (y' + y'') + 2g}{h (x' + x'') + b (y' + y'') + 2f}$

The equation to any secant is therefore,

$$y - y' = -\dfrac{a (x' + x'') + h (y' + y'') + 2g}{h (x' + x'') + b (y' + y'') + 2f} (x - x') \qquad ...(6)$$

To obtain the equation to the tangent at (x', y'), we put $x'' = x'$ and $y'' = y'$ in this equation, and it becomes

$$y - y' = -\dfrac{ax' + hy' + g}{hx' + by' + f} (x - x')$$

i.e., $\quad (ax' + hy' + g) x + (hx' + by' + f) y$
$$= ax'^2 + 2hx'y' + by'^2 + gx' + fy'$$
$$= - gx' - fy' - c \qquad \text{[by equation (3)]}$$

The required equation is therefore,

$$axx' + h(xy' + x'y) + byy' + g(x + x') + f(y + y') + c = 0 \qquad ...(7)$$

Cor. 1.: The equation (7) may be written down, from the general equation of the second degree, by substituting xx' for x^2, yy' for y^2, $xy' + x'y$ for $2xy$, $x + x'$ for $2x$ and $y + y'$ for $2y$. (Cf. Art. 152.)

Cor. 2.: If the conic pass through the origin we have $c = 0$, and then the tangent at the origin (where $x' = 0$ and $y' = 0$) is

$$gx + fy = 0.$$

i.e., the equation to the tangent at the origin is obtained by equating to zero the terms of the lowest degree in the equation to the conic.

➤ **373.** The equation of the previous article may also be obtained as follows; if (x', y') and (x'', y'') be two points on the conic section, the equation to the line joining them is

$$a (x - x') (x - x'') + h [(x - x') (y - y'') + (x - x'') (y - y')] + b (y - y') (y - y'')$$
$$= ax^2 + 2hxy + by^2 + 2gx + 2fy + c \qquad ...(1)$$

For the terms of the second degree on the two sides of (1) cancel, and the equation reduces to one of the first degree, thus representing a straight line.

Also, since (x', y') lies on the curve, the equation is satisfied by putting $x = x'$ and $y = y'$

Hence, (x', y') is point lying on (1).

So, (x'', y'') lies on (1)

It therefore, is the straight line joining them.

Putting $x'' = x'$ and $y'' = y'$ we have, as the equation to the tangent at (x', y'),

$$a(x - x')^2 + 2h(x - x')(y - y') + b(y - y')^2$$
$$= ax^2 + 2hxy + by^2 + 2gx + 2fy + c$$

i.e., $2axx' + 2h(x'y + xy') + 2byy' + 2gx + 2fy + c$
$$= ax'^2 + 2hx'y' + by'^2$$
$$= -2gx' - 2fy' - c, \text{ since } (x', y') \text{ lies on the conic.}$$

Hence, the equation (7) of the last article.

➤ **374.** *To find the condition that any straight line*

$$lx + my + n = 0 \qquad \qquad \text{...(1)}$$

may touch the conic

$$ax^2 + 2hxy + by^2 + 2gx + 2fy + c = 0 \qquad \qquad \text{...(2)}$$

Substituting for y in (2) from (1), we have for the equation giving the abscissae of the points of intersection of (1) and (2),

$$x^2(am^2 - 2hlm + bl^2) - 2x(hmn - bln - gm^2 + flm)$$
$$+ bn^2 - 2fmn + cm^2 = 0 \qquad \qquad \text{...(3)}$$

If (1) be a tangent, the values of x given by (3) must be equal. The condition for this is, (Art. 1)

$$(hmn - bln - gm^2 + flm)^2 = (am^2 - 2hlm + bl^2)(bn^2 - 2fmn + cm^2).$$

On simplifying, we have, after division by m^2

$$l^2(bc - f^2) + m^2(ca - g^2) + n^2(ab - h^2) + 2mn(gh - af)$$
$$+ 2nl(hf - bg) + 2lm(fg - ch) = 0$$

EXAMPLE   *Find the equations o the tangents to the conic*

$$x^2 + 4xy + 3y^2 - 5x - 6y + 3 = 0 \qquad \qquad \text{...(1)}$$

which are parallel to the straight line $x + 4y = 0.$

The equation to any such tangent is

$$x + 4y + c = 0 \qquad \qquad \text{...(2)}$$

where c is to be determined

This straight line meets (1) in points given by

$$3x^2 - 2x(5c + 28) + 3c^2 + 24c + 48 = 0$$

The roots of this equation are equal, *i.e.*, the line (2) is a tangent, if

$$\{2(5c + 28)\}^2 = 4 \cdot 3 \cdot (3c^2 + 24c + 48)$$

i.e., if $c = -5 \text{ or } -8$

The required tangents are therefore

$$x + 4y - 5 = 0 \quad \text{and} \quad x + 4y - 8 = 0$$

➤ **375.** As in Arts. 214 and 274 it may be proved that the polar of (x', y') with respect to $\phi(x, y) = 0$ is

$$(ax' + hy' + g)x + (hx' + by' + f)y + gx' + fy' + c = 0$$

The form of the equation to a polar is therefore the same as that of a tangent.

Just as in Art. 217 it may now be shewn that, if the polar of P passes through T, the polar of T passes through P.

The chord of the conic which is bisected at (x', y'), being parallel to the polar of (x', y') [Arts. 221 and 280], has an equation

$$(ax' + hy' + g)(x - x') + (hx' + by' + f)(y - y') = 0$$

➤ **376.** *To find the equation to the diameter bisecting all chords parallel to the straight line $y = mx$. (See fig. Art. 279)*

Any such chord is $y = mx + K$ ...(1)

This meets the conic section

$$ax^2 + 2hxy + by^2 + 2gx + 2fy + c = 0$$

in points whose abscissae are given by

$$ax^2 + 2hx(mx + K) + b(mx + K)^2 + 2gx + 2f(mx + K) + c = 0$$

i.e., by $x^2(a + 2hm + bm^2) + 2x(hK + bmK + g + fm) + bK^2 + 2fK + c = 0$

If x_1 and x_2 be the roots of this equation, we therefore have

$$x_1 + x_2 = -2\frac{(h + bm)K + g + fm}{a + 2hm + bm^2}$$

Let (X, Y) be the middle point of the required chord, so that

$$X = \frac{x_1 + x_2}{2} = -\frac{(h + bm)K + g + fm}{a + 2hm + bm^2} \quad \text{...(2)}$$

Also, since (X, Y) lies on (1) we have

$$Y = mX + K \quad \text{...(3)}$$

If between (2) and (3) we eliminate K, we have a relation between X and Y.

This relation is

$$- (a + 2hm + bm^2) X = (h + bm) (Y - mX) + g + fm.$$

i.e., $$X (a + hm) + Y (h + bm) + g + fm = 0$$

The locus of the required middle point is therefore the straight line whose equation is

$$x (a + hm) + y (h + bm) + g + fm = 0$$

If this be parallel to the straight line $y = m'x$, we have

$$m' = -\frac{a + hm}{h + bm} \qquad \ldots(4)$$

i.e., $$a + h (m + m') + bmm' = 0 \qquad \ldots(5)$$

This is therefore, the condition that the two straight lines $y = mx$ and $y = m'x$ may be parallel to conjugate diameters of the conic given by the general equation.

➤ **377.** *To find the condition that the pair of straight lines, whose equation is*

$$Ax^2 + 2Hxy + By^2 = 0 \qquad \ldots(1)$$

may be parallel to conjugate diameters of the general conic

$$ax^2 + 2hxy + by^2 + 2gx + 2fy + c = 0 \qquad \ldots(2)$$

Let the equations of the straight lines represented by (1) be $y = mx$ and $y = m'x$, so that (1) is equivalent to

$$B (y - mx) (y - m'x) = 0$$

and hence, $$m + m' = -\frac{2H}{B} \quad \text{and} \quad mm' = \frac{A}{B}$$

By the condition of the last article it therefore follows that the lines (1) are parallel to conjugate diameters if

$$a + h \left(-\frac{2H}{B} \right) + b \frac{A}{B} = 0$$

i.e., if $$Ab - 2Hh + Ba = 0$$

➤ **378.** *To prove that two concentric conic sections always have a pair, and only one pair, of common conjugate diameters and to find their equation.*

Let the two concentric conic sections be

$$ax^2 + 2hxy + by^2 = 1 \qquad \ldots(1)$$

and $$a'x^2 + 2h'xy + b'y^2 = 1 \qquad \ldots(2)$$

The straight lines

$$Ax^2 + 2Hxy + By^2 = 0 \qquad \ldots(3)$$

are conjugate diameters of both (1) and (2) if

$$Ab - 2Hh + Ba = 0$$

and $$Ab' - 2Hh' + Ba' = 0$$

Solving these two equations we have

$$\frac{A}{ha' - h'a} = \frac{-2H}{ab' - a'b} = \frac{B}{bh' - b'h}$$

Substituting these values in (3), we see that the straight lines

$$x^2 (ha' - h'a) - xy (ab' - a'b) + y^2 (bh' - b'h) = 0 \qquad \text{...(4)}$$

are always conjugate diameters of both (1) and (2).

Hence, there is always a pair of conjugate diameters, real, coincident, or imaginary, which are common to any two concentric conic sections.

═══ EXAMPLES XLII ═══

1. How many other conditions can a conic section satisfy when we are given (1) its centre, (2) its focus, (3) its eccentricity, (4) the positions of its axes, (5) a tangent, (6) a tangent and its point of contact, (7) the position of one of its asymptotes?

2. Find the condition that the straight line $lx + my = 1$ may touch the parabola $(ax - by)^2 - 2 (a^2 + b^2) (ax + by) + (a^2 + b^2)^2 = 0$, and shew that if this straight line meet the axes in P and Q, then PQ will, when it is a tangent, subtend a right angle at the point (a, b).

3. Two parabolas have a common focus; prove that the perpendicular from it upon the common tangent passes through the intersection of the directrices.

4. Shew that the conic $\dfrac{x^2}{a^2} + \dfrac{2xy}{ab} \cos \alpha + \dfrac{y^2}{b^2} = \sin^2 \alpha$ is inscribed in the rectangle, the equations to whose sides are $x^2 = a^2$ and $y^2 = b^2$ and that the quadrilateral formed by joining the points of contact is of constant perimeter $4 \sqrt{a^2 + b^2}$, whatever be the value of α.

5. A variable tangent to a conic meets two fixed tangents in two points, P and Q; prove that the locus of the middle point of PQ is a conic which becomes a straight line when the given conic is a parabola.

6. Prove that the chord of contact of tangents, drawn from an external point to the conic $ax^2 + 2hxy + by^2 = 1$, subtends a right angle at the centre if the point lie on the conic

$$x^2 (a^2 + h^2) + 2h (a + b) xy + y^2 (h^2 + b^2) = a + b.$$

7. Given the focus and directrix of a conic, prove that the polar of a given point with respect to it passes through another fixed point.

8. Prove that the locus of the centres of conics which touch the axes at distances a and b from the origin is the straight line $ay = bx$.

9. Prove that the locus of the poles of tangents to the conic $ax^2 + 2hxy + by^2 = 1$ with respect to the conic $a'x^2 + 2h'xy + b'y^2 = 1$ is the conic

$$a (h'x + b'y)^2 - 2h (a'x + h'y) (h'x + b'y) + b (a'x + h'y)^2 = ab - h^2.$$

10. Find the equations to the straight lines which are conjugate to the coordinate axes with respect to the conic $Ax^2 + 2Hxy + By^2 = 1$.

Find the condition that they may coincide, and interpret the result.

11. Find the equation to the common conjugate diameters of the conics

(1) $x^2 + 4xy + 6y^2 = 1$ and $2x^2 + 6xy + 9y^2 = 1$ and

(2) $2x^2 - 5xy + 3y^2 = 1$ and $2x^2 + 3xy - 9y^2 = 1$

12. Prove that the points of intersection of the conics

$$ax^2 + 2hxy + by^2 = 1 \quad \text{and} \quad a'x^2 + 2h'xy + b'y^2 = 1$$

are at the ends of conjugate diameters of the first conic, if

$$ab' + a'b - 2hh' = 2(ab - h^2).$$

13. Prove that the equation to the equi-conjugate diameters of the conic $ax^2 + 2hxy + by^2 = 1$ is

$$\frac{ax^2 + 2hxy + by^2}{ab - h^2} = \frac{2 (x^2 + y^2)}{a + b}.$$

➤ **379.** *Two conics, in general, intersect in four points, real or imaginary.*

For the general equation to two conics can be written in the form

$$ax^2 + 2x (hy + g) + by^2 + 2fy + c = 0$$

and $\qquad a'x^2 + 2x (h'y + g') + b'y^2 + 2f'y + c' = 0.$

Eliminating x from these equations, we find that the result is an equation of the fourth degree in y, giving therefore, four values, real or imaginary, for y. Also, by eliminating x^2 from these two equations, we see that there is only one value of x for each value of y. There are therefore, only four points of intersection.

➤ **380.** *Equation to any conic passing through the intersection of two given conics.*

Let $\qquad S \equiv ax^2 + 2hxy + by^2 + 2gx + 2fy + c = 0 \qquad$ ...(1)

and $\qquad S' \equiv a'x^2 + 2h'xy + b'y^2 + 2g'x + 2f'y + c' = 0 \qquad$ ...(2)

be the equations to the two given conics.

Then $\qquad\qquad\qquad\qquad S - \lambda S' = 0 \qquad$ ...(3)

is the equation to any conic passing through the intersections of (1) and (2).

For, since S and S' are both of the second degree in x and y, the (3) is of the second degree, and hence, represents a conic section.

Also, since (3) is satisfied when both S and S' are zero, it is satisfied by the points (real or imaginary) which are common to (1) and (2).

Hence, (3) is a conic which passes through the intersections of (1) and (2).

➤ **381.** *To find the equations to the straight lines passing through the intersections of two conics given by the general equations.*

As in the last article, the equation,

$$(a - \lambda a') x^2 + 2(h - \lambda h') xy + (b - \lambda b') y^2 + 2(g - \lambda g') x$$
$$+ 2 (f - \lambda f') y + (c - \lambda c') = 0 \qquad \ldots(1)$$

represents some conic through the intersections of the given conics.

Now, by Art. 116, (1) represents straight lines if

$$(a - \lambda a') (b - \lambda b') (c - \lambda c') + 2 (f - \lambda f') (g - \lambda g') (h - \lambda h') - (a - \lambda a') (f - \lambda f')^2$$
$$- (b - \lambda b') (g - \lambda g')^2 - (c - \lambda c') (h - \lambda h')^2 = 0 \qquad \ldots(2)$$

Now (2) is a cubic equation. The three values of λ found from it will, when substituted successively in (1), give the three pairs of straight lines which can be drawn through the (real or imaginary) intersections of the two conics.

Also, since a cubic equation always has at least one real root, one value of λ is always real, and it will be shown that there can always be drawn at least one pair of real straight lines through the intersections of two conics. [See Part II, Art. 96]

➤ **382.** *All conics which pass through the intersections of two rectangular hyperbolas are themselves rectangular hyperbolas.*

In this case, if $S = 0$ and $S' = 0$ be the two rectangular hyperbolas, we have

$$a + b = 0 \quad \text{and} \quad a' + b' = 0 \qquad \text{(Art. 358)}$$

Hence, in the conic $S - \lambda S' = 0$, the sum of the coefficients of x^2 and y^2

$$= (a - \lambda a') + (b - \lambda b') = (a + b) - \lambda (a' + b') = 0.$$

Hence, the conic $S - \lambda S' = 0$, *i.e.*, any conic through the intersections of the two rectangular hyperbolas, is itself a rectangular hyperbola.

Cor. : If two rectangular hyperbolas intersect in four points A, B, C and D, the two straight lines AD and BC, which are a conic through the intersection of the two hyperbolas, must be a rectangular hyperbola. Hence, AD and BC must be at right angles. Similarly, BD

and CA, and CD and AB, must be at right angles. Hence, D is the orthocentre of the triangle ABC.

Therefore, if two rectangular hyperbolas intersect in four points each point is the orthocentre of the triangle formed by the other three.

➤ **383.** *If $L = 0$, $M = 0$, $N = 0$, and $R = 0$ be the equations to the four sides of a quadrilateral taken in order, the equation to any conic passing through its angular points is*

$$LN = \lambda \cdot MR \qquad \qquad \dots(1)$$

For $L = 0$ passes through one pair of its angular points and $N = 0$ passes through the other pair. Hence, $LN = 0$ is the equation to a conic (*viz.* a pair of straight lines) passing through the four angular points.

Similarly, $MR = 0$ is the equation to another conic passing through the four points.

Hence, $LN = \lambda \cdot MR$ is the equation to any conic through the four points.

Geometrical meaning : Since L is proportional to the perpendicular from any point (x, y) upon the straight line $L = 0$, the relation (1) states that the product of the perpendiculars from any point of the curve upon the straight lines $L = 0$ and $N = 0$ is proportional to the product of the perpendiculars from the same point upon $M = 0$ and $R = 0$.

Hence, *if a conic circumscribe a quadrilateral, the ratio of the product of the perpendiculars from any point P of the conic upon two opposite sides of the quadrilateral to the product of the perpendiculars from P upon the other two sides is the same for all positions of P.*

➤ **384.** *Equations to the conic sections passing through the intersections of a conic and two given straight lines.*

Let $S = 0$ be the equation to the given conic.

Let $u = 0$ and $v = 0$ be the equations to the two given straight lines where

$$u \equiv ax + by + c$$

and

$$v \equiv a'x + b'y + c'$$

Let the straight line $u = 0$ meet the conic $S = 0$ in the points P and R and let $v = 0$ meet it in the points Q and T.

The equation to any conic which passes through the points P, Q, R and T will be of the form

$$S = \lambda \cdot u \cdot v \qquad \qquad \dots(1)$$

For (1) is satisfied by the coordinates of any point which lies both on $S = 0$ and on $u = 0$; for its coordinates on being substituted in (1) make both its members zero.

But the points P and R are the only points which lie both on $S = 0$ and on $u = 0$.

The equation (1) therefore, denotes a conic passing through P and R.

Similarly it goes through the intersections of $S = 0$ and $v = 0$, i.e., through the points Q and T.

Thus, (1) represents some conic going through the four points P, Q, R and T.

Also (1) represents any conic going through these four points. For the quantity λ may be so chosen that it shall go through any fifth point, or to make it satisfy any fifth condition; also five conditions completely determine a conic section.

EXAMPLE *Find the equation to the conic which passes through the point (1, 1) and also through the intersections of the conic*
$$x^2 + 2xy + 5y^2 - 7x - 3y + 6 = 0$$
with the straight lines $2x - y - 5 = 0$ and $3x + y - 11 = 0$. Find also the parabolas passing through the same points.

The equation to the required conic must by the last article be of the form
$$x^2 + 2xy + 5y^2 - 7x - 8y + 6 = \lambda (2x - y - 5)(3x + y - 11) \qquad \ldots(1)$$
This passes through the point (1, 1) if
$$1 + 2 + 5 - 7 - 8 + 6 = \lambda (2 - 1 - 5)(3 + 1 - 11)$$
i.e., if
$$\lambda = -\frac{1}{28}$$

The required equation then becomes
$$28(x^2 + 2xy + 5y^2 - 7x - 8y + 6) + (2x - y - 5)(3x + y - 11) = 0$$
i.e.,
$$34x^2 + 55xy + 139y^2 - 233x - 218y + 223 = 0$$
The equation to the required parabola will also be of the form (1),

i.e., $\quad x^2(1 - 6\lambda) + xy(2 + \lambda) + y^2(5 + \lambda) - x(7 - 37\lambda)$
$$- y(8 + 6\lambda) + 6 - 55\lambda = 0$$
This is a parabola (Art. 357) if $(2 + \lambda)^2 = 4(1 - 6\lambda)(5 + \lambda)$

i.e., if
$$\lambda = \frac{1}{5}[-12 \pm 4\sqrt{10}\,]$$

Substituting these values in (1), we have the required equations.

➤ **385. Particular cases of the equation,**

$$S = \lambda uv$$

I. Let $u = 0$ and $v = 0$ intersect on the curve, *i.e.*, in the figure of Art. 384 let the points P and Q coincide.

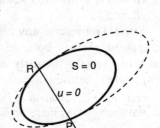

The conic $S = \lambda uv$ then goes through two coincident points at P and therefore, touches the original conic at P as in the figure.

II. Let $u = 0$ and $v = 0$ coincide, so that $v = u$.

In this case the point T also moves up to coincidence with R and the second conic touches the original conic at both the points P and R.

The equation to the second conic now becomes $S = \lambda u^2$.

When a conic touches a second conic at each of two points, the two conics are said to have **double contact** with one another.

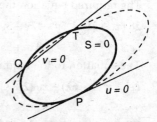

The two conics $S = \lambda u^2$ and $S = 0$ therefore, have double contact with one another, the straight line $u = 0$ passing through the two points of contact.

As a particular case we see that if $u = 0$, $v = 0$ and $w = 0$ be the equations to three straight lines then the equation $vw = \lambda u^2$ represents a conic touching the conic $vw = 0$ where $u = 0$ meets it, *i.e.*, it is a conic to which $v = 0$ and $w = 0$ are tangents and $u = 0$ is the chord of contact.

III. Let $u = 0$ be a tangent to the original conic.

In this case the two points P and R coincide, and the conic $S = \lambda uv$ touches $S = 0$ where $u = 0$ touches it, and $v = 0$ is the equation to the straight line joining the other points of intersection of the two conics.

If, in addition, $v = 0$ goes through the point of contact of $u = 0$, we have the equation to a conic which goes through three coincident points at P, the point of contact of $u = 0$; also the straight line joining P to the other point of intersection of the two conics is $v = 0$.

IV. Finally, let $v = 0$ and $u = 0$ coincide and be tangents at P. The equation $S = \lambda u^2$ now represents a conic section passing through four coincident points at the point where $u = 0$ touches $S = 0$.

➤ **386. Line at infinity :** We have shewn, in Art. 60, that the straight line, whose equation is

$$0 \cdot x + 0 \cdot y + C = 0$$

is altogether at an infinite distance. This straight line is called The Line at Infinity. Its equation may for brevity be written in the form $C = 0$.

We can shew that parallel lines meet on the line at infinity.

For the equations to any two parallel straight lines are

$$Ax + By + C = 0 \qquad \qquad \dots(1)$$

and $$Ax + By + C' = 0 \qquad \qquad \dots(2)$$

Now, (2) may be written in the form

$$Ax + By + C + \frac{C' - C}{C} \, (0 \cdot x + 0 \cdot y + C) = 0$$

and hence, by Art. 97, we see that it passes through the intersection of (1) and the straight line

$$0 \cdot x + 0 \cdot y + C = 0$$

Hence, (1), (2) and the line at infinity meet in a point.

➤ **387.** *Geometrical meaning of the equation*

$$S = \lambda u \qquad \qquad \dots(1)$$

where λ is a constant, and $u = 0$ is the equation of a straight line.

The equation (1) can be written in the form

$$S = \lambda u \times (0 \cdot x + 0 \cdot y + 1)$$

and hence, by Art. 384, represents a conic passing through the intersection of the conic $S = 0$ with the straight lines

$$u = 0 \quad \text{and} \quad 0 \cdot x + 0 \cdot y + 1 = 0$$

Hence, (1) passes through the intersection of $S = 0$ with the line at infinity.

Since $S = 0$ and $S = \lambda u$ have the same intersections with the line at infinity, it follows that these two conics have their asymptotes in the same direction.

Particular Case : Let

$$S \equiv x^2 + y^2 - a^2$$

so that $S = 0$ represents a circle.

Any other circle is

$$x^2 + y^2 - 2gx - 2fy + c = 0$$

i.e., $$x^2 + y^2 - a^2 = 2gx + 2fy - a^2 - c$$

so that its equation is of the form $S = \lambda u$.

It therefore, follows that any two circles must be looked upon as intersecting the line at infinity in the same two (imaginary) points. These imaginary points are called the Circular Points at Infinity.

➤ **388** *Geometrical meaning of the equation $S = \lambda$, where λ is a constant.* This equation can be written in the form

$$S = \lambda \, (0 \cdot x + 0 \cdot y + 1)^2$$

and therefore, by Art. 385, has double contact with $S = 0$ where the straight line $0 \cdot x + 0 \cdot y + 1 = 0$ meets it, *i.e.*, the tangents to the two conics at the points where they meet the line at infinity are the same.

The conics $S = 0$ and $S = \lambda$ therefore, have the same (real or imaginary) asymptotes.

Particular Case : Let $S = 0$ denote a circle. Then $S = \lambda$ (being an equation which differs from $S = 0$ only in its constant term) represents a concentric circle.

Two concentric circles must therefore, be looked upon as touching one another at the imaginary points where they meet the Line at Infinity.

Two concentric circles thus have double contact at the Circular Points at Infinity.

EXAMPLES XLIII

1. What is the geometrical meaning of the equations $S = \lambda \cdot T$ and $S = u^2 + ku$, where $S = 0$ is the equation of a conic, $T = 0$ is the equation of a tangent to it, and $u = 0$ is the equation of any straight line?

2. If the major axes of two conics be parallel, prove that the four points in which they meet are concyclic.

3. Prove that in general two parabolas can be drawn to pass through the intersections of the conics

$$ax^2 + 2hxy + by^2 + 2gx + 2fy + c = 0$$

and $\qquad a'x^2 + 2h'xy + b'y^2 + 2g'x + 2f'y + c' = 0$

and that their axes are at right angles if $h\,(a' - b') = h'\,(a - b)$.

4. Through a focus of an ellipse two chords are drawn and a conic is described to pass through their extremities, and also through the centre of the ellipse; prove that it cuts the major axis in another fixed point.

5. Through the extremities of a normal chord of an ellipse a circle is drawn such that its other common chord passes through the centre of the ellipse. Prove that the locus of the intersection of these common chords is an ellipse similar to the given ellipse. If the

eccentricity of the given ellipse be $\sqrt{2}\,(\sqrt{2}-1)$, prove that the two ellipses are equal.

6. If two rectangular hyperbolas intersect in four points A, B, C and D, prove that the circles described on AB and CD as diameters cut one another orthogonally.

7. A circle is drawn through the centre of the rectangular hyperbola $xy = c^2$ to touch the curve and meet it again in two points; prove that the locus of the feet of the perpendicular let fall from the centre upon the common chord is the hyperbola $4xy = c^2$.

8. If a circle touches an ellipse and passes through its centre, prove that the rectangle contained by the perpendiculars from the centre of the ellipse upon the common tangent and the common chord is constant for all points of contact.

9. From a point T whose coordinates are (x', y') a pair of tangents TP and TQ are drawn to the parabola $y^2 = 4ax$; prove that the line joining the other pair of points in which the circumcircle of the triangle TPQ meets the parabola is the polar of the point $(2a - x', -y')$ and hence that, if the circle touch the parabola, the line PQ touches an equal parabola.

10. Prove that the equation to the circle, having double contact with the ellipse $\dfrac{x^2}{a^2} + \dfrac{y^2}{b^2} = 1$ at the ends of a latus rectum, is

$$x^2 + y^2 - 2ae^3x = a^2\,(1 - e^2 - e^4)$$

11. Two circles have double contact with a conic, their chords of contact being parallel. Prove that the radical axis of the two circles is midway between the two chords of contact.

12. If a circle and an ellipse have double contact with one another, prove that the length of the tangent drawn from any point of the ellipse to the circle varies as the distance of that point from the chord of contact.

13. Two conics, A and B, have double contact with a third conic C. Prove that two of the common chords of A and B, and their chords of contact with C, meet in a point.

14. Prove that the general equation to the ellipse, having double contact with the circle $x^2 + y^2 = a^2$ and touching the axis of x at the origin, is
$$c^2x^2 + (a^2 + c^2)\,y^2 - 2a^2cy = 0.$$

15. A rectangular hyperbola has double contact with a fixed central conic. If the chord of contact always passes through a fixed point, prove that the locus of the centre of the hyperbola is a circle passing through the centre of the fixed conic.

16. A rectangular hyperbola has double contact with a parabola; prove that the centre of the hyperbola and the pole of the chord of contact are equidistant from the directrix of the parabola.

➤ **389.** *To find the equation of the pair of tangents that can be drawn from any point* (x', y') *to the general conic*

$$\phi(x, y) \equiv ax^2 + 2hxy + by^2 + 2gx + 2fy + c = 0$$

Let T be the given point (x', y'), and let P and R be the points where the tangents from T touch the conic.

The equation to PR is therefore,

$$u = 0$$

where $u \equiv (ax' + hy' + g) x + (hx' + by' + f) y$
$$+ gx' + fy' + c$$

The equation to any conic which touches $S = 0$ at both of the points P and R is

$$S = \lambda u^2 \qquad \text{(Art. 385)}$$

i.e., $ax^2 + 2hxy + by^2 + 2gx + 2fy + c$
$$= \lambda \left[(ax' + hy' + g)x + (hx' + by' + f) y + gx' + fy' + c \right]^2 \qquad \ldots(1)$$

Now, the pair of straight lines TP and TR is a conic section which touches the given conic at P and R and which also goes through the point T.

Also, we can only draw one conic to go through five points, *viz*, T, two points at P, and two points at R.

If then we find λ so that (1) goes through the point T, it must represent the two tangents TP and TR.

The equation (1) is satisfied by x' and y' if

$$ax'^2 + 2hx'y' + by'^2 + 2gx' + 2fy' + c$$
$$= \lambda(ax'^2 + 2hx'y' + by'^2 + 2gx' + 2fy' + c)^2$$

i.e., if $\qquad \lambda = \dfrac{1}{\phi(x', y')}$

The required equation (1), then becomes

$$\phi(x', y')(ax^2 + 2hxy + by^2 + 2gx + 2fy + c)$$
$$= [(ax' + hy' + g) x + (hx' + by' + f) y + gx' + fy' + c]^2$$

i.e., $\qquad \phi(x, y) \times \phi(x', y') = u^2$

where $u = 0$ is the equation to the chord of contact.

➤ **390.** *Director circle of a conic given by the general equation of the second degree.*

The equation to the two tangents from (x', y') to the conic are, by the last article,

$$x^2 \left[a\phi(x', y') - (ax' + hy' + g)^2 \right]$$
$$+ 2xy \left[h\phi(x', y') - (ax' + hy' + g)(hx' + by' + f) \right]$$
$$+ y^2 \left[b\phi(x', y') - (hx' + by' + f)^2 \right] + \text{other terms} = 0 \quad \dots(1)$$

If (x', y') be a point on the director circle of the conic, the two tangents from it to the conic are at right angles.

Now, (1) represents two straight lines at right angles if the sum of the coefficients of x^2 and y^2 in it be zero,

i.e., if $(a + b)\,\phi(x', y') - (ax' + hy' + g)^2 - (hx' + by' + f)^2 = 0$

Hence, the locus of the point (x', y') is

$$(a + b)(ax^2 + 2hxy + by^2 + 2gx + 2fy + c)$$
$$- (ax + hy + g)^2 - (hx + by + f)^2 = 0$$

i.e., the circle whose equation is

$$(x^2 + y^2)(ab - h^2) + 2x(bg - fh) + 2y(af - gh) + c(a + b) - g^2 - f^2 = 0.$$

Cor. : If the given conic be a parabola, then $ab = h$ and the locus becomes a straight line, *viz.*, the directrix of the parabola. (Art. 211)

➤ **391.** The equation to the director circle may also be obtained in another manner. For it is a circle, whose centre is at the centre of the conic, and the square of whose radius is equal to the sum of the squares of the semi-axes of the conic.

The centre is, Art. 352, the point $\left(\dfrac{hf - bg}{ab - h^2}, \ \dfrac{gh - af}{ab - h^2} \right)$

Also, if the equation to the conic be reduced to the form

$$ax^2 + 2hxy + by^2 + c' = 0$$

and if α and β be its semi-axes, we have, (Art. 364)

$$\frac{1}{\alpha^2} + \frac{1}{\beta^2} = \frac{a + b}{-c'} \quad \text{and} \quad \frac{1}{\alpha^2 \beta^2} = \frac{ab - h^2}{c'^2}$$

so that, by division, $\alpha^2 + \beta^2 = \dfrac{-(a + b)\,c'}{ab - h^2}$.

The equation to the required circle is therefore,

$$\left(x - \frac{hf - bg}{ab - h^2} \right)^2 + \left(y - \frac{gh - af}{ab - h^2} \right)^2 = -\frac{(a + b)\,c'}{ab - h^2}$$

$$= -\frac{(a + b)(abc + 2fgh - af^2 - bg^2 - ch^2)}{(ab - h^2)^2}$$

(Art. 352)

➤ **392.** *The equation to the (imaginary) tangents drawn from the focus of a conic to touch the conic satisfies the analytical condition for being a circle.*

Take the focus of the conic as origin, and let the axis of x be perpendicular to its directrix, so that the equation to the latter may be written in the form $x + k = 0$.

The equation to the conic, e being its eccentricity, is therefore,

$$x^2 + y^2 = e^2 (x + k)^2$$

i.e.,
$$x^2 (1 - e^2) + y^2 - 2e^2 kx - e^2 k^2 = 0$$

The equation to the pair of tangents drawn from the origin is therefore, by Art. 389.

$$[x^2 (1 - e^2) + y^2 - 2e^2 kx - e^2 k^2] [- e^2 k^2] = [- e^2 kx - e^2 k^2]^2$$

i.e.,
$$x^2 (1 - e^2) + y^2 - 2e^2 kx - e^2 k^2 = - e^2 [x + k]^2$$

i.e.,
$$x^2 + y^2 = 0 \qquad \qquad \dots(1)$$

Here, the coefficients of x^2 and y^2 are equal and the coefficient of xy is zero.

However the axes and origin of coordinates be changed, it follows, on making the substitutions of Art. 129, that in (1) the coefficients of x^2 and y^2 will still be equal and the coefficient of xy zero.

Hence, whatever be the conic and however its equation may be written, the equation to the tangents from the focus always satisfies the analytical conditions for being a circle.

➤ **393.** *To find the foci of the conic given by the general equation of the second degree*

$$ax^2 + 2hxy + by^2 + 2gx + 2fy + c = 0.$$

Let (x', y') be a focus. By the last article the equation to the pair of tangents drawn from it satisfies the conditions for being a circle.

The equation to the pair of tangents is

$$\phi (x', y') [ax^2 + 2hxy + by^2 + 2gx + 2fy + c]$$
$$= [x (ax' + hy' + g) + y (hx' + by' + f) + (gx' + fy' + c)]^2$$

In this equation the coefficients of x^2 and y^2 must be equal and the coefficient of xy must be zero.

We therefore, have

$$a\phi (x', y') - (ax' + hy' + g)^2 = b\phi (x', y') - (hx' + by' + f)^2,$$

and
$$h\phi (x', y') = (ax' + hy' + g) (hx' + by' + f)$$

$$i.e., \quad \frac{(ax' + hy' + g)^2 - (hx' + by' + f)^2}{a - b} = \frac{(ax' + hy' + g)(hx' + by' + f)}{h}$$

$$= \phi(x', y') \qquad \ldots(4)$$

These equations, on being solved, give the foci.

Cor. : Since the directrices are the polars of the foci, we easily obtain their equations.

➤ **394.** The (4) of the previous article give, in general, four values for x' and four corresponding values for y'. Two of these would be found to be real and two imaginary.

In the case of the ellipse the two imaginary foci lie on the minor axis. That these imaginary foci exist follows from Art. 247, by writing the standard equation in the form

$$x^2 + \{y - \sqrt{b^2 - a^2}\}^2 = \frac{b^2 - a^2}{b^2} \left\{ y - \frac{b^2}{\sqrt{b^2 - a^2}} \right\}^2 .$$

This shews that the imaginary point $\{0, \sqrt{b^2 - a^2}\}$ is a focus, the imaginary line $y - \dfrac{b^2}{\sqrt{b^2 - a^2}} = 0$ is a directrix, and that the corresponding eccentricity is the imaginary quantity $\sqrt{\dfrac{b^2 - a^2}{b^2}}$.

Similarly, for the hyperbola, except that, in this case, the eccentricity is real.

In the case of the parabola, two of the foci are at infinity and are imaginary, whilst a third is at infinity and is real.

➤ **395.**

EXAMPLE 1 *Find the focus of the parabola*

$$16x^2 - 24xy + 9y^2 - 80x - 140y + 100 = 0.$$

The focus is given by the equations

$$\frac{(16x' - 12y' - 40)^2 - (-12x' + 9y' - 70)^2}{7}$$

$$= \frac{(16x' - 12y' - 40)(-12x' + 9y' - 70)}{-12}$$

$$= 16x'^2 - 24x'y' + 9y'^2 - 80x' - 140y' + 100 \qquad \ldots(1)$$

The first pair of (1) give

$$12(16x' - 12y' - 40)^2 + 7(16x' - 12y' - 40)(-12x' + 9y' - 70)$$
$$- 12(-12x' + 9y' - 70)^2 = 0$$

i.e., $\{4(16x' - 12y' - 40) - 3(-12x' + 9y' - 70)\}$

$$\times \{3(16x' - 12y' - 40) + 4(-12x' + 9y' - 70)\} = 0$$

i.e., $(100x' - 75y' + 50) \times (-400) = 0$

so that $y' = \dfrac{4x' + 2}{3}.$

We then have $16x' - 12y' - 40 = -48$

and $-12x' + 9y' - 70 = -64$

The second pair of equation (1) then gives

$$-\frac{48 \times 64}{12} = x'(16x' - 12y' - 40) + y'(-12x' + 9y' - 70) - 40x' - 70y' + 100$$

$$= -48x' - 64y' - 40x' - 70y' + 100$$

$$= -88x' - 134y' + 100$$

i.e., $-256 = -88x' - \dfrac{536x' + 268}{3} + 100$

so that $x' = 1$, and then $y' = 2$

The focus is therefore, the point (1, 2).

In the case of a parabola, we may also find the equation to the directrix, by Art. 390, and then find the coordinates of the focus, which is the pole of the directrix.

EXAMPLE 2 *Find the foci of the conic*

$$55x^2 - 30xy + 39y^2 - 40x - 24y - 464 = 0.$$

The foci are given by the equation

$$\frac{(55x' - 15y' - 20)^2 - (-15x' + 39y' - 12)^2}{16}$$

$$= \frac{(55x - 15y' - 20)(-15x' + 39y' - 12)}{-15}$$

$$= 55x'^2 - 30x'y' + 39y'^2 - 40x' - 24y' - 464 \qquad \dots(1)$$

The first pair of equations (1) gives

$$15(55x' - 15y' - 20)^2 + 16(55x' - 15y' - 20)(-15x' + 39y' - 12)$$

$$- 15(-15x' + 39y' - 12)^2 = 0$$

i.e., $\{5(55x' - 15y' - 20) - 3(-15x' + 39y' - 12)\}$

$$\{3(55x' - 15y' - 20) + 5(-15x' + 39y' - 12)\} = 0$$

i.e., $(5x' - 3y' - 1)(3x' + 5y' - 4) = 0$

∴ $y' = \dfrac{5x' - 1}{3} \qquad \dots(2)$

or $y' = -\dfrac{3x' - 4}{5} \qquad \dots(3)$

Substituting this first value of y' in the second pair of equation (1), we obtain

$$-25\,(2x'-1)^2 = \frac{340x'^2 - 340x' - 1355}{3}$$

giving
$$x'^2 = 2 \quad \text{or} \quad -1.$$

Hence, from (2)
$$y' = 3 \quad \text{or} \quad -2$$

On substituting the second value of y' in the same pair of equation(1), we finally have

$$2x'^2 - 2x' + 13 = 0$$

the roots of which are imaginary.

We should thus, obtain two imaginary foci which would be found to lie on the minor axis of the conic section. The real foci are therefore, the points (2, 3) and (−1, −2).

➤ **396. Equation to the axes of the general conic.**

By Art. 393, the equation

$$\frac{(ax + hy + g)^2 - (hx + by + f)^2}{a - b} = \frac{(ax + hy + g)\,(hx + by + f)}{h} \qquad \dots(1)$$

represents some conic passing through the foci.

But, since it could be solved as a quadratic equation to give $\dfrac{ax + hy + g}{hx + by + f}$ it represents two straight lines.

The equation (1) therefore, represents the axes of the general conic.

➤ **397.** *To find the length of the straight lines drawn through a given point in a given direction to meet a given conic.*

Let the equation to the conic be

$$\phi\,(x, y) = ax^2 + 2hxy + by^2 + 2gx + 2fy + c = 0 \qquad \dots(1)$$

Let P be any point (x', y'), and through it let there be drawn a straight line at an angle θ with the axis of x to meet the curve in Q and Q'.

The coordinates of any point on this line distant r from P are

$x' + r\cos\theta$ and $y' + r\sin\theta$ (Art. 86)

If this point be on (1), we have

$$a\,(x' + r\cos\theta)^2 + 2h\,(x' + r\cos\theta)\,(y' + r\sin\theta) + b\,(y' + r\sin\theta)^2$$
$$+ 2g\,(x' + r\cos\theta) + 2f\,(y' + r\sin\theta) + c = 0$$

i.e.,
$$r^2\,[a\cos^2\theta + 2h\cos\theta\sin\theta + b\sin^2\theta]$$
$$+ 2r\,[(ax' + hy' + g)\cos\theta + (hx' + by' + f)\sin\theta] + \phi\,(x', y') = 0 \quad \dots(2)$$

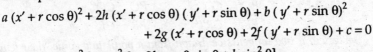

For any given value of θ this is a quadratic equation in r, and therefore, for any straight line drawn at an inclination θ it gives the values of PQ and PQ'.

If the two values of r given by equation (2) be of opposite sign, the points Q and Q' lie on opposite sides of P.

If P be on the curve, then $\phi(x', y')$ is zero and one value of r obtained from equation (2) is zero.

➤ **398.** *If two chords PQQ' and PRR' be drawn in given directions through any point P to meet the curve in Q, Q' and R, R' respectively, the ratio of the rectangle PQ·PQ' to the rectangle PR·PR' is the same for all points, and is therefore equal to the ratio of the squares of the diameters of the conic which are drawn in the given directions.*

The values of PQ and PQ' are given by the equation of the last article, and therefore,

$$PQ \cdot PQ' = \text{product of the roots}$$
$$= \frac{\phi(x', y')}{a\cos^2\theta + 2h\cos\theta\sin\theta + b\sin^2\theta} \qquad \ldots(1)$$

So, if PRR' be drawn at an angle θ' to the axis, we have

$$PR \cdot PR' = \frac{\phi(x', y')}{a\cos^2\theta' + 2h\cos\theta'\sin\theta' + b\sin^2\theta'} \qquad \ldots(2)$$

On dividing (1) by (2), we have

$$\frac{PQ \cdot PQ'}{PR \cdot PR'} = \frac{a\cos^2\theta' + 2h\cos\theta'\sin\theta' + b\sin^2\theta'}{a\cos^2\theta + 2h\cos\theta\sin\theta + b\sin^2\theta}.$$

The right-hand member of this equation does not contain x' or y *i.e.*, it does not depend on the position of P but only on the directions θ and θ'.

The quantity $\dfrac{PQ \cdot PQ'}{PR \cdot PR'}$ is therefore, the same for all positions of P.

In the particular case when P is at the centre of the conic this ratio becomes $\dfrac{CQ''^2}{CR''^2}$ where C is the centre and CQ' and CR'' are parallel to the two given directions.

Cor. : If Q and Q' coincide, and also R and R', the two lines PQQ' and PRR' become the tangents from P, and the above relation then gives

$$\frac{PQ^2}{PR^2} = \frac{CQ''^2}{CR''^2} \quad i.e., \quad \frac{PQ}{PR} = \frac{CQ''}{CR''}$$

Hence, *if two tangents be drawn from a point to a conic, their lengths are to one another in the ratio of the parallel semi-diameters of the conic.*

➤ **399.** *If PQQ' and $P_1Q_1Q_1'$ be two chords drawn in parallel directions from two points P and P_1 to meet a conic in Q and Q', and Q_1 and Q_1', respectively, then the ratio of the rectangles $PQ \cdot PQ'$ and $P_1Q_1 \cdot P_1Q_1'$ is independent of the direction of the chords.*

For, if P and P_1 be respectively the points (x', y') and (x'', y''), and θ be the angle that each chord makes with the axis, we have, as in the last article,

$$PQ \cdot PQ' = \frac{\phi(x', y')}{a\cos^2\theta + 2h\cos\theta\sin\theta + b\sin^2\theta}$$

and

$$P_1Q_1 \cdot P_1Q_1' = \frac{\phi(x'', y'')}{a\cos^2\theta + 2h\cos\theta\sin\theta + b\sin^2\theta}$$

so that

$$\frac{PQ \cdot PQ'}{P_1Q_1 \cdot P_1Q_1'} = \frac{\phi(x', y')}{\phi(x'', y'')}$$

➤ **400.** *If a circle and a conic section cut one another in four points, the straight line joining one pair of points of intersection and the straight line joining the other pair are equally inclined to the axis of the conic.*

For (Fig. Art. 397) let the circle and conic intersect in the four points Q, Q' and R, R' and let QQ' and RR' meet in P.

Then

$$\frac{PQ \cdot PQ'}{PR \cdot PR'} = \frac{CQ''^2}{CR''^2} \qquad \text{(Art. 398)}.$$

But, since Q, Q', R, and R' are four points on a circle, we have

$$PQ \cdot PQ' = PR \cdot PR'$$

∴

$$CQ'' = CR''.$$

Also in any conic equal radii from the centre are equally inclined to the axis of the conic.

Hence, CQ'' and CR'', and therefore, PQQ' and PRR', are equally inclined to the axis of the conic.

➤ **401.** *To shew that any chord of a conic is cut harmonically by the curve, any point on the chord, and the polar of this point with respect to the conic.*

Take the point as origin, and let the equation to the conic be

$$ax^2 + 2hxy + by^2 + 2gx + 2fy + c = 0 \qquad ...(1)$$

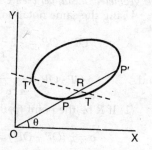

or, in polar coordinates,

$$r^2 (a \cos^2 \theta + 2h \cos \theta \sin \theta + b \sin^2 \theta) + 2r (g \cos \theta + f \sin \theta) + c = 0$$

i.e., $c \cdot \dfrac{1}{r^2} + 2 \cdot \dfrac{1}{r} \cdot (g \cos \theta + f \sin \theta) + a \cos^2 \theta$

$$+ 2h \cos \theta \sin \theta + b \sin^2 \theta = 0$$

Hence, if the chord OPP' be drawn at an angle θ to OX, we have

$$\dfrac{1}{OP} + \dfrac{1}{OP'} = \text{sum of the roots of this equation in } \dfrac{1}{r}$$

$$= -2 \cdot \dfrac{g \cos \theta + f \sin \theta}{c}$$

Let R be a point on this chord such that

$$\dfrac{2}{OR} = \dfrac{1}{OP} + \dfrac{1}{OP'}$$

Then, if $OR = \rho$ we have

$$\dfrac{2}{\rho} = -2 \dfrac{g \cos \theta + f \sin \theta}{c}$$

so that the locus of R is

$$g \cdot \rho \cos \theta + f \cdot \rho \sin \theta + c = 0$$

or, in Cartesian coordinates,

$$gx + fy + c = 0 \qquad\qquad \text{...(2)}$$

But (2) is the polar of the origin with respect to the conic (1), so that the locus of R is the polar of O.

The straight line PP' is therefore, cut harmonically by O and the point in which it cuts the polar of O.

EXAMPLE *Through any point O is drawn a straight line to cut a conic in P and P' and on it is taken a point R such that OR is (1) the arithmetic mean, and (2) the geometric mean, between OP and OP'. Find in each case the locus of R.*

Using the same notation as in the last article, we have

$$OP + OP' = -2 \dfrac{g \cos \theta + f \sin \theta}{a \cos^2 \theta + 2h \cos \theta \sin \theta + b \sin^2 \theta}$$

and

$$OP \cdot OP' = \dfrac{c}{a \cos^2 \theta + 2h \cos \theta \sin \theta + b \sin^2 \theta}$$

(1) If R be the point (ρ, θ), we have

$$\rho = \dfrac{1}{2}(OP + OP') = -\dfrac{g \cos \theta + f \sin \theta}{a \cos^2 \theta + 2h \cos \theta \sin \theta + b \sin^2 \theta}$$

i.e., $a\rho \cos^2 \theta + 2h\rho \cos \theta \sin \theta + b\rho \sin^2 \theta + g \cos \theta + f \sin \theta = 0$

i.e., in Cartesian coordinates,

$$ax^2 + 2hxy + by^2 + gx + fy = 0$$

The locus is therefore, a conic passing through O and the intersection of the conic and the polar of O, *i.e.*, through the points T and T', and having its asymptotes parallel to those of the given conic.

(2) If R be the point (ρ, θ), we have in this case

$$\rho^2 = OP \cdot OP' = \frac{c}{a \cos^2 \theta + 2h \cos \theta \sin \theta + b \sin^2 \theta},$$

i.e., $a\rho^2 \cos^2 \theta + 2h\rho^2 \cos \theta \sin \theta + b\rho^2 \sin^2 \theta = c$

i.e., $$ax^2 + 2hxy + by^2 = c$$

The locus is therefore, a conic, having its centre at O and passing through T and T', and having its asymptotes parallel to those of the given conic.

➤ **402.** *To find the locus of the middle points of parallel chords of a conic.* [*Cf. Art. 376.*]

The lengths of the segments of the chord drawn through the point (x', y') at an angle θ to the axis of x is given by equation (2) of Art. 397.

If (x', y') be the middle point of the chord the roots of this equation are equal in magnitude but opposite in sign, so that their algebraic sum is zero.

The coefficient of r in this equation is therefore, zero, so that

$$(ax' + hy' + g) \cos \theta + (hx' + by' + f) \sin \theta = 0$$

The locus of the middle point of chords inclined at an angle θ to the axis of x is therefore, the straight line

$$(ax + hy + g) + (hx + by + f) \tan \theta = 0$$

Hence, the locus of the middle points of chords parallel to the line $y = mx$ is

$$(ax + hy + g) + (hx + by + f) m = 0$$

i.e., $$x (a + hm) + (h + bm) y + g + fm = 0$$

This is parallel to the line $y = m'x$ if

$$m' = -\frac{a + hm}{h + bm}$$

i.e., if $$a + h (m + m') + bmm' = 0$$

This is therefore, the condition that $y = mx$ and $y = m'x$ should be parallel to conjugate diameters.

➤ **403.** *Equation to the pair of tangents drawn from a given point* (x', y') *to a given conic.* [*Cf. Art. 389.*]

If a straight line be drawn through (x', y'), the point P, to meet the conic in Q and Q', the lengths of PQ and PQ' are given by the equation

$$r^2 (a \cos^2 \theta + 2h \cos \theta \sin \theta + b \sin^2 \theta)$$
$$+ 2r [(ax' + hy' + g) \cos \theta + (hx' + by' + f) \sin \theta] + \phi (x', y') = 0$$

The roots of this equation are equal, *i.e.* the corresponding lines touch the conic, if

$$(a \cos^2 \theta + 2h \cos \theta \sin \theta + b \sin^2 \theta) \times \phi (x', y')$$
$$= [(ax' + hy' + g) \cos \theta + (hx' + by' + f) \sin \theta]^2,$$

i.e., if $(a + 2h \tan \theta + b \tan^2 \theta) \times \phi (x', y')$

$$= [(ax' + hy' + g) + (hx' + by' + f) \tan \theta]^2 \qquad \ldots(1)$$

The roots of this equation give the corresponding directions of the tangents through P.

Also the equation to the line through P inclined at an angle θ to the axis of x is

$$\frac{y - y'}{x - x'} = \tan \theta \qquad \ldots(2)$$

If we substitute for $\tan \theta$ in (1) from (2) we shall get the equation to the pair of tangents from P.

On substitution we have

$$\{a(x - x')^2 + 2h (x - x') (y - y') + b (y - y')^2\} \phi (x', y')$$
$$= [(ax' + hy' + g) (x - x') + (hx' + by' + f) (y - y')]^2$$

This equation reduces to the form of Art. 389.

EXAMPLES XLIV

1. Two tangents are drawn to an ellipse from a point P; if the points in which these tangents meet the axes of the ellipse be concyclic, prove that the locus of P is a rectangular hyperbola.

2. A pair of tangents to the conic $Ax^2 + By^2 = 1$ intercept a constant distance $2k$ on the axis of x; prove that the locus of their point of intersection is the curve

$$By^2 (Ax^2 + By^2 - 1) = Ak^2 (By^2 - 1)^2$$

3. Pairs of tangents are drawn to the conic $\alpha x^2 + \beta y^2 = 1$ so as to be always parallel to conjugate diameters of the conic

$$ax^2 + 2hxy + by^2 = 1;$$

shew that the locus of their point of intersection is the conic

$$ax^2 + 2hxy + by^2 = \frac{a}{\alpha} + \frac{b}{\beta}.$$

4. Prove that the director circles of all conics which touch two given straight lines at given points have a common radical axis.
5. A parabola circumscribes a right-angled triangle. Taking its sides as the axes of coordinates, prove that the locus of the foot of the perpendicular from the right angle upon the directrix is the curve whose equation is.

$$2xy \, (x^2 + y^2) \, (hy + kx) + h^2 y^4 + k^2 x^4 = 0$$

and that the axis is one of the family of straight lines

$$y = mx - \frac{m^3 h - k}{1 + m^2}$$

where m is an arbitrary parameter and $2h$ and $2k$ are the sides of the triangle.
Find the foci of the curves:
6. $300x^2 + 320xy + 144y^2 - 1220x - 768y + 199 = 0$
7. $16x^2 - 24xy + 9y^2 + 28x + 14y + 21 = 0$
8. $144x^2 - 120xy + 25y^2 + 67x - 42y + 13 = 0$
9. $x^2 - 6xy + y^2 - 10x - 10y - 19 = 0$ and also its directrices.
10. Prove that the foci of the conic

$$ax^2 + 2hxy + by^2 = 1$$

are given by the equations

$$\frac{x^2 - y^2}{a - b} = \frac{xy}{h} = \frac{1}{h^2 - ab}.$$

11. Prove that the locus of the foci of all conics which touch the four lines $x = \pm a$ and $y = \pm b$ is the hyperbola $x^2 - y^2 = a^2 - b^2$.
12. Given the centre of a conic and two tangents; prove that the locus of the foci is a hyperbola.
[Take the two tangents as axes, their inclination being ω; let (x_1, y_1) and (x_2, y_2) be the foci, and (h, k) the given centre. Then $x_1 + x_2 = 2h$ and $y_1 + y_2 = 2k$; also, by Art. 270 (β), we have

$$y_1 y_2 \sin^2 \omega = x_1 x_2 \sin^2 \omega = (\text{semi–minor axis})^2.$$

From these equations, eliminating x_2 and y_2, we have:

$$x_1{}^2 - y_1{}^2 = 2hx_1 - 2ky_1].$$

13. A given ellipse, of semi-axes a and b, slides between two perpendicular lines; prove that the locus of its focus is the curve

$$(x^2 + y^2) \, (x^2 y^2 + b^4) = 4a^2 x^2 y^2.$$

14. Conics are drawn touching both the axes, supposed oblique, at the same given distance a from the origin. Prove that the foci lie either on the straight line $x = y$, or on the circle

$$x^2 + y^2 + 2xy \cos \omega = a (x + y).$$

15. Find the locus of the foci of conics which have a common point and a common director circle.

16. Find the locus of the focus of a rectangular hyperbola a diameter of which is given in magnitude and position.

17. Through a fixed point O chords POP' and QOQ' are drawn at right angles to one another to meet a given conic in P, P', Q and Q'.

Prove that $\dfrac{1}{PO \cdot OP'} + \dfrac{1}{QO \cdot OQ'}$ is constant.

18. A point is taken on the major axis of an ellipse whose abscissa is $ae \div \sqrt{2 - e^2}$; prove that the sum of the squares of the reciprocals of the segments of any chord through it is constant.

19. Through a fixed point O is drawn a line OPP' to meet a conic in P and P'; prove that the locus of a point Q on OPP', such that

$\dfrac{1}{OQ^2} = \dfrac{1}{OP^2} + \dfrac{1}{OP'^2}$ is another conic whose centre is O.

20. Prove Carnot's theorem, viz., if a conic section cut the side BC of a triangle ABC in the points A' and A'', and, similarly, the side CA in B' and B'', and AB in C' and C'', then

$$BA' \cdot BA'' \cdot CB' \cdot CB'' \cdot AC' \cdot AC'' = CA' \cdot CA'' \cdot AB' \cdot AB'' \cdot BC' \cdot BC''.$$

[Use Art. 398.]

21. Obtain the equations giving the foci of the general conic by making use of the fact that, if S be a focus and PSP' any chord of the conic passing through it, then $\dfrac{1}{SP} + \dfrac{1}{SP'}$ is the same for all directions of the chord.

22. Obtain the equations for the foci also from the fact that the product of the perpendiculars drawn from them upon any tangent is the same for all tangents.

➤ **404.** *To find the equation to a conic, the axes of coordinates being a tangent and normal to the conic.*

Since, the origin is on the curve, the equation to the curve must be satisfied by the coordinates $(0, 0)$ so that the equation has no constant term and therefore, is of the form

$$ax^2 + 2hxy + by^2 + 2gx + 2fy = 0$$

If this curve touch the axis of x at the origin, then, when $y = 0$, we must have a perfect square and therefore, $g = 0$.

The required equation is therefore,

$$ax^2 + 2hxy + by^2 + 2fy = 0 \qquad \qquad ...(1)$$

EXAMPLE *O is any point on a conic and PQ a chord; prove that*

(1) *if PQ subtend a right angle at O, it passes through a fixed point on the normal at O, and*

(2) *If OP and OQ be equally inclined to the normal at O, then PQ passes through a fixed point on the tangent at O.*

Take the tangent and normal at O as axes, so that the equation to the conic is (1).

Let the equation to, $\quad PQ \quad$ be $\quad y = mx + c \qquad$ ...(2)

Then, by Art. 122, the equation to the lines OP and OQ is

$$c(ax^2 + 2hxy + by^2) + 2fy(y - mx) = 0 \qquad \text{...(3)}$$

(1) If the lines OP and OQ be at right angles then (Art. 66), we have

$$ac + bc + 2f = 0$$

i.e., $\qquad\qquad c = -\dfrac{2f}{a+b}$

$\qquad\qquad\qquad\qquad$ = a constant for all positions of PQ.

But c is the intercept of PQ on the axis of y, *i.e.,* on the normal at O. The straight line PQ therefore, passes through a fixed point on the normal at O which is distant $\dfrac{-2f}{a+b}$ from O.

This point is often called the Fregier Point.

(2) If again OP and OQ be equally inclined to the axis of y then, in equation (3), the coefficient of xy must be zero, and hence

$$2hc - 2fm = 0$$

i.e., $\qquad\qquad \dfrac{c}{m} = \dfrac{f}{h} = \text{constant.}$

But $\dfrac{-c}{m}$ is the intercept on the axis of x of the line PQ.

Hence, in this case, PQ passes through a fixed point on the tangent at O.

➤ **405.** *General equation to conics passing through four given points.*

Let A, B, C, and D be the four points, and let BA and CD meet in O. Take OAB and ODC as the axes, and let $OA = \lambda$, $OB = \lambda'$, $OD = \mu$, and $OC = \mu'$.

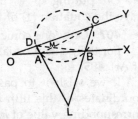

Let any conic passing through the four points be

$$ax^2 + 2h'xy + by^2 + 2gx + 2fy + c = 0 \quad \text{...(1)}$$

If we put $y = 0$ in this equation the roots of the resulting equation must be λ and λ'.

Hence, $\qquad\qquad 2g = -a(\lambda + \lambda')$ and $c = a\lambda\lambda'$, *i.e.,* $\qquad\qquad a = \dfrac{c}{\lambda\lambda'}$ and $2g = -c\,\dfrac{\lambda + \lambda'}{\lambda\lambda'}$

Similarly, $\qquad b = \dfrac{c}{\mu\mu'}$ and $2f = -c\,\dfrac{\mu + \mu'}{\mu\mu'}$

On substituting in (1) we have

$$\mu\mu' x^2 + 2hxy + \lambda\lambda' y^2 - \mu\mu'\,(\lambda + \lambda')\,x - \lambda\lambda'\,(\mu + \mu')\,y + \lambda\lambda'\,\mu\mu' = 0 \qquad \ldots(1)$$

where $\qquad\qquad\qquad\qquad h = h'\,\dfrac{\lambda\lambda'\mu\mu'}{c}$

This is the required equation, h being a constant as yet undetermined and depending on which of the conics through A, B, C and D we are considering.

➤ **406. Aliter.** We have proved in Art. 383 that the equation $k\,LN = MR$, k being any constant, represents any conic circumscribing the quadrilateral formed by the four straight lines $L = 0$, $M = 0$, $N = 0$ and $R = 0$ taken in this order.

With the notation of the previous article the equations to the four lines AB, BC, CD and DA are

$$y = 0, \quad \frac{x}{\lambda'} + \frac{y}{\mu'} - 1 = 0, \quad x = 0,$$

and $\qquad\qquad\qquad\qquad \dfrac{x}{\lambda} + \dfrac{y}{\mu} - 1 = 0$

The equation to any conic circumscribing the quadrilateral $ABCD$ is therefore,

$$kxy = \left(\frac{x}{\lambda'} + \frac{y}{\lambda'} - 1 \right)\left(\frac{x}{\lambda} + \frac{y}{\mu} - 1 \right) \qquad \ldots(1)$$

i.e., $\quad \mu\mu' x^2 + xy\,(\lambda\mu' + \lambda'\mu - k\lambda\lambda'\mu\mu') + \lambda\lambda'\,y^2$

$$- \mu\mu'\,(\lambda + \lambda')\,x - \lambda\lambda'\,(\mu + \mu')\,y + \lambda\lambda'\,\mu\mu' = 0.$$

On putting $\lambda\mu' + \lambda'\mu - k\,\lambda\lambda'\,\mu\mu'$ equal to another constant $2h$ we have the equation (1) of the previous article.

➤ **407.** Only one conic can be drawn through any five points.

For the general equation to a conic through four points is Eq. (1) of Art. 405.

If we wish it to pass through a fifth point, we substitute the coordinates of this fifth point in this equation, and thus obtain the corresponding value of h. Except when three of the five points lie on a straight line a value of h will always be found and only one.

EXAMPLE *Find the equation to the conic section which passes through the five points* $A, B, C, D,$ *and* $E,$ *whose coordinates are* $(1, 2), (3, -4), (-1, 3),$ $(-2, -3),$ *and* $(5, 6).$

The equations to $AB, BC, CD,$ and DA are easily found to be

$$y + 3x - 5 = 0, \ 4y + 7x - 5 = 0, \ 6x - y + 9 = 0, \text{ and } 5x - 3y + 1 = 0$$

The equation to any conic through the four points $A, B, C,$ and D is therefore

$$(y + 3x - 5)(6x - y + 9) = \lambda(4y + 7x - 5)(5x - 3y + 1) \qquad \ldots(1)$$

If this conic pass through the point $E,$ the (1) must be satisfied by the values $x = 5$ and $y = 6.$

We thus have $\lambda = \dfrac{11}{9}$ and, on substitution in (1), the required equation is

$$223x^2 - 38xy - 123y^2 - 171x + 83y + 350 = 0$$

which represents a hyperbola.

➤ **408.** *To find the general equation to a conic section which touches four given straight lines, i.e., which is inscribed in a given quadrilateral.*

Let the four straight lines form the sides of the quadrilateral $ABCD.$ Let BA and CD meet in $O,$ and take OAB and ODC as the axes of x and $y,$ and let the equations to the other two sides BC and DA be

$$l_1 x + m_1 y - 1 = 0$$

and $\qquad l_2 x + m_2 y - 1 = 0$

Let the equation to the straight line joining the points of contact of any conic touching the axes at P and Q be

$$ax + by - 1 = 0$$

By Art. 385, II, the equation to the conic is then

$$2\lambda xy = (ax + by - 1)^2 \qquad \ldots(1)$$

The condition that the straight line BC should touch this conic is, as in Art. 374, found to be

$$\lambda = 2(a - l_1)(b - m_1) \qquad \ldots(2)$$

Similarly, it will be touched by AD if

$$\lambda = 2(a - l_2)(b - m_2) \qquad \ldots(3)$$

The required conic has therefore, (1) as its equation, the values of a and b being given in terms of the quantity λ by means of (2) and (3).

Also λ is any quantity we may choose. Hence we have the system of conics touching the four given lines.

If we solve (2) and (3), we obtain

$$\frac{2b - (m_1 + m_2)}{m_1 - m_2} = -\frac{2a - (l_1 + l_2)}{l_1 - l_2} = \pm \sqrt{1 - \frac{2\lambda}{(l_1 - l_2)(m_1 - m_2)}}.$$

➤ **409.** *The conic $LM = R^2$, where $L = 0$, $M = 0$, and $R = 0$ are the equations of straight lines.*

The equation $LM = 0$ represents a conic, *viz.*, two straight lines. Hence, by Art. 385, II, the equation

$$LM = R^2 \qquad \qquad \text{...(1)}$$

represents a conic touching the straight lines $L = 0$, and $M = 0$, where $R = 0$ meets them.

Thus, $L = 0$ and $M = 0$ are a pair of tangents and $R = 0$ the corresponding chord of contact.

Every point which satisfies the equations $M = \mu^2 L$ and $R = \mu L$ clearly lies on (1).

Hence, the point of intersection of the straight lines $M = \mu^2 L$ and $R = \mu L$ lies on the conic (1) for all values of μ. This point may be called the point "μ".

➤ **410.** To find the equation to the straight line joining two points "μ" and "μ'" and the equation to the tangent at the point "μ".

Consider the equation

$$aL + bM + R = 0 \qquad \qquad \text{...(1)}$$

Since it is of the first degree and contains two constants a and b, at our disposal, it can be made to represent any straight line.

If it pass through the point "μ" it must be satisfied by the substitutions $M = \mu^2 L$ and $R = \mu L$.

Hence, $$a + b\mu^2 + \mu = 0 \qquad \qquad \text{...(2)}$$

Similarly, if it pass through the point "μ'" we have

$$a + b\mu'^2 + \mu' = 0 \qquad \qquad \text{...(3)}$$

Solving (2) and (3), we have

$$\frac{a}{\mu\mu'} = b = \frac{-1}{\mu + \mu'}$$

On substitution in (1), the equation to the joining line is

$$L\mu\mu' + M - (\mu + \mu')R = 0$$

By putting $\mu' = \mu$ we have, as the equation to the tangent at the point "μ"

$$L\mu^2 + M - 2\mu R = 0.$$

EXAMPLES XLV

1. Prove that the locus of the foot of the perpendicular let fall from the origin upon tangents to the conic $ax^2 + 2hxy + by^2 = 2x$ is the curve
$$(h^2 - ab)(x^2 + y^2)^2 + 2(x^2 + y^2)(bx - hy) + y^2 = 0.$$

2. In the conic $ax^2 + 2hxy + by^2 = 2y$, prove that the rectangle contained by the focal distances of the origin is $\dfrac{1}{ab - h^2}$.

3. Tangents are drawn to the conic $ax^2 + 2hxy + by^2 = 2x$ from two points on the axis of x equidistant from the origin; prove that their four points of intersection lie on the conic $by^2 + hxy = x$.

   If the tangents be drawn from two points on the axis of y equidistant from the origin, prove that the points of intersection are on a straight line.

4. A system of conics is drawn to pass through four fixed points; prove that
   (1) the polars of a given point all pass through a fixed point, and
   (2) the locus of the pole of a given line is a conic section.

5. Find the equation to the conic passing through the origin and the points (1, 1), (–1, 1), (2, 0), and (3, –2). Determine its species.

6. Prove that the locus of the centre of all conics circumscribing the quadrilateral formed by the straight lines $y = 0$, $x = 0$, $x + y = 1$ and $y - x = 2$ is the conic $2x^2 - 2y^2 + 4xy + 5y - 2 = 0$.

7. Prove that the locus of the centres of all conics, which pass through the centres of the inscribed and escribed circles of a triangle, is the circumscribing circle of the triangle.

8. Prove that the locus of the extremities of the principal axes of all conics, which can be described through the four points $(\pm a, 0)$ and $(0, \pm b)$, is the curve
$$\left(\frac{x^2}{a^2} - \frac{y^2}{b^2}\right)(x^2 + y^2) = x^2 - y^2.$$

9. A, B, C and D are four fixed points and AB and CD meet in O; any straight line passing through O meets AD and BC in R and R' respectively, and any conic passing through the four given points in S and S'; prove that
$$\frac{1}{OR} + \frac{1}{OR'} = \frac{1}{OS} + \frac{1}{OS'}.$$

10. Prove that, in general, two parabolas can be drawn through four points, and that either two, or none, can be drawn.

   [For a parabola we have $h = \pm \sqrt{\lambda\lambda' \mu\mu'}$].

11. Prove that the locus of the centres of the conics circumscribing a quadrilateral $ABCD$ (Fig. Art. 405) is a conic passing through the vertices $O, L,$ and M of the quadrilateral and through the middle points of AB, AC, AD, BC, BD and CD.

   Prove also that its asymptotes are parallel to the axes of the parabolas through the four points.

   [The required locus is obtained by eliminating h from the equations $2\mu\mu'x + 2hy - \mu\mu'(\lambda + \lambda') = 0$, and $2hx + 2\lambda\lambda'y - \lambda\lambda'(\mu + \mu') = 0$]

12. By taking the case when $\lambda\lambda' = -\mu\mu'$ and when AB and CD are perpendicular (in which case ABC is a triangle having D as its orthocentre and AL, BM and CO are the perpendiculars on its sides) prove that all conics passing through the vertices of a triangle and its orthocentre are rectangular hyperbolas.

   From Ex. 11 prove also that the locus of its centre is the nine point circle of the triangle.

13. Prove that the triangle OML (Fig. Art. 405) is such that each angular point is the pole of the opposite side with respect to any conic passing through the angular points A, B, C and D of the quadrilateral.

   [Such a triangle is called a **Self Conjugate Triangle.**]

14. Prove that only one rectangular hyperbola can be drawn through four given points. Prove also that the nine point circles of the four triangles that can be formed by four given points meet in a point, viz., the centre of the rectangular hyperbola passing through the four points.

15. By using the result of Art. 374, prove that in general, two conics can be drawn through four points to touch a given straight line.

   A system of conics is inscribed in the same quadrilateral; prove that

16. The locus of the pole of a given straight line with respect to this system is a straight line.

17. The locus of their centres is a straight line passing through the middle points of the diagonals of the quadrilaterals.

18. Prove that the triangle formed by the three diagonals OL, AC and BD (Fig. Art. 408) is such that each of its angular points is the pole of the opposite side with respect to any conic inscribed in the quadrilateral.

19. Prove that only one parabola can be drawn to touch any four given lines.

   Hence prove that, if the four triangles that can be made by four lines be drawn, the orthocentres of these four triangles lie on a straight line, and their circumcircles meet in a point.

17

MISCELLANEOUS PROPOSITIONS

On the four normals that can be drawn from any point in the plane of a central conic to the conic.

➤ **411.** Let the equation to the conic be

$$Ax^2 + By^2 = 1 \qquad \qquad \text{...(1)}$$

[If A and B be both positive, it is an ellipse; if one be positive and the other negative, it is a hyperbola.]

The equation to the normal at any point (x', y') of the curve is

$$\frac{x - x'}{Ax'} = \frac{y - y'}{By'}$$

[If this normal pass through the given point (h, k), we have

$$\frac{h - x'}{Ax'} = \frac{k - y'}{By'},$$

i.e., $$(A - B)x'y' + Bhy' - Akx' = 0 \qquad \text{...(2)}$$

This is an equation to determine the point (x', y') such that the normal at it goes through the point (h, k). It shews that the point (x', y') lies on the rectangular hyperbola

$$(A - B)xy + Bhy - Akx = 0 \qquad \qquad \text{...(3)}$$

The point (x', y') is therefore, both on the curve (3) and on the curve (1). Also these two conics intersect in four points, real or imaginary. There are therefore, four points, in general, lying on (1), such that the normals at them pass through the given point (h, k).

Also the hyperbola (3) passes through the origin and the point (h, k) and its asymptotes are parallel to the axes.

Hence, *from a given point four normals can in general be drawn to a given central conic, and their feet all lie on a certain rectangular hyperbola, which passes through the given point and the centre of the conic, and has its asymptotes parallel to the axes of the given conic.*

➤ **412.** *To find the conditions that the normals at the points where two given straigh lines meet a central conic may meet in a point.*

Let the conic be

$$Ax^2 + By^2 = 1 \qquad \dots(1)$$

and let the normals to it at the points where it is met by the straight lines

$$l_1x + m_1y = 1 \qquad \dots(2)$$

and

$$l_2x + m_2y = 1 \qquad \dots(3)$$

meet in the point (h, k).

By Art. 384, the equation to any conic passing through the intersection of (1) with (2) and (3) is

$$Ax^2 + By^2 - 1 + \lambda(l_1x + m_1y - 1)(l_2x + m_2y - 1) = 0 \qquad \dots(4)$$

Since, these intersections are the feet of the four normals drawn from (h, k), then, by the last article, the conic

$$(A - B)xy + Bhy - Akx = 0 \qquad \dots(5)$$

passes through the same four points.

For some value of λ it therefore, follows that (4) and (5) are the same.

Comparing these equations, we have, since the coefficients of x^2 and y^2 and the constant term in (5) are all zero,

$$A + \lambda l_1 l_2 = 0, \quad B + \lambda m_1 m_2 = 0, \quad \text{and} \quad -1 + \lambda = 0.$$

Therefore, $\lambda = 1$, and hence,

$$l_1 l_2 = -A, \quad \text{and} \quad m_1 m_2 = -B \qquad \dots(6)$$

The relations (6) are the required conditions.

Also, comparing the remaining coefficients in (4) and (5), we have

$$\frac{\lambda(l_1m_2 + l_2m_1)}{A - B} = \frac{-\lambda(l_1 + l_2)}{-Ak} = \frac{-\lambda(m_1 + m_2)}{Bh},$$

so that

$$h = \frac{A - B}{B} \frac{m_1 + m_2}{l_1m_2 + l_2m_1} \qquad \dots(7)$$

and

$$k = \frac{A - B}{A} \frac{l_1 + l_2}{l_1m_2 + l_2m_1} \qquad \dots(8)$$

Cor. 1. : If the given conic be an ellipse, we have

$$A = \frac{1}{a^2} \quad \text{and} \quad B = \frac{1}{b^2}$$

The relations (6) then give

$$a^2 l_1 l_2 = b^2 m_1 m_2 = -1 \qquad \ldots(9)$$

and the coordinates of the point of concurrence are

$$h = \frac{a^2 - b^2}{a^2} \cdot \frac{m_1 + m_2}{l_1 m_2 + l_2 m_1} = l_1(a^2 - b^2) \cdot \frac{1 - b^2 m_1^2}{a^2 l_1^2 + b^2 m_1^2},$$

and

$$k = -\frac{a^2 - b^2}{b^2} \cdot \frac{l_1 + l_2}{l_1 m_2 + l_2 m_1} = -m_1(a^2 - b^2) \cdot \frac{1 - a^2 l_1^2}{a^2 l_1^2 + b^2 m_1^2}$$

Cor. 2. : If the equations to the straight lines be given in the form $y = mx + c$ and $y = m'x + c'$, we have

$$m = -\frac{l_1}{m_1}, \ c = \frac{1}{m_1}, \ m' = -\frac{l_2}{m_2}, \text{ and } c' = \frac{1}{m_2}$$

The relations (9) then give

$$mm' = \frac{b^2}{a^2} \quad \text{and} \quad cc' = -b^2.$$

➤ **413.** If the normals at four points P, Q, R and S of an ellipse meet in a point, the sum of the their eccentric angles is equal to an odd multiple of two right angles. [Cf. Art. 293.]

If α, β, γ and δ be the eccentric angles of the four points, the equations to *PQ* and *RS* are

$$y = -x \cdot \frac{b}{a} \cot \frac{\alpha + \beta}{2} + \frac{b \cos \dfrac{\alpha - \beta}{2}}{\sin \dfrac{\alpha + \beta}{2}}$$

and

$$y = -x \cdot \frac{b}{a} \cot \frac{\gamma + \delta}{2} + \frac{b \cos \dfrac{\gamma - \delta}{2}}{\sin \dfrac{\gamma + \delta}{2}} \qquad \text{[Art. 259.]}$$

Since, the normals at these points meet in a point, we have, by Art. 412, Cor. 2,

$$\frac{b^2}{a^2} = mm' = \frac{b^2}{a^2} \cot \frac{\alpha + \beta}{2} \cot \frac{\gamma + \delta}{2}$$

∴

$$\tan \frac{\alpha + \beta}{2} = \cot \frac{\gamma + \delta}{2} = \tan \left(\frac{\pi}{2} - \frac{\gamma + \delta}{2} \right)$$

∴

$$\frac{\alpha + \beta}{2} = n\pi + \frac{\pi}{2} - \frac{\gamma + \delta}{2}$$

i.e.,

$$\alpha + \beta + \gamma + \delta = (2n + 1) \pi.$$

➤ 414.

EXAMPLE 1 *If the normals at the points A, B, C and D of an ellipse meet in a point O, prove that* $SA \cdot SB \cdot SC \cdot SD = \lambda^2 \cdot SO^2$, *where S is one of the foci and* λ *is a constant.*

Let the equation to the ellipse be

$$\frac{x^2}{a^2} + \frac{y^2}{b^2} = 1 \qquad \qquad \dots(1)$$

and let O be the point (h, k).

As in Art. 411, the feet of the normals drawn from O lie on the hyperbola

$$\left(\frac{1}{a^2} - \frac{1}{b^2}\right)xy + \frac{hy}{b^2} - \frac{kx}{a^2} = 0,$$

i.e., $\qquad\qquad a^2 e^2 xy = a^2 hy - b^2 kx \qquad \qquad \dots(2)$

The coordinates, of the points A, B, C and D are therefore, found by solving (1) and (2).

From (2) we have $y = \dfrac{b^2 kx}{a^2(h - e^2 x)}$

Substituting in (1) and simplifying, we obtain

$$x^4 a^2 e^4 - 2ha^2 e^2 x^3 + x^2(a^2 h^2 + b^2 k^2 - a^4 e^4) + 2he^2 a^4 x - a^4 h^2 = 0 \qquad \dots(3$$

If x_1, x_2, x_3 and x_4 be the roots of this equation, we have (Art. 2),

$$\Sigma x_1 = \frac{2h}{e^2}, \ \Sigma x_1 x_2 = \frac{a^2 h^2 + b^2 k^2 - a^4 e^4}{a^2 e^4},$$

$$\Sigma x_1 x_2 x_3 = -\frac{2ha^2}{e^2} \quad \text{and} \quad x_1 x_2 x_3 x_4 = -\frac{a^2 h^2}{e^4}$$

If S be the point $(-ae, 0)$ we have, by Art. 251,

$$SA = a + ex_1$$

$$\therefore \ SA \cdot SB \cdot SC \cdot SD = (a + ex_1)(a + ex_2)(a + ex_3)(a + ex_4)$$

$$= a^4 + a^3 e \Sigma x_1 + a^2 e^2 \Sigma x_1 x_2 + ae^3 \Sigma x_1 x_2 x_3 + e^4 x_1 x_2 x_3 x_4$$

$$= \frac{b^2}{e^2} \{(h + ae)^2 + k^2\}, \text{ on substitution and simplificatio}$$

$$= \frac{b^2}{e^2} \cdot SO^2.$$

Aliter. If ρ stand for one of the quantities SA, SB, SC or SD we have

$$\rho = a + ex$$

i.e.,

$$x = \frac{1}{e}(\rho - a)$$

Substituting this value in (3) we obtain an equation in the fourth degree, and easily have

$$\rho_1 \rho_2 \rho_3 \rho_4 = \frac{b^2}{e^2}[(h + ae)^2 + k^2], \text{ as before.}$$

EXAMPLE 2 *If the normals at four points P, Q, R, and S of a central conic meet in a point, and if PQ pass through a fixed point, find the locus of the middle point of RS.*

Let the equation to PQ be

$$y = m_1 x + c_1 \qquad \qquad \ldots(1)$$

and that to RS $\qquad y = m_2 x + c_2 \qquad \qquad \ldots(2)$

If the equation to the given conic be $Ax^2 + By^2 = 1$, we then have (by Art. 412, Cor. 2)

$$\dot{m}_1 m_2 = \frac{A}{B} \qquad \qquad \ldots(3)$$

and $\qquad \qquad c_1 c_2 = -\frac{1}{B} \qquad \qquad \ldots(4)$

If (f, g) be the fixed point through which PQ passes, we have

$$g = m_1 f + c_1 \qquad \qquad \ldots(5)$$

Now, the middle point of RS lies on the diameter conjugate to it, *i.e.*, by Art. 376, on the diameter

$$y = -\frac{A}{Bm_2}x,$$

i.e., by Eq. (3),

$$y = -m_1 x \qquad \qquad \ldots(6)$$

Now, from (4) and (5),

$$c_2 = -\frac{1}{B(g - fm_1)}$$

so that, by (3), the equation to RS is

$$y = \frac{A}{Bm_1}x - \frac{1}{B(g - fm_1)} \qquad \qquad \ldots(7)$$

Eliminating m_1 between (6) and (7), we easily have, as the equation to the required locus,

$$(Ax^2 + By^2)(gx + fy) + xy = 0$$

Cor. : From (6) it follows that the diameter conjugate to RS is equall inclined with PQ to the axis, and hence, that the points P and Q and th ends of the diameter conjugate to RS are concyclic (Art. 400).

EXAMPLES XLVI

1. If the sum of the squares of the four normals drawn from a poi O to an ellipse be constant, prove that the locus of O is a conic.

2. If the sum of the reciprocals of the distances from a focus of the fe of the four normals drawn from a point O to an ellipse $\dfrac{4}{\text{lat. rect.}}$, prove that the locus of O is a parabola passing throu that focus.

3. If four normals be drawn from a point O to an ellipse and if t sum of the squares of the reciprocals of perpendiculars from t centre upon the tangents drawn at their feet be constant, prove th the locus of O is a hyperbola.

4. The normals at four points of an ellipse are concurrent and th meet the major axis in G_1, G_2, G_3 and G_4; prove that

$$\frac{1}{CG_1} + \frac{1}{CG_2} + \frac{1}{CG_3} + \frac{1}{CG_4} = \frac{4}{CG_1 + CG_2 + CG_3 + CG_4}.$$

5. If the normals to a central conic at four points L, M, N, and P concurrent, and if the circle through L, M and N meet the cu again in P', prove that PP' is a diameter.

6. Shew that the locus of the foci of the rectangular hyperbolas wh pass through the four points in which the normals drawn from a point on a given straight line meet an ellipse is a pair of conics

7. If the normals at points of an ellipse, whose eccentric angles α, β and γ, meet in a point, prove that
$$\sin(\beta + \gamma) + \sin(\gamma + \alpha) + \sin(\alpha + \beta) = 0.$$
Hence, by page 217, Ex. 15, shew that if PQR be a maximum triar inscribed in an ellipse, the normals at P, Q and R are concurrer

8. Prove that the normals at the points where the straight
$$\frac{x}{a \cos \alpha} + \frac{y}{b \sin \alpha} = 1 \text{ meets the ellipse } \frac{x^2}{a^2} + \frac{y^2}{b^2} = 1 \text{ meet at the po}$$
$$\left(-ae^2 \cos^3 \alpha, \frac{a^2 e^2}{b} \sin^3 \alpha \right)$$

9. Prove that the loci of the point of intersection of normals at the e of focal chords of an ellipse are the two ellipses
$$a^2 y^2 (1 + e^2)^2 + b^2 (x \pm ae)(x \mp ae^3) = 0.$$

10. Tangents to the ellipse $\dfrac{x^2}{a^2} + \dfrac{y^2}{b^2} = 1$ are drawn from any point or

ellipse $\dfrac{x^2}{a^2} + \dfrac{y^2}{b^2} = 4$; prove that the normals at the points of contact

meet on the ellipse $a^2x^2 + b^2y^2 = \dfrac{1}{4}(a^2 - b^2)^2$.

11. Any tangent to the rectangular hyperbola $4xy = ab$ meets the ellipse
$\dfrac{x^2}{a^2} + \dfrac{y^2}{b^2} = 1$ in the points P and Q; prove that the normals at P and
Q meet on a fixed diameter.

12. Chords of an ellipse meet the major axis in the point whose distance
from the centre is $a\sqrt{\dfrac{a-b}{a+b}}$; prove that the normals at its ends meet
on a circle.

13. From any point on the normal to the ellipse at the point whose
eccentric angle is α two other normals are drawn to it; prove that
the locus of the point of intersection of the corresponding tangents
is the curve
$$xy + bx \sin \alpha + ay \cos \alpha = 0.$$

14. Shew that the locus of the intersection of two perpendicular normals
to an ellipse is the curve
$$(a^2 + b^2)(x^2 + y^2)(a^2y^2 + b^2x^2)^2 = (a^2 - b^2)^2(a^2y^2 - b^2x^2)^2.$$

15. ABC is a triangle inscribed in the ellipse $\dfrac{x^2}{a^2} + \dfrac{y^2}{b^2} = 1$ having each side

parallel to the tangent at the opposite angular point; prove that the
normals at A, B and C meet at a point which lies on the ellipse
$$a^2x^2 + b^2y^2 = \dfrac{1}{4}(a^2 - b^2)^2.$$

16. The normals at four points of an ellipse meet in a point (h, k). Find
the equations of the axes of the two parabolas which pass through
the four points. Prove that the angle between them is $2 \tan^{-1} \dfrac{b}{a}$ and
that they are parallel to one or other of the equi-conjugates of the
ellipse.

17. Prove that the centre of mean position of the four points on the
ellipse $\dfrac{x^2}{a^2} + \dfrac{y^2}{b^2} = 1$, the normals at which pass through the point
(α, β), is the point
$$\left(\dfrac{1}{2} \dfrac{a^2\alpha}{a^2 - b^2}, -\dfrac{1}{2} \dfrac{b^2\beta}{a^2 - b^2} \right)$$

18. Prove that the product of the three normals drawn from any point
to a parabola, divided by the product of the two tangents from the
same point, is equal to one quarter of the latus rectum.

19. Prove that the conic $2aky = (2a - h)y^2 + 4a.x^2$ intersects the parabola $y^2 = 4ax$ at the feet of the normals drawn to it from the point (h, k).

20. From a point (h, k) four normals are drawn to the rectangular hyperbola $xy = c^2$; prove that the centre of mean position of their feet is the point $\left(\dfrac{h}{4}, \dfrac{k}{4}\right)$, and that the four feet are such that each is the orthocentre of the triangle formed by the other three.

CONFOCAL CONICS

➤ **415. Def.** Two conics are said to be confocal when they have both foci common.

To find the equation to conics which are confocal with the ellipse

$$\frac{x^2}{a^2} + \frac{y^2}{b^2} = 1 \qquad \ldots(1)$$

All conics having the same foci have the same centre and axes.

The equation to any conic having the same centre and axes as the given conic is

$$\frac{x^2}{A} + \frac{y^2}{B} = 1 \qquad \ldots(2)$$

The foci of (1) are at the points $(\pm \sqrt{a^2 - b^2}, 0)$.

The foci of (2) are at the points $(\pm \sqrt{A - B}, 0)$.

These foci are the same if

$$A - B = a^2 - b^2$$

i.e., if $\qquad A - a^2 = B - b^2 = \lambda \text{ (say)}$

$\therefore \qquad A = a^2 + \lambda \quad \text{and} \quad B = b^2 + \lambda$

The equation (2) then becomes

$$\frac{x^2}{a^2 + \lambda} + \frac{y^2}{b^2 + \lambda} = 1,$$

which is therefore, the required equation, the quantity λ determining the particular confocal.

➤ **416.** *For different values of λ to trace the conic given by the equation*

$$\frac{x^2}{a^2 + \lambda} + \frac{y^2}{b^2 + \lambda} = 1 \qquad \ldots(1)$$

First, let λ be very great; then $a^2 + \lambda$ and $b^2 + \lambda$ are both very great and, the greater that λ is, the more nearly do these quantities approach to equality. A circle of infinitely great radius is therefore a confocal of the system.

Let λ gradually decrease from infinity to zero; the semi-major axis $\sqrt{a^2 + \lambda}$ gradually decreases from infinity to a, and the semi-minor axis from infinity to b. When λ is positive, the equation (1) therefore, represents an ellipse gradually decreasing in size from an infinite circle to the standard ellipse

$$\frac{x^2}{a^2} + \frac{y^2}{b^2} = 1$$

This latter ellipse is marked I in the figure.

Next, let λ gradually decrease from 0 to $-b^2$. The semi-major axis decreases from a to $\sqrt{a^2 - b^2}$, and the semi-minor axis from b to 0.

For these values of λ the confocal is still an ellipse, which always lies within the ellipse I; it gradually decreases in size until, when λ is a quantity very slightly greater than $-b^2$, it is an extremely narrow ellipse very nearly coinciding with the line SH, which joins the two foci of all curves of the system.

Next, let λ be less than $-b^2$; the semi-minor axis $\sqrt{b^2 + \lambda}$ now, becomes imaginary and the curve is a hyperbola; when λ is very slightly less than $-b^2$ the curve is a hyperbola very nearly coinciding with the straight lines SX and HX'.

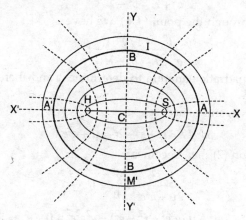

[As λ passes through the value $-b^2$ it will be noted that the confocal instantaneously changes from the line-ellipse SH to the line-hyperbola SX and HX'.]

As λ gets less and less, the semi-transverse axis $\sqrt{a^2 + \lambda}$ becomes less and less, so that the ends of the transverse axis of the hyperbola gradually approach to C, and the hyperbola widens out as in the figure.

When $\lambda = -a^2$, the transverse axis of the hyperbola vanishes, and the hyperbola degenerates into the infinite double line YCY'.

When λ is less than $-a^2$, both semi-axes of the conic become imaginary, and therefore, the confocal becomes wholly imaginary.

➤ **417.** *Through any point in the plane of a given conic there can be drawn two conics confocal with it; also one of these is an ellipse and the other a hyperbola.*

Let the equation to the given conic be

$$\frac{x^2}{a^2} + \frac{y^2}{b^2} = 1,$$

and let the given point be (f, g).

Any conic confocal with the given conic is

$$\frac{x^2}{a^2 + \lambda} + \frac{y^2}{b^2 + \lambda} = 1 \qquad \text{...(1)}$$

If this go through the point (f, g), we have

$$\frac{f^2}{a^2 + \lambda} + \frac{g^2}{b^2 + \lambda} = 1 \qquad \text{...(2)}$$

This is a quadratic equation to determine λ and therefore, gives two values of λ.

Put $b^2 + \lambda = \mu$, and hence,

$$a^2 + \lambda = \mu + a^2 - b^2 = \mu + a^2 e^2$$

The equation (2) then becomes

$$\frac{f^2}{\mu + a^2 e^2} + \frac{g^2}{\mu} = 1$$

i.e.,
$$\mu^2 + \mu(a^2 e^2 - f^2 - g^2) - g^2 a^2 e^2 = 0 \qquad \text{...(3)}$$

On applying the criterion of Art. 1 we at once see that the roots of this equation are both real.

Also, since its last term is negative, the product of these roots is negative, and therefore, one value of μ is positive and the other is negative.

The two values of $b^2 + \lambda$ are therefore, one positive and the other negative. Similarly, the two values of $a^2 + \lambda$ can be shewn to be both positive.

On substituting in (2) we thus obtain an ellipse and a hyperbola.

➤ **418.** *Confocal conics cut at right angles.*

Let the confocals be

$$\frac{x^2}{a^2 + \lambda_1} + \frac{y^2}{b^2 + \lambda_1} = 1, \text{ and } \frac{x^2}{a^2 + \lambda_2} + \frac{y^2}{b^2 + \lambda_2} = 1,$$

and let them meet at the point (x', y').

The equations to the tangents at this point are

$$\frac{xx'}{a^2 + \lambda_1} + \frac{yy'}{b^2 + \lambda_1} = 1, \text{ and } \frac{xx'}{a^2 + \lambda_2} + \frac{yy'}{b^2 + \lambda_2} = 1.$$

These cut at right angles if (Art. 69)

$$\frac{x'^2}{(a^2 + \lambda_1)(a^2 + \lambda_2)} + \frac{y'^2}{(b^2 + \lambda_1)(b^2 + \lambda_2)} = 0 \qquad \text{...(1)}$$

But, since (x', y') is a common point of the two confocals, we have

$$\frac{x'^2}{a^2 + \lambda_1} + \frac{y'^2}{b^2 + \lambda_1} = 1, \text{ and } \frac{x'^2}{a^2 + \lambda_2} + \frac{y'^2}{b^2 + \lambda_2} = 1.$$

By subtraction, we have

$$x'^2 \left(\frac{1}{a^2 + \lambda_1} - \frac{1}{a^2 + \lambda_2} \right) + y'^2 \left(\frac{1}{b^2 + \lambda_1} - \frac{1}{b^2 + \lambda_2} \right) = 0$$

i.e.,

$$\frac{x'^2}{(a^2 + \lambda_1)(a^2 + \lambda_2)} + \frac{y'^2}{(b^2 + \lambda_1)(b^2 + \lambda_2)} = 0 \qquad \text{...(2)}$$

The condition (1) is therefore, satisfied and hence, the two confocals cut at right angles.

Cor. : From equation (2) it is clear that the quantities $b^2 + \lambda_1$ and $b^2 + \lambda_2$ have opposite signs; for otherwise we should have the sum of two positive quanities equal to zero. Two confocals, therefore, which intersect, are one an ellipse and the other a hyperbola.

➤ **419.** *One conic and only one conic, confocal with the conic* $\frac{x^2}{a^2} + \frac{y^2}{b^2} = 1$, *can be drawn to touch a given straight line.*

Let the equation to the given straight line be

$$x \cos \alpha + y \sin \alpha = p \qquad \text{...(1)}$$

Any confocal of the system is

$$\frac{x^2}{a^2 + \lambda} + \frac{y^2}{b^2 + \lambda} = 1 \qquad \ldots(2)$$

The straight line (1) touches has (2) if

$$p^2 = (a^2 + \lambda) \cos^2 \alpha + (b^2 + \lambda) \sin^2 \alpha \qquad \text{(Art. 264)},$$

i.e., if $\qquad \lambda = p^2 - a^2 \cos^2 \alpha - b^2 \sin^2 \alpha.$

This only gives one value for λ and therefore, there is only one conic of the form (2) which touches the straight line (1).

Also, $\lambda + a^2 = p^2 + (a^2 - b^2) \sin^2 \alpha = $ a real quantity. The conic is therefore, real.

EXAMPLES XLVII

1. Prove that the difference of the squares of the perpendiculars drawn from the centre upon parallel tangents to two given confocal conics is constant.

2. Prove that the equation to the hyperbola drawn through the point of the ellipse, whose eccentric angle is α, and which is confocal with the ellipse, is

$$\frac{x^2}{\cos^2 \alpha} - \frac{y^2}{\sin^2 \alpha} = a^2 - b^2.$$

3. Prove that the locus of the points lying on a system of confocal ellipses, which have the same eccentric angle α, is a confocal hyperbola whose asymptotes are inclined at an angle 2α.

4. Shew that the locus of the point of contact of tangents drawn from a given point to a system of confocal conics is a cubic curve, which passes through the given point and the foci.

   If the given point be on the major axis, prove that the cubic reduces to a circle.

5. Shew that only one of a given system of confocals can have a given straight line as a normal.

6. Prove that the locus of the feet of the normals, drawn from the fixed point (h, k) to each of the series of confocals given by the equation

$$\frac{x^2}{a^2 + \lambda} + \frac{y^2}{b^2 + \lambda} = 1,$$

is the cubic curve

$$\frac{x}{y - k} + \frac{y}{x - h} = \frac{a^2 - b^2}{hy - kx}.$$

Shew also from geometrical considerations that this curve passes through the fixed point and the foci of the confocals.

7. Two tangents at right angles to one another are drawn from a point P, one to each of two confocal ellipses; prove that P lies on a fixed circle. Shew also that the line joining the points of contact is bisected by the line joining P to the common centre.

8. From a given point a pair of tangents is drawn to each of a given system of confocals; prove that the normals at the points of contact meet on a straight line.

9. Tangents are drawn to the parabola $y^2 = 4x\sqrt{a^2 - b^2}$, and on each is taken the point at which it touches one of the confocals

$$\frac{x^2}{a^2 + \lambda} + \frac{y^2}{b^2 + \lambda} = 1.$$

prove that the locus of such points is a straight line.

10. Normals are drawn from a given point to each of a system of confocal conics, and tangents at the feet of these normals; prove that the locus of the middle points of the portions of these tangents intercepted between the axes of the confocals is a straight line.

11. Prove that the locus of the pole of a given straight line with respect to a series of confocals is a straight line which is the normal to that confocal which the straight line touches.

12. A series of parallel tangents is drawn to a system of confocal conics; prove that the locus of the points of contact is a rectangular hyperbola.

Shew also that the locus of the vertices of these rectangular hyperbolas, for different directions of the tangents, is the curve $r^2 = c^2 \cos 2\theta$, where $2c$ is the distance between the foci of the confocals.

13. The locus of the pole of any tangent to a confocal with respect to any circle, whose centre is one of the foci, is obtained and found to be a circle; prove that, if the circle corresponding to each confocal be taken, they are all coaxal.

14. Prove that the two conics

$$ax^2 + 2hxy + by^2 = 1 \quad \text{and} \quad a'x^2 + 2h'xy + b'y^2 = 1$$

can be placed so as to be confocal, if

$$\frac{(a-b)^2 + 4h^2}{(ab - h^2)^2} = \frac{(a' - b')^2 + 4h'^2}{(a'b' - h'^2)^2}.$$

CURVATURE

➤ **420. Circle of Curvature. Def. :** If P, Q and R be any three points on a conic section, one circle and only one circle can be drawn to pass through them. Also this circle is completely determined by the three points.

Let now, the point Q and R move up to, and ultimately coincide with the point P ; then the limiting position of the above circle is called the circle of curvature at P ; also the radius of this circle is called the radius of curvature at P, and its centre is called the centre of curvature at P.

➤ **421.** Since, the circle of curvature at P meets the conic in three coincident points at P, it will cut the curve in one other point P'. The line PP' which is the line joining P to the other point of intersection of the conic and the circle of curvature is called the common chord of curvature.

We shewed, in Art. 400, that, if a circle and a conic intersect in four points, the line joining one pair of points of intersection and the line joining the other pair are equally inclined to the axis. In our case, one pair of points is two of the coincident points at P, and the line joining them therefore, the tangent at P ; the other pair of points is the third point at P and the point P', and the line joining them the chord of curvature PP'. Hence, *the tangent at P and the chord of curvature PP' are, in any conic, equally inclined to the axis.*

➤ **422.** *To find the equation to the circle of curvature and the length of the radius of curvature at any point $(at^2, 2at)$ of the parabola $y^2 = 4ax$.*

If $S = 0$ be the equation to a conic, $T = 0$ the equation to the tangent at the point P, whose coordinates are at^2 and $2at$, and $L = 0$ the equation to any straight line passing through P, we know, by Art. 384, that $S + \lambda \cdot L \cdot T = 0$ is the equation to the conic section passing through three coincident points at P and through the other point in which $L = 0$ meets $S = 0$.

If λ and L be so chosen that this conic is a circle, it will be the circle of curvature at P, and, by the last article, we know that $L = 0$ will be equally inclined to the axis with $T = 0$.

In the case of a parabola

$$S \equiv y^2 - 4ax \text{ and } T \equiv ty - x - at^2. \qquad \text{(Art. 229)}$$

Also the equation to a line through $(at^2, 2at)$ equally inclined with $T = 0$ to the axis is

$$t(y - 2at) + x - at^2 = 0,$$

so that　　　　　　　　$L \equiv ty + x - 3at^2.$

The equation to the circle of curvature is therefore

$$y^2 - 4ax + \lambda(ty - x - at^2)(ty + x - 3at^2) = 0$$

where　　　　　　$1 + \lambda t^2 = -\lambda, \quad i.e., \quad \lambda = -\dfrac{1}{1 + t^2}.$

On substituting this value of λ, we have, as the required equation,

$$x^2 + y^2 - 2ax(3t^2 + 2) + 4ayt^3 - 3a^2t^4 = 0,$$

i.e., $$[x - a(2 + 3t^2)]^2 + [y + 2at^3]^2 = 4a^2(1 + t^2)^3.$$

The circle of curvature has therefore, its centre at the point $(2a + 3at^2, -2at^3)$ and its radius equal to

$$2a (1 + t^2)^{3/2}.$$

Cor. : If S be the focus, we have SP equal to $a + at^2$, so that the radius of curvature is equal to $\dfrac{2 \cdot SP^{3/2}}{\sqrt{a}}$.

➤ **423.** To find the equation to the circle of curvature at the point $P(a \cos \phi, b \sin \phi)$ of the ellipse $\dfrac{x^2}{a^2} + \dfrac{y^2}{b^2} = 1$.

The tangent at the point P is

$$\frac{x}{a} \cos \phi + \frac{y}{b} \sin \phi = 1$$

The straight line passing through P and equally inclined with this line to the axis is

$$\frac{\cos \phi}{a} (x - a \cos \phi) - \frac{\sin \phi}{b} (y - b \sin \phi) = 0$$

i.e., $$\frac{x}{a} \cos \phi - \frac{y}{b} \sin \phi - \cos 2\phi = 0.$$

The equation to the circle of curvature is therefore, of the form

$$\frac{x^2}{a^2} + \frac{y^2}{b^2} - 1 + \lambda \left[\frac{x}{a} \cos \phi + \frac{y}{b} \sin \phi - 1 \right]$$

$$\left[\frac{x}{a} \cos \phi - \frac{y}{b} \sin \phi - \cos 2\phi \right] = 0 \quad \dots(1)$$

Since, it is a circle, the coefficients of x^2 and y^2 must be equal, so that

$$\frac{1}{a^2} + \lambda \frac{\cos^2 \phi}{a^2} = \frac{1}{b^2} - \lambda \frac{\sin^2 \phi}{b^2}$$

and therefore, $$\lambda = \frac{a^2 - b^2}{b^2 \cos^2 \phi + a^2 \sin^2 \phi}.$$

On substitution in (1), the equation to the circle of curvature is

$$(b^2 \cos^2 \phi + a^2 \sin^2 \phi)\left(\frac{x^2}{a^2} + \frac{y^2}{b^2} - 1\right) + (a^2 - b^2)\left[\frac{x^2}{a^2} \cos^2 \phi - \frac{y^2}{b^2} \sin^2 \phi\right.$$
$$\left. - \frac{x \cos \phi}{a}(1 + \cos 2\phi) + \frac{y \sin \phi}{b}(1 - \cos 2\phi) + \cos 2\phi\right] = 0$$

i.e., $\quad x^2 + y^2 - (a^2 - b^2)\left[\dfrac{2x \cos^3 \phi}{a} - \dfrac{2y \sin^3 \phi}{b}\right]$
$$+ a^2(\cos^2 \phi - 2 \sin^2 \phi) - b^2(2 \cos^2 \phi - \sin^3 \phi) = 0$$

The equation to the circle of curvature is then

$$\left\{x - \frac{a^2 - b^2}{a} \cos^3 \phi\right\}^2 + \left\{y + \frac{a^2 - b^2}{b} \sin^3 \phi\right\}^2$$

$$= (a^2 - b^2)^2 \left\{\frac{\cos^6 \phi}{a^2} + \frac{\sin^6 \phi}{b^2}\right\} - a^2 \{\cos^2 \phi - 2 \sin^2 \phi\}$$

$$+ b^2 \{2 \cos^2 \phi - \sin^2 \phi\}$$

$$= \frac{(a^2 \sin^2 \phi + b^2 \cos^2 \phi)^3}{a^2 b^2}, \text{ after some reduction.}$$

The centre is therefore, the point whose coordinates are $\left(\dfrac{a^2 - b^2}{a} \cos^3 \phi, \ -\dfrac{a^2 - b^2}{b} \sin^3 \phi\right)$ and whose radius is

$$\frac{(a^2 \sin^2 \phi + b^2 \cos^2 \phi)^{3/2}}{ab}.$$

Cor. 1. : If CD be the semi-diameter which is conjugate to CP, then D is the point $(90° + \phi)$, so that its coordiantes are $- a \sin \phi$ and $b \cos \phi$, (Art. 285).

Hence, $\qquad CD^2 = a^2 \sin^2 \phi + b^2 \cos^2 \phi$

and therefore, the radius of curvature $\rho = \dfrac{CD^3}{ab}$.

Cor. 2. : If the point P have as coordiantes x' and y' then, since $x' = a \cos \phi$ and $y' = b \sin \phi$, the equation to the circle of curvature is

$$\left(x - \frac{a^2 - b^2}{a^4} x'^3\right)^2 + \left(y + \frac{a^2 - b^2}{b^4} y'^3\right)^2 = \frac{(a^2 + b^2 - x'^2 - y'^2)^3}{a^2 b^2}$$

Cor. 3. : In a similar manner it may be shewn that the equation to the circle of curvature at any point (x', y') of the hyperbola $\dfrac{x^2}{a^2} - \dfrac{y^2}{b^2} = 1$ is

$$\left(x - \frac{a^2 + b^2}{a^4} x'^3\right)^2 + \left(y + \frac{a^2 + b^2}{b^4} y'^3\right)^2 = \frac{(a^2 - b^2 - x'^2 - y'^2)^3}{-a^2 b^2}$$
$$= \frac{(x'^2 + y'^2 - a^2 + b^2)^3}{a^2 b^2}$$

➤ **424.** If a circle and an ellipse intersect in four points, the sum of their eccentric angles is euqal to an even multiple of π. [Page 218, Ex. 18.]

If then the circle of curvature at a point P, whose eccentric angle is θ, meet the curve again in Q, whose eccentric angle is ϕ, three of these four points coincide at P, so that three of these eccentric angles are equal to θ, whilst the fourth is equal to ϕ. We therefore, have

$$3\theta + \phi = \text{an even multiple of } \pi = 2n\pi.$$

Hence, if ϕ be supposed given, *i.e.*, if Q be given, we have

$$\theta = \frac{2n\pi - \phi}{3}.$$

Giving n in succession the values 1, 2, and 3, we see that θ equals $\dfrac{2\pi - \phi}{3}$, $\dfrac{4\pi - \phi}{3}$ or $\dfrac{6\pi - \phi}{3}$.

Hence, the circles of curvature at the points, whose eccentric angles are $\dfrac{2\pi - \phi}{3}$, $\dfrac{4\pi - \phi}{3}$ and $\dfrac{6\pi - \phi}{3}$, all pass through the point whose eccentric angle is ϕ.

Also since $\dfrac{2\pi - \phi}{3} + \dfrac{4\pi - \phi}{3} + \dfrac{6\pi - \phi}{3} + \phi = 4\pi = $ an even multiple of π, we see that the points $\dfrac{2\pi - \phi}{3}$, $\dfrac{4\pi - \phi}{3}$, $\dfrac{6\pi - \phi}{3}$ and ϕ all lie on a circle.

Hence, *through any point Q on an ellipse can be drawn three circles which are the circles of curvature at three points P_1, P_2 and P_3. Also the four points P_1, P_2, P_3, and Q all lie on another circle.*

➤ **425. Evolute of a Curve**: The locus of the centres of curvature at different points of a curve is called the evolute of the curve.

➤ **426.** *Evolute of the parabola $y^2 = 4ax$.*

Let, $(\bar{x}, \bar{y})$ be the centre of curvature at the point $(at^2, 2at)$ of this curve.

Then, $\bar{x} = a(2 + 3t^2)$ and $\bar{y} = -2at^3$.   (Art. 422.)

$\therefore$ $(\bar{x} - 2a)^3 = 27a^3 t^6 = \dfrac{27}{4} a\bar{y}^2$

i.e., the locus of the centre of curvature is the curve

$$27ay^2 = 4(x - 2a)^3$$

This curve meets the axis of x in the point $(2a, 0)$.

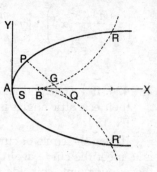

It also meets the parabola where

$$27a^2x = (x - 2a)^3$$

i.e., where $x = 8a$,

and therefore, $y = \pm 4\sqrt{2}a$

Hence, it meets the parabola at the points

$$(8a, \pm 4\sqrt{2}a)$$

The curve is called a semi-cubical parabola and could be shewn to be of the shape of the dotted curve in the figure.

➤ **427.** *Evolute of the ellipse* $\dfrac{x^2}{a^2} + \dfrac{y^2}{b^2} = 1$.

If $(\bar{x}, \bar{y})$ be the centre of curvature corresponding to the point $(a\cos\phi, b\sin\phi)$ of the ellipse, we have

$$\bar{x} = \frac{a^2 - b^2}{a}\cos^3\phi \quad \text{and} \quad \bar{y} = -\frac{a^2 - b^2}{b}\sin^3\phi$$

Hence,

$$(a\bar{x})^{2/3} + (b\bar{y})^{2/3} = (a^2 - b^2)^{2/3}\{\cos^2\phi + \sin^2\phi\}$$
$$= (a^2 - b^2)^{2/3}$$

Hence, the locus of the point $(\bar{x}, \bar{y})$ is the curve

$$(ax)^{2/3} + (by)^{2/3} = (a^2 - b^2)^{2/3}$$

This curve could be shewn to be of the shape shewn in the figure where

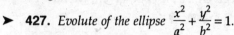

$$CL = CL' = \frac{a^2 - b^2}{a}$$

and

$$CM = CM' = \frac{a^2 - b^2}{b}$$

The equation to the evolute of the hyperbola would be found to be

$$(ax)^{2/3} - (by)^{2/3} = (a^2 + b^2)^{2/3}$$

➤ **428. Contact of different orders :** If two conics, or curves touch, *i.e.*, have two coincident points in common they are said to have contact of the first order. The tangent to a conic therefore has contact of the first order with it.

If two conics have three coincident points in common, they are said to have contact of the second order. The circle of curvature of a conic therefore, has contact of the second order with it.

If two conics have four coincident points in common, they are said to have contact of the third order. No conics, which are not coincident, can have more than four coincident points; for a conic is completely determined if five points on it be given. Contact of the third order is therefore, all that two conics can have, and then they are said to osculate one another.

Since a circle is completely determined when three points on it are given we cannot, in general, obtain a circle to have contact of a higher order than the second with a given conic. The circle of curvature is therefore ,often called the osculating circle.

In general, one curve osculates another when it has the highest possible order of contact with the second curve.

➤ **429.** *Equation to a conic osculating another conic.*

If $S = 0$ be the equation to a conic and $T = 0$ the tangent at any point of it, the conic $S = \lambda T^2$ passes through four coincident points of $S = 0$ at the point where $T = 0$ touches it. (Art. 385, IV)

Hence, $S = \lambda T^2$ is the equation to the required osculating conic.

EXAMPLE *The equation of any conic osculating the conic*

$$ax^2 + 2hxy + by^2 - 2fy = 0 \qquad \qquad ...(1)$$

as the origin is

$$ax^2 + 2hxy + by^2 - 2fy + \lambda y^2 = 0 \qquad \qquad ...(2)$$

For the tangent to (1) at the origin is $y = 0$.

If (2) be a parabola, we have $h^2 = a(b + \lambda)$, so that its equation is

$$(ax + hy)^2 = 2afy$$

If (2) be a rectangular hyperbola, we have $a + b + \lambda = 0$, and the equation to the osculating rectangular hyperbola is

$$a(x^2 - y^2) + 2hxy - 2fy = 0.$$

EXAMPLES XLVIII

1. If the normal at a point P of a parabola meet the directrix in L, prove that the radius of curvature at P is equal to $2PL$.

2. If ρ_1 and ρ_2 be the radii of curvature at the ends of a focal chord of the parabola, prove that

$$\rho_1^{-2/3} + \rho_2^{-2/3} = (2a)^{-2/3}.$$

3. PQ is the common chord of the parabola and its circle of curvature at P; prove that the ordinate of Q is three times that of P, and that the locus of the middle point of PQ is another parabola.

4. If ρ and ρ' be the radii of curvature at the ends, P and D, of conjugate diameters of the ellipse, prove that

$$\rho^{2/3} + \rho'^{2/3} = \frac{a^2 + b^2}{(ab)^{2/3}}$$

and that the locus of the middle point of the line joining the centres of curvature at P and D is

$$(ax + by)^{2/3} + (ax - by)^{2/3} = (a^2 - b^2)^{2/3}.$$

5. O is the centre of curvature at any point of an ellipse, and Q and R are the feet of the other normals drawn from O; prove that the locus of the intersection of tangents at Q and R is $\dfrac{a^2}{x^2} + \dfrac{x^2}{y^2} = 1$, and that the line QR is a normal to the ellipse

$$\frac{x^2}{b^2} + \frac{y^2}{a^2} = \frac{a^2 b^2}{(a^2 - b^2)^2}.$$

6. If four normals be drawn to an ellipse from any point on the evolute, prove that the locus of the centre of the rectangular hyperbola through their feet is the curve

$$\left(\frac{x}{a}\right)^{2/3} + \left(\frac{y}{b}\right)^{2/3} = 1.$$

7. In general, prove that there are six points on an ellipse the circles of curvature at which pass through a given point O, not on the ellipse. If O be on the ellipse, why is the number of circles of curvature passing through it only four?

8. The circles of curvature at three points of an ellipse meet in a point P on the curve. Prove that (1) the normals at these three points meet on the normal drawn at the other end of the diameter throguh P, and (2) the locus of these points of intersection for different positions of P is the ellipse

$$4 (a^2 x^2 + b^2 y^2) = (a^2 - b^2)^2.$$

9. Prove that the equation to the circle of curvature at any point (x', y') of the rectangular hyperbola $x^2 - y^2 = a^2$ is

$$a^2 (x^2 + y^2) - 4xx'^3 + 4yy'^3 + 3a^2 (x'^2 + y'^2) = 0.$$

10. Shew that the equation to the chord of curvature of the rectangular hyperbola $xy = c^2$ at the point "t" is $ty + t^3 x = c (1 + t^4)$, and that the centre of curvature is the point

$$\left(c\,\frac{1+3t^4}{2t^3},\ c\,\frac{3+t^4}{2t} \right)$$

Prove also that the locus of the pole of the chord of curvature is the curve $r^2 = 2c^2 \sin 2\theta$.

11. PQ is the normal at any point of a rectangular hyperbola and meets the curve again in Q; the diameter through Q meets the curve again in R; shew that PR is the chord of curvature at P, and that PQ is equal to the diameter of curvature at P.

12. Prove that the equation to the circle of curvature of the conic $ax^2 + 2hxy + by^2 = 2y$ at the origin is

$$a\,(x^2 + y^2) = 2y.$$

13. If two confocal conics intersect, prove that the centre of curvature of either curve at a point of intersection is the pole of the tangent at that point with regard to the other curve.

14. Shew that the equation to the parabola, having contact of the third order with the rectangular hyperbola $xy = c^2$ at the point $\left(ct, \dfrac{c}{t} \right)$,

is $\qquad (x - yt^2)^2 - 4ct\,(x + yt^2) + 8c^2t^2 = 0$

Prove also that its directrix bisects, and is perpendicular to, the radius vector of the hyperbola from the centre to the point of contact.

15. Prove that the equation to the parabola, which passes through the origin and has contact of the second order with the parabola $y^2 = 4ax$ at the point $(at^2, 2at)$, is

$$(4x - 3ty)^2 + 4at^2\,(3x - 2ty) = 0.$$

16. Prove that the equation to the rectangular hyperbola, having contact of the third order with the parabola $y^2 = 4ax$ at the point $(at^2, 2at)$, is

$$x^2 - 2txy - y^2 + 2ax\,(2 + 3t^2) - 2at^3y + a^2t^4 = 0$$

Prove also that the locus of the centres of these hyperbolas is an equal parabola having the same axis and directrix as the original parabola.

17. Through every point of a circle is drawn the rectangular hyperbola of closest contact; prove that the centres of all these hyperbolas lie on a concentric circle of twice its radius.

18. A rectangular hyperbola is drawn to have contract of the third order with the ellipse $\dfrac{x^2}{a^2} + \dfrac{y^2}{b^2} = 1$; find its equation and prove that the locus of its centre is the curve

$$\left(\frac{x^2 + y^2}{a^2 + b^2} \right)^2 = \frac{x^2}{a^2} + \frac{y^2}{b^2}$$

ENVELOPES

➤ **430.** Consider any point P on a circle whose centre is O and whose radius is a. The straight line through P at right angles to OP is a tangent to the circle at P. Conversely, if through O we draw any straight line OP of length a, and if through the end P we draw a straight line perpendicular to OP, this latter straight line touches, or envelopes, a circle of radius a and centre O, and this circle is said to be the envelope of the straight lines drawn in this manner.

Again, if S be the focus of a parabola, and PY be the tangent at any point P of it meeting the tangent at the vertex in the point Y, then we know (Art. 211, δ) that SYP is a right angle. Conversely, if S be joined to any point Y on a given line, and a straight line be drawn through Y perpendicular to SY, this line, so drawn, always touches, or envelopes, a parabola whose focus is S and such that the given line is the tangent at its vertex.

➤ **431. Envelope. Def.:** The curve which is touched by each of a series of lines, which are all drawn to satisfy some given condition, is called the Envelope of these lines.

As an example, consider the series of straight lines which are drawn so that each of them cuts off from a pair of fixed straight lines a triangle of constant area.

We know (Art. 330) that any tangent to a hyperbola always cuts off a triangle of constant area from its asymptotes.

Conversely, we conclude that, if a variable straight line cuts off a constant area from two given straight lines, it always touches a hyperbola whose asymptotes are the two given straight lines, *i.e.*, that its envelope is a hyperbola.

➤ **432.** *If the equation to any curve involve a variable parameter, in the first degree only, the curve always passes through a fixed point or points.*

For if λ be the variable parameter, the equation to the curve can be written in the form $S + \lambda S' = 0$, and this equation is always satisfied by the points which satisfy $S = 0$ and $S' = 0$, *i.e.*, the curve always passes through the point, or points, of intersection of $S = 0$ and $S' = 0$ [compare Art. 97].

➤ **433.** *Curve touched by a variable straight line whose equation involves, in the second degree, a variable parameter.*

As an example, let us find the envelope of the straight lines given by the equation

$$m^2x - my + a = 0$$

I (Pages 12–14)

1. 5. **2.** 13. **3.** $3\sqrt{7}$. **4.** $\sqrt{a^2+b^2}$.

5. $\sqrt{a^2+2b^2+c^2-2ab-2bc}$.

6. $2a\sin\dfrac{\alpha-\beta}{2}$. **7.** $a(m_1-m_2)\sqrt{(m_1+m_2)^2+4}$. **9.** $3\pm2\sqrt{15}$.

15. $\left(\dfrac{10}{7},\dfrac{33}{7}\right)$. **16.** $(-2,-9)$ **17.** $\left(1,-\dfrac{4}{5}\right);(-11,16)$.

18. $\left(-5\dfrac{11}{12},2\dfrac{5}{12}\right);\left(-20\dfrac{1}{2},34\dfrac{1}{2}\right)$. **19.** $\left(-\dfrac{1}{3},0\right);\left(-\dfrac{5}{3},2\right)$.

20. $\left(\dfrac{-5}{2},\dfrac{9}{2}\right);(1,1);\left(\dfrac{9}{2},-\dfrac{5}{2}\right)$.

21. $\left(\dfrac{a^2+b^2}{a+b},\dfrac{a^2+2ab-b^2}{a+b}\right);\left(\dfrac{a^2-2ab-b^2}{a-b},\dfrac{a^2+b^2}{a-b}\right)$

22. $\left(\dfrac{kx_1+lx_2+mx_3}{k+l+m},\dfrac{ky_1+ly_2+my_3}{k+l+m}\right)$.

II (Page 17)

1. 10. **2.** 1. **3.** 29. **4.** $2ac$. **5.** a^2.

6. $2ab\sin\dfrac{\phi_2-\phi_3}{2}\sin\dfrac{\phi_3-\phi_1}{2}\sin\dfrac{\phi_1-\phi_2}{2}$.

7. $a^2(m_2-m_3)(m_3-m_1)(m_1-m_2)$.

8. $\dfrac{1}{2}a^2(m_2-m_3)(m_3-m_1)(m_1-m_2)$.

9. $\dfrac{1}{2}a^2(m_2-m_3)(m_3-m_1)(m_1-m_2)\div m_1m_2m_3$.

13. $20\dfrac{1}{2}$. **14.** 96.

III (Pages 21, 22)

12. $2\sqrt{5}$. **13.** $\sqrt{79}$. **14.** $\sqrt{7}a$. **16.** $\dfrac{1}{4}(8-3\sqrt{3})$. **17.** $\dfrac{7\sqrt{3}}{2}$.

18. $\frac{1}{4} a^2 \sqrt{3}$.   **25.** $r^2 = a^2$.   **26.** $\theta = \alpha$.   **27.** $r = 2a \cos \theta$.

28. $r \cos 2\theta = 2a \sin\theta$.   **29.** $r \cos \theta = 2a \sin^2 \theta$.   **30.** $r^2 = a^2 \cos 2\theta$.

31. $x^2 + y^2 = a^2$ **32.** $y = mx$.   **33.** $x^2 + y^2 = ax$.

34. $(x^2 + y^2)^3 = 4a^2 x^2 y^2$.   **35.** $(x^2 + y^2)^2 = a^2 (x^2 - y^2)$.

36. $xy = a^2$ **37.** $x^2 - y^2 = a^2$.   **38.** $y^2 + 4ax = 4a^2$.

39. $4(x^2 + y^2)(x^2 + y^2 + ax) a^2 y^2$.

40. $x^3 - 3xy^2 + 3x^2 y - y^3 = 5kxy$.

IV (Page 28)

8. $2ax + k^2 = 0$.   **9.** $(n^2 - 1)(x^2 + y^2 + a^2) + 2ax (n^2 + 1) = 0$.

10. $4x^2 (c^2 - 4a^2) + 4c^2 y^2 = c^2 (c^2 - 4a^2)$.   **11.** $(6a - 2c) x = a^2 - c^2$.

12. $y^2 - 4y - 2x + 5 = 0$.   **13.** $4y + 2x + 3 = 0$ **14.** $x + y = 7$.

15. $y = x$ **16.** $y = 3x$ **17.** $15x^2 - y^2 + 2ax = a^2$ **18.** $x^2 + y^2 = 3$.

19. $x^2 + y^2 = 4y$.   **20.** $8x^2 + 8y^2 + 6x - 36y + 27 = 0$

21. $x^2 = 3y^2$.   **22.** $x^2 + 2ay = a^2$

23. (1) $4x^2 + 3y^2 + 2ay = a^2$;   (2) $x^2 - 3y^2 + 8ay = 4a^2$

V (Pages 38, 39)

1. $y = x + 1$. **2.** $x - y - 5 = 0$.   **3.** $x - y\sqrt{3} - 2\sqrt{3} = 0$

4. $5y - 3x + 15 = 0$. **5.** $2x + 3y = 6$. **6.** $6x - 5y + 30 = 0$

7. (1) $x + y = 11$; (2) $y - x = 1$.   **8.** $x + y + 1 = 0$; $x - y = 3$

9. $xy' + x'y = 2x'y'$.   **10.** $20y - 9x = 96$.

15. $x + y = 0$. **16.** $y - x = 1$.   **17.** $7y + 10x = 11$.   **18.** $ax - by = ab$.

19. $(a - 2b) x - by + b^2 + 2ab - a^2 = 0$ **20.** $y (t_1 + t_2) - 2x = 2at_1 t_2$

21. $t_1 t_2 y + x = a (t_1 + t_2)$

22. $x \cos \frac{1}{2} (\phi_1 + \phi_2) + y \sin \frac{1}{2} (\phi_1 + \phi_2) = a \cos \frac{1}{2} (\phi_1 - \phi_2)$

23. $\frac{x}{a} \cos \frac{\phi_1 + \phi_2}{2} + \frac{y}{b} \sin \frac{\phi_1 + \phi_2}{2} = \cos \frac{\phi_1 - \phi_2}{2}$.

24. $bx \cos \frac{1}{2} (\phi_1 - \phi_2) - ay \sin \frac{1}{2} (\phi_1 + \phi_2) = ab \cos \frac{1}{2} (\phi_1 + \phi_2)$.

25. $x + 3y + 7 = 0$; $y - 3x = 1$; $y + 7x = 11$.

26. $2x - 3y = 4$; $y - 3x = 1$; $x + 2y = 2$.

27. $y(a' - a) - x(b' - b) = a'b - ab'$; $y(a' - a) + x(b' - b) = a'b' - ab$.

28. $2ay - ab'x = ab - a'b'$. **29.** $y = 6x$; $2y = 3x$.

VI (Pages 45–47)

1. $90°$. **2.** $\tan^{-1}\dfrac{23}{10}$. **3.** $\tan^{-1}\dfrac{4}{3}$. **4.** $60°$. **5.** $\tan^{-1}\dfrac{4m^2 n^2}{m^4 - n^4}$.

6. $\tan^{-1}\dfrac{a^2 - b^2}{2ab}$ **7.** $\tan^{-1}(2)$ **8.** $4y + 3x = 18$

9. $7y - 8x = 118$ **10.** $4y + 11x = 10$ **11.** $x + 4y + 16 = 0$

12. $ax + by = a^2$ **13.** $2x(a - a') + 2y(b - b') = a^2 - a'^2 + b^2 - b'^2$.

15. $yx' - xy' = 0$; $a^2 xy' - b^2 x'y = (a^2 - b^2)x'y'$; $xx' - yy' = x^2 - y^2$

16. $121y - 88x = 371$; $33y - 24x = 1043$.

17. $x = 3$; $y = 4$; $4\dfrac{1}{2}$ **19.** $x = 0$; $y + \sqrt{3}x = 0$

20. $y = k$; $(1 - m^2)(y - k) = 2m(x - h)$

21. $\tan^{-1}\dfrac{33}{55}$; $9x - 7y = 1$; $7x + 9y = 73$.

VII (Pages 50, 51)

1. $4\dfrac{2}{5}$ **2.** $2\dfrac{2}{5}$ **3.** $5\dfrac{1}{13}$ **4.** $\dfrac{a^2 + ab - b^2}{\sqrt{a^2 + b^2}}$ **5.** $a\cos\dfrac{1}{2}(\alpha - \beta)$

8. $\dfrac{c - d}{\sqrt{1 + m^2}}$ **9.** $\left\{\dfrac{a}{b}(b \pm \sqrt{a^2 + b^2}, 0\right\}$ **11.** $\dfrac{1}{2}(2 + \sqrt{3})$.

VIII (Pages 58–61)

1. $\left(\dfrac{-11}{29}, \dfrac{41}{29}\right)$ **2.** $\left(\dfrac{ab}{a + b}, \dfrac{ab}{a\ b}\right)$.   **3.** $\left\{\dfrac{a}{m_1 m_2}, a\left(\dfrac{1}{m_1} + \dfrac{1}{m_2}\right)\right\}$.

4. $\{a\cos\dfrac{1}{2}(\phi_1 + \phi_2)\sec\dfrac{1}{2}(\phi_1 - \phi_2), a\sin\dfrac{1}{2}(\phi_1 + \phi_2)\sec\dfrac{1}{2}(\phi_1 - \phi_2)\}$.

5. $\left(\dfrac{a(b - b')}{b + b'}, \dfrac{2bb'}{b + b'}\right)$ **6.** $\dfrac{130}{17\sqrt{29}}$.   **8.** $y = a$; $3y = 4x + 3a$.

9. $(1, 1)$; $45°$. **10.** $\left(\dfrac{5}{2}, \dfrac{1}{4}\right)$; $\tan^{-1} 60$. **11.** $(-1, -3)$; $(3, 1)$; $(5, 3)$.

12. $(2, 1)$; $\tan^{-1} \dfrac{7}{17}$.   **13.** $45°$; $(-5, 3)$; $x - 3y = 9$; $2x - y = 8$

14. 3 and $-\dfrac{3}{2}$ **19.** $m_1 (a_2 - a_3) + m_2 (a_3 - a_1) + m_3 (a_1 - a_2) = 0$.

20. $(-4, -3)$.   **21.** $\left(\dfrac{11}{13}, -\dfrac{7}{13} \right)$ **23.** $43x - 29y = 71$.

24. $x - y = 11$.   **25.** $y = 3x$ **26.** $y = x$

27. $a^2 y - b^2 x = ab (a - b)$.   **28.** $3x + 4y = 5a$.   **29.** $x + y + 2 = 0$.

30. $23x + 23y = 11$.   **31.** $13x - 23y = 64$.

33. $Ax + By + C + \lambda (A'x + B'y + C') = 0$ where λ is

     (1) $-\dfrac{C}{C'}$, (2) $-\dfrac{B}{B'}$, (3) $-\dfrac{Ba + C}{B'a + C'}$ and (4) $-\dfrac{Ax' + By + C}{A'x + B'y + C'}$

37. $y = 2$; $x = 6$ **38.** $99x + 77y + 71 = 0$; $7x - 9y - 37 = 0$.

39. $x - 2y + 1 = 0$; $2x + y = 3$

40. $x (2\sqrt{2} - 3) + y (\sqrt{2} - 1) = 4\sqrt{2} - 5$;

     $x (2\sqrt{2} + 3) + y (\sqrt{2} + 1) = 4\sqrt{2} + 5$.

41. $(y - b) (m + m') + (x - a) (1 - mm') = 0$;

     $(y - b) (1 - mm') - (x - a) (m + m') = 0$.

42. $33x + 9y = 31$; $112x - 64y + 141 = 0$; $7y - x = 18$.

43. $x (3 + \sqrt{17}) + y (5 + \sqrt{17}) = 15 + 4\sqrt{17}$;

     $x (4 + \sqrt{10}) + y (2 + \sqrt{10}) = 4\sqrt{10} + 12$;

     $x (2\sqrt{34} - 3\sqrt{5}) + y (\sqrt{34} - 5\sqrt{5}) = 6\sqrt{34} - 15\sqrt{5}$.

44. $A (y - k) - B (x - h) = \pm (Ax + By + C)$.

45. At an angle of $15°$ or $75°$ to the axis of x.

IX (Pages 67, 68)

1. (1) $\tan^{-1} \dfrac{\sqrt{3}}{2}$;   (2) $15°$.   **2.** $\tan^{-1} \dfrac{30\sqrt{3}}{37}$.

3. $\tan^{-1} \left(\dfrac{m^2 + 1}{m^2 - 1} \tan \omega \right)$.

7. $y = 0$, $y = x - a$, $x = 2a, y = 2a, y = x + a, x = 0, y = x, x = a$,   and $y = a$, where a is the length of a side.

10. $y (6 - \sqrt{3}) + x (3\sqrt{3} - 2) = 22 - 9\sqrt{3}$.   **11.** $\dfrac{5}{6}$.

12. $10y - 11x + 1 = 0$; $\dfrac{6}{37} \sqrt{111}$.

ANSWERS

X (Pages 73–75)

4. $(-7, 3)$.　　**5.** $\left(-\dfrac{13}{28}, \dfrac{5}{4}\right)$; $\dfrac{157}{140}$.

6. $\left(\dfrac{-85 - 7\sqrt{5}}{120}, \dfrac{21\sqrt{5} - 65}{120}\right)$; $\dfrac{35 - 7\sqrt{5}}{120}$.　　**7.** $\left(\dfrac{7}{9}, \dfrac{14}{27}\right)$; $\dfrac{14}{27}$.

8. $\left\{\dfrac{6 + \sqrt{10}}{2}, \dfrac{2 + \sqrt{10}}{2}\right\}$; $\left(\dfrac{6 - \sqrt{10}}{2}, \dfrac{2 - \sqrt{10}}{2}\right)$; $\left(\dfrac{8 - \sqrt{10}}{6}, \dfrac{16 + \sqrt{10}}{6}\right)$

9. $\left(\dfrac{9}{2}, \dfrac{9}{2}\right)$ $(2, 12)$, $(12, 2)$, and $(-3, -3)$; $\dfrac{3}{2}\sqrt{2}$, $4\sqrt{2}$, $4\sqrt{2}$, and $6\sqrt{2}$.

10. $\left(-13\dfrac{1}{2}, 19\dfrac{1}{2}\right)$.　**11.** 4.　**12.** $7\dfrac{25}{48}$.　**13.** $\dfrac{3}{2}$.　**14.** $\dfrac{17a^2}{26}$.

15. $\dfrac{1}{2}(b - c)(c - a)(a - b)$.

16. $a^2(m_2 - m_3)(m_3 - m_1)(m_1 - m_2) \div 2m_1^2 m_2^2 m_3^2$.

17. $\dfrac{1}{2}(c_1 - c_2)^2 \div (m_1 - m_2)$. **18.** $\dfrac{1}{2}\left\{\dfrac{(c_2 - c_3)^2}{m_2 - m_3} + \dfrac{(c_3 - c_1)^2}{m_3 - m_1} + \dfrac{(c_1 - c_2)^2}{m_1 - m_2}\right\}$.

23. $\left(\dfrac{5}{2}, \dfrac{5}{2}\right)$.

24. $10y + 32x + 43 = 0$; $25x + 29y + 5 = 0$; $y = 5x + 2$; $52x + 80y = 47$.

26. $\left(4 + \dfrac{1}{2}\sqrt{3}, \dfrac{3}{2} + \sqrt{3}\right)$; $\left(4 + \dfrac{1}{6}\sqrt{3}, \dfrac{3}{2} + \dfrac{1}{3}\sqrt{3}\right)$.

XI (Pages 79, 80)

1. $x^2 + 2xy \cot \alpha - y^2 = a^2$.　　**2.** $y^2 + \lambda x^2 = \lambda a^2$.

3. $(m + 1)x = (m - 1)a$　**4.** $(m + n)(x^2 + y^2 + a^2) - 2ax(m - n) = c^2$.

5. $x + y = c \sec^2 \dfrac{\omega}{2}$.　　**6.** $x - y = d \csc^2 \dfrac{\omega}{2}$.

7. $x + y = 2c \csc \omega$.　　**8.** $y - x = 2c \csc \omega$.

9. $x^2 + 2xy \cos \omega + y^2 = 4c^2 \csc^2 \omega$.

10. $(x^2 + y^2)\cos \omega + xy(1 + \cos^2 \omega) = x(a \cos \omega + b) + y(b \cos \omega + a)$

11. $x(m + \cos \omega) + y(1 + m \cos \omega) = 0$.

12. (i) $x + y - a - b = 0$; (ii) $y = x$.

19. A straight line.　　**20.** A circle, centre O.

25. A straight line.

27. If P be the point (h, k), the equation to the locus of S is

$$\frac{h}{x} + \frac{k}{y} = 1.$$

XII (Page 86)

1. $(x - 3y)(x - 4y) = 0$; $\tan^{-1}\frac{1}{13}$ **2.** $(2x - 11y)(2x - y) = 0$; $\tan^{-1}\frac{4}{3}$.

3. $(11x + 2y)(3x - 7y) = 0$; $\tan^{-1}\left(\frac{83}{19}\right)$ **4.** $x = 1$; $x = 2$; $x = 3$.

5. $y = \pm 4$.   **6.** $(y + 4x)(y - 2x)(y - 3x) = 0$; $\tan^{-1}\left(-\frac{6}{7}\right)$; $\tan^{-1}\left(\frac{1}{7}\right)$

7. $x(1 - \sin\theta) + y\cos\theta = 0$; $x(1 + \sin\theta) + y\cos\theta = 0$; θ.

8. $y\sin\theta + x\cos\theta = \pm x\sqrt{\cos 2\theta}$; $\tan^{-1}(\text{cosec }\theta\sqrt{\cos 2\theta})$.

9. $12x^2 - 7xy - 12y^2 = 0$; $71x^2 + 94xy - 71y^2 = 0$; $x^2 - y^2 = 0$; $x^2 - y^2 = 0$.

XIII (Pages 90, 91)

1. $\left(\frac{6}{5}, -\frac{12}{5}\right)$; $45°$.   **2.** $(2, 1)$; $\tan^{-1}\frac{3}{5}$.   **3.** $\left(\frac{-3}{2}, -\frac{5}{2}\right)$; $90°$.

4. $(-1, 1)$; $\tan^{-1}3$ **6.** -15.   **7.** 2 **8.** -10 or $-17\frac{1}{2}$ **9.** -12.

10. 6 **11.** 6 **12.** 14 **13.** -3.   **14.** $\frac{5}{2}$ or $\frac{10}{3}$

16. (i) $c(a + b) = 0$; (ii) $e = 0$, or $ae = bd$.

17. $5y + 6x = 56$; $5y - 6x = 14$.

XV (Page 103)

1. (i) $y'^2 = 4x'$; (ii) $2x'^2 + y'^2 = 6$

2. (i) $x'^2 + y'^2 = 2cx'$; (ii) $x'^2 + y'^2 = 2cy'$.

3. $(a - b)^2(x'^2 + y'^2) = a^2b^2$.

4. (i) $2x'y' + a^2 = 0$; $9x'^2 + 25y'^2 = 225$; $x'^4 + y'^4 = 1$.

5. $x'^2 + y'^2 = r^2$; $x'^2 - y'^2 = a^2\cos 2\alpha$.   **6.** $x'^2 - 4y'^2 = a^2$.

8. $\tan^{-1}\frac{B}{A}$; $-C + \sqrt{A^2 + B^2}$.

XVI (Pages 108, 109)

1. $2x' - \sqrt{6}\,y' + 1 = 0.$ **2.** $x'^2 + \sqrt{3}\,x'y' = 1.$ **3.** $x'^2 + y'^2 = 8.$

4. $y'^2 = 4x' \operatorname{cosec}^2 \alpha.$

XVII (Pages 115–117)

1. $x^2 + y^2 + 2x - 4y = 4.$ **2.** $x^2 + y^2 + 10x + 12y = 39.$

3. $x^2 + y^2 - 2ax + 2by = 2ab.$ **4.** $x^2 + y^2 + 2ax + 2by + 2b^2 = 0.$

5. $(2, 4); \sqrt{61}.$ **6.** $\left(\dfrac{5}{6}, 1\right); \dfrac{1}{6}\sqrt{13}.$ **7.** $\left(\dfrac{k}{2}, 0\right); \dfrac{\sqrt{5}}{2}\,k.$

8. $(g, -f); \sqrt{f^2 + g^2}.$ **9.** $\left(\dfrac{c}{\sqrt{1 + m^2}}, \dfrac{mc}{\sqrt{1 + m^2}}\right); c.$

13. $15x^2 + 15y^2 - 94x + 18y + 55 = 0.$

14. $b\,(x^2 + y^2 - a^2) = x\,(b^2 + h^2 - a^2).$ **15.** $x^2 + y^2 - ax - by = 0.$

16. $x^2 + y^2 - 22x - 4y + 25 = 0.$ **17.** $x^2 + y^2 - 5x - y + 4 = 0.$

18. $3x^2 + 3y^2 - 29x - 19y + 56 = 0.$

19. $b\,(x^2 + y^2) - (a^2 + b^2)\,x + (a - b)\,(a^2 + b^2) = 0.$

21. $x^2 + y^2 - 3x - 4y = 0.$

22. $x^2 + y^2 - \dfrac{a^2 + b^2}{a + b}\,(x + y) = 0 \; ; \dfrac{a^2 + b^2}{a + b}.$

23. $x^2 + y^2 - hx - ky = 0.$

24. $x^2 + y^2 \pm 2y\sqrt{a^2 - b^2} = b^2.$

25. $x^2 + y^2 - 10x - 10y + 25 = 0.$

26. $x^2 + y^2 \pm 2ax \pm 2ay + a^2 = 0.$

27. $x^2 + y^2 + 2\,(5 \pm \sqrt{12})\,(x + y) + 37 \pm 10\sqrt{12} = 0.$

28. $x^2 + y^2 - 6x + 4y + 9 = 0,$ or $x^2 + y^2 + 10x + 20y + 25 = 0.$

29. $b\,(x^2 + y^2) = x\,(b^2 + c^2).$

30. $x^2 + y^2 \pm 6\sqrt{2}\,y - 6x + 9 = 0.$

31. $x^2 + y^2 - 3x + 2 = 0 \; ; \; 2x^2 + 2y^2 - 5x - \sqrt{3}\,y + 3 = 0;$

$2x^2 + 2y^2 - 7x - \sqrt{3}\,y + 6 = 0$

33. $(x + 21)^2 + (y + 13)^2 = 65^2.$ **34.** $8x^2 + 8y^2 - 25x - 3y + 18 = 0.$

36. $x^2 + y^2 = a^2 + b^2; x^2 + y^2 - 2\,(a + b)\,x + 2\,(a - b)\,y + a^2 + b^2 = 0.$

XVIII (Pages 124–126)

1. $5x - 12y = 152$.
2. $24x + 10y + 151 = 0$.
3. $x + 2y = \pm 2\sqrt{5}$.

4. $x + 2y + g + 2f = \pm\sqrt{5}\sqrt{g^2 + f^2 - c}$.
5. $\left(-\dfrac{c}{\sqrt{2}}, \dfrac{c}{\sqrt{2}}\right)$.

6. $c = a$; $(0, b)$.
7. Yes.
8. $k = 40$ or -10

9. $a\cos^2\alpha + b\sin^2\alpha \pm \sqrt{a^2 + b^2\sin^2\alpha}$.

10. $Aa + Bb + C = \pm c\sqrt{A^2 + B^2}$.

11. (1) $y = mx \pm a\sqrt{1 + m^2}$; (2) $my + x = \pm a\sqrt{1 + m^2}$;

  (3) $ax \pm y\sqrt{b^2 - a^2} = ab$; (4) $x + y = a\sqrt{2}$.

12. $2\sqrt{r^2 - \dfrac{a^2 b^2}{a^2 + b^2}}$.
13. $x^2 + y^2 \pm \sqrt{2}\,ax = 0$; $x^2 + y^2 \pm \sqrt{2}\,ay = 0$.

14. $c = b - am$; $c = b - am \pm \sqrt{(1 + m^2)(a^2 + b^2)}$.

15. $x^2 + y^2 - 6x - 8y + \dfrac{381}{169} = 0$.

16. $x^2 + y^2 - 2cx - 2cy + c^2 = 0$, where $2c = a + b \pm \sqrt{a^2 + b^2}$.

17. $5x^2 + 5y^2 - 10x + 30y + 49 = 0$.
18. $x^2 + y^2 - 2cx - 2cy + c^2 = 0$.

19. $(x - r)^2 + (y - h)^2 = r^2$.
20. $x^2 + y^2 - 2\alpha x - 2\beta y = 0$.

XIX (Pages 133–135)

1. $x + 2y = 7$.
2. $8x - 2y = 11$.
3. $x = 0$.

4. $23x + 5y = 57$.
5. $by - ax = a^2$.
6. $(5, 10)$.

7. $\left(\dfrac{3}{5}, -\dfrac{3}{10}\right)$
8. $(1, -2)$
9. $\left(\dfrac{1}{2}, -\dfrac{1}{3}\right)$

10. $(-2a, -2b)$.
11. $\left(6, -\dfrac{18}{5}\right)$

12. $3y - 2x = 13$; $\left(-\dfrac{162}{13}, \dfrac{243}{13}\right)$.
13. $(2, -1)$.
14. $x'^2 + y'^2 = 2a^2$.

18. $\dfrac{1}{2}\sqrt{46}$.
19. 9.
20. $\sqrt{2a^2 + 2ab + b^2}$.
21. $\left(\dfrac{33}{4}, 2\right)$; $\dfrac{1}{4}$.

23. (1) $28x^2 + 33xy - 28y^2 - 715x - 195y + 4225 = 0$;

  (2) $123x^2 - 64xy + 3y^2 - 664x + 226y + 763 = 0$.

XX (Page 137)

1. $\left(\dfrac{1}{2}\sqrt{A^2+B^2}, \tan^{-1}\dfrac{B}{A}\right)$.

2. $r^2 - 2ra \operatorname{cosec} a. \cos(\theta-\alpha) + a^2\cot^2\alpha = 0,\ r = 2a\sin\theta$.

6. $r^2 - r[a\cos(\theta-\alpha) + b\cos(\theta-\beta)] + ab\cos(\alpha-\beta) = 0$.

8. $b^2c^2 + 2ac = 1$.

XXI (Pages 138, 139)

1. $120°;\left(\dfrac{4g+2f}{3}, \dfrac{4f+2g}{3}\right);\ \dfrac{2\sqrt3}{3}\sqrt{f^2+g^2+fg}$.

2. $30°;\ (8-6\sqrt3, 12-4\sqrt3);\ \sqrt{47-24\sqrt3}$.

3. $\left(\dfrac{g-f\cos\omega}{\sin^2\omega}, \dfrac{f-g\cos\omega}{\sin^2\omega}\right);\ \dfrac{\sqrt{f^2+g^2-2fg\cos\omega}}{\sin\omega}$

4. $x^2 + \sqrt2\,xy + y^2 - x(4+3\sqrt2) - 2y(3+\sqrt2) + 3(2\sqrt2-1) = 0$.

5. $x^2 + xy + y^2 + 11x + 13y + 13 = 0$.

8. $(x-x')(x-x'') + y - y'(y-y') + \cos\omega[(x-x')(x-y'')$
$\qquad\qquad\qquad\qquad\qquad + (x-x'')(y-y')] = 0$

XXII (Pages 145–148)

4. A circle.   5. A circle.   6. A circle.

9. $x^2 + y^2 - 2xy\cos\omega = \dfrac{a^2\sin^2\omega}{4}$, the given radii being the axes.

11. A circle.   12. A circle.

16. (1) A circle;   (2) A circle;   (3) The polar of O.

17. The curve $r = a + a\cos\theta$, the fixed point O being the origin and the centre of the circle on the initial line.

24. The same circle in each case.

33. $2ab \div \sqrt{a^2+b^2}$.

35. $8a\sqrt{\dfrac{14}{65}};\ x = 4a;\ 63x + 16y + 100a = 0$.

36. (i) $x = 0$, $3x + 4y = 10$, $y = 4$, and $3y = 4x$.

(ii) $y = mx + c\sqrt{1 + m^2}$, where

$$m = \frac{\pm (b + c)}{\sqrt{a^2 - (b + c)^2}}, \quad \text{or} \quad \frac{\pm (b - c)}{\sqrt{a^2 - (b - c)^2}}.$$

XXIII (Pages 152, 153)

3. $3x^2 + 3y^2 - 8x + 29y = 0$ **4.** $15x - 11y = 144$.

5. $x + 10y = 2$.   **6.** $6x - 7y + 12 = 0$.   **7.** $\left(-\dfrac{2}{3}, -\dfrac{2}{3}\right)$.

8. $\left(\dfrac{26}{25}, \dfrac{13}{50}\right)$ **11.** $(\lambda + 1)(x^2 + y^2) + 2\lambda(x + 2y) = 4 + 6\lambda$.

12. $(y - x)^2 = 0$.   **13.** Take the equations to the circles as in Art. 192

XXIV (Pages 159, 160)

8. $x^2 - y^2 + 2mxy = c$.   **12.** $k(x^2 + y^2) + (a - c)y - ck = 0$.

13. $x^2 + y^2 - cx - by + a^2 = 0$ **14.** $x^2 + y^2 - 16x - 18y - 4 = 0$.

XXV (Pages 164–166)

1. $(7x + 6y)^2 - 570x + 750y + 2100 = 0$.

2. $(ax - by)^2 - 2a^3x - 2b^3y + a^4 + a^2b^2 + b^4 = 0$.

3. $(-1, 2)$; $y = 2$; 4; $(0, 2)$.   **4.** $\left(4, \dfrac{9}{2}\right)$; $x = 4$; 2; $(4, 4)$.

5. $\left(a, \dfrac{a}{2}\right)$; $x = a$; $2a$; $(a, 0)$.   **6.** $(1, 2)$; $y = 2$; 4; $(0, 2)$.

8. (i) $\dfrac{1}{3}$; (ii) 4.   **9.** $(2, 6)$.   **11.** $y = -2x$; $y - 12 = m(x - 24)$.

12. $\left(\dfrac{B^2 - C}{2A}, -B\right)$; $x = \dfrac{B^2 - A^2 - C}{2A}$.   **15.** $9y^2 = 4ax$.

XXVI (Pages 171–173)

1. $4y = 3x + 12$; $4x + 3y = 34$.   **2.** $4y - x = 24$; $4x + y = 108$.

3. $y - x = 3$; $y + x = 9$; $x + y + 3 = 0$: $x - y = 9$;

4. $y = x$; $x + y = 4a$; $y + x = 0$; $x - y = 4a$.

5. $4y = x + 28$; $(28, 14)$. **6.** $\left(\dfrac{a}{3}, \dfrac{2a}{\sqrt{3}} \right)$

7. $y + 2x + 1 = 0$; $\left(\dfrac{1}{2}, -2 \right)$; $2y = x + 8$; $(8, 8)$.

8. $(3a, 2\sqrt{3}\,a)$; $\left(\dfrac{a}{3}, -\dfrac{2\sqrt{3}}{3}\,a \right)$.

9. $4y = 9x + 4$; $4y = x + 36$.

13. $\left(\dfrac{\sqrt{17} + 1}{8}\,a, \dfrac{a}{2}\sqrt{2\sqrt{17} + 2} \right)$; $(3a, 2\sqrt{3}\,a)$.

14. $b^{1/3} + a^{1/3}x + a^{2/3}\,b^{2/3} = 0$. **15.** $x = 0$. **25.** a ; $10a$.

XXVII (Pages 182, 183)

4. $4x + 3y + 1 = 0$. **5.** $56y = 25$.

XXVIII (Pages 188–190)

25. Take the general equation to the circle and introduce the condition that the point $(at^2, 2at)$ lies on it; the sum of the roots of the resulting equation in t is then found to be zero.

28. It can be shewn that the normals at the points "t_1" and "t_2" meet on the parabola when $t_1 t_2 = 2$; then use the previous examples

XXIX (Pages 195–197)

1. $y = bx$. **2.** $cx = a$. **3.** $y = ad$.

4. $y = (x - a)\tan 2\alpha$. **5.** $y^2 - \lambda x^2 = 2ax$.

6. $x^2 = \mu^2 [(x - a)^2 + y^2]$. **19.** $y^2 = 2a(x - a)$.

20. $y^2 - ky = 2a(x - h)$. **21.** $y^2(y^2 - 2ax + 4a^2) + 8a^4 = 0$.

22. $(8a^2 + y^2 + 2ax)^2 \tan^2 a = a6a^2(4ax - y^2)$

23. $y^4 + 4ay^2(a - x) - 16a^3x + a^2 f^2 = 0$

24. The parabola $y^2 = 2a(x + 2a)$.

XXX (Pages 200–202)

1. $y^2 = a(x - a)$. **2.** $y^2 = 4ax$. **3.** $27ay^2 = (2x - a)(x - 5a)^2$.

4. A parabola. **5.** A straight line.

6. $27ay^2 - 4(x - 2a)^3 = $ constant

$$\left[\textbf{N.B. } (m_1 - m_2)^2 \right.$$

$$= m_1{}^2 + m_2{}^2 - 2m_1m_2 = m_1(-m_2 - m_3) + m_2(-m_3 - m_1) - 2m_1m_2$$

$$\left. = -[m_2m_3 + m_3m_1 + m_1m_2] - 3m_1m_2 = \frac{h - 2a}{a} + \frac{3k}{am_3} \right].$$

7. A straight line, itself a normal.

XXXII (Pages 216–218)

1. (α) $3x^2 + 5y^2 = 32$;   (β) $3x^2 + 7y^2 = 115$

2. $20x^2 + 36y^2 = 405$ **3.** $x^2 + 2y^2 = 100$ **4.** $8x^2 + 9y^2 = 1152$.

5. (1) $\frac{2a}{3}$; $\frac{1}{3}\sqrt{6}$; $\left(\pm\frac{a}{3}\sqrt{6}, 0\right)$;   (2) $\frac{4}{5}$; $\frac{1}{5}\sqrt{5}$; $\left(0, \pm\frac{1}{10}\sqrt{5}\right)$;

(3) $\frac{10}{3}$; $\frac{2}{3}$; $(0, 5)$ and $(0, 1)$.

6. $\frac{\sqrt{3}}{2}$.   **7.** $7x^2 + 2xy + 7y^2 + 10x - 10y + 7 = 0$.   **8.** Without.

9. $x + 4\sqrt{3}y = 24\sqrt{3}$; $11x - 4\sqrt{3}y = 24\sqrt{3}$;   7 and 13.

11. (1) $\tan^{-1}\frac{b}{a}$; (2) $\tan^{-1}\sqrt{\frac{b}{a}}$; (3) 45°. **12.** $\frac{x^2}{a^2} + \frac{y^2}{b^2} = \frac{y}{b}$.

XXXIII (Pages 227–230)

1. $x + 3y = 5$; $9x - 3y - 5 = 0$.   **2.** $25x + 6y = 137$; $6x - 25y + 20 = 0$.

3. $\pm x\sqrt{7} \pm 4y = 16$; $\pm 4x \mp y\sqrt{7} = \frac{7}{4}\sqrt{7}$.

5. $y = 3x \pm \frac{1}{2}\sqrt{\frac{155}{3}}$; $\left(\pm\frac{3}{26}\sqrt{65}, \mp\frac{2}{39}\sqrt{195}\right)$.

31. Use Arts. 145 and 260.

XXXIV (Pages 242–245)

1. $x + 2y = 4$.   **2.** $2x - 7y + 8 = 0$; $\left(-\frac{3}{2}, -\frac{1}{2}\right)$ **3.** $3x + 8y = 9$; $2x = 3y$

4. $9x^2 - 24xy - 4y^2 + 30x + 40y - 55 = 0$.

5. $a^2y + b^2x = 0$; $a^2y - b^2x = 0$; $a^3y + b^3x = 0$; $ay + bx = 0$.

XXXV (Pages 249–251)

1. $x^2 - 2xy \cot 2\alpha - y^2 = a^2 - b^2$ 2. $cx^2 - 2xy = ca^2$.

3. $d^2(x^2 - a^2)^2 = 4(b^2x^2 + a^2y^2 - a^2b^2)$.

4. $\lambda(x^2 - a^2)^2 = 2(x^2y^2 + b^2x^2 + a^2y^2 - a^2b^2)$.

5. $(x^2 + y^2 - a^2 - b^2)^2 = 4\cot^2\alpha\ (b^2x^2 + a^2y^2 - a^2b^2)$.

6. $ay = bx \tan\alpha$.   7. $b^2x^2 + a^2y^2 = 4a^2b^2$.

8. $b^4x^2 + a^4y^2 = a^2b^2(a^2 + b^2)$.

9. $b^2x^2 + a^2y^2 = 2a^2by$.   10. $(b^2x^2 + a^2y^2)^2 = c^2(b^4x^2 + a^4y^2)$.

11. $(a^2 + b^2)(b^2x^2 + a^2y^2)^2 = a^2b^2(b^4x^2 + a^4y^2)$.

12. $b^2x(x - h) + a^2y(y - k) = 0$.

13. $c^2a^2b^2(b^2x^2 + a^2y^2) + (b^2x^2 + a^2y^2 - a^2b^2)(b^4x^2 + a^4y^2) = 0$.

14. $(b^2x^2 + a^2y^2)^2 = a^2b^4(x^2 + y^2)$.

15. $a^4b^4(x^2 + y^2) = (a^2 + b^2)(b^2x^2 + a^2y^2)^2$

29. If the chords be PK and PK', let the equation to KK' be $y = mx + c$; transform the origin to P and, by means of Art. 122, find the condition that the angle KPK' is a right angle; substitute for c in the equation to KK', and find the point of intersection of KK' and the normal at P. See also Art. 404.

XXXVI (Pages 261–263)

1. $16x^2 - 9y^2 = 36$.   2. $25x^2 - 144y^2 = 900$.   3. $65x^2 - 36y^2 = 441$.

4. $x^2 - y^2 = 32$.   5. $6, 4, (\pm\sqrt{13}, 0), 2\frac{2}{3}$.   6. $3x^2 - y^2 = 3a^2$.

7. $7y^2 + 24xy - 24ax - 6ay + 15a^2 = 0$; $\left(-\dfrac{a}{3}, a\right)$; $12x - 9y + 29a = 0$.

8. $\left(5, -\dfrac{20}{3}\right)$.   9. $24y - 30x = \pm\sqrt{161}$.

14. $y = \pm x \pm \sqrt{a^2 - b^2}$; $(a^2 + b^2)\sqrt{\dfrac{2}{a^2 - b^2}}$.   15. $9y = 32x$

16. $125x - 48y = 481$.

29. (1) $b^4x^2 + a^4y^2 = a^2b^2(b^2 - a^2)$; (2) $x = a \cdot \dfrac{a^2 - b^2}{a^2 + b^2}$;

   (3) $x^2(a^2 + 2b^2) - a^2y^2 - 2a^3ex + a^2(a^2 - b^2) = 0$.

XXXVII (Pages 273, 274)

1. At the points $(a, \pm b\sqrt{2}.)$

8. $(2x + y + 2)(x + 2y + 1) = 0$, $(2x + y + 2)(x + 2y + 1) = $ constant.

9. $3x^2 + 10xy + 8y^2 + 14x + 22y + 7 = 0$;
$3x^2 + 10xy + 8y^2 + 14x + 22y + 23 = 0$.

XXXVIII (Pages 280–283)

16. $\left(\pm\frac{3}{4}\sqrt{6}a, \mp\frac{1}{4}\sqrt{6}a\right)$; $\left(\pm\frac{1}{3}\sqrt{6}a, \pm\sqrt{6}a\right)$

XXXIX (Pages 296–298)

19. Transform the equation of the previous example to Cartesian coordinates.

XL (Pages 307, 308)

1. A hyperbola; $(2, 1)$; $c' = -26$ **2.** An ellipse; $\left(-\frac{1}{4}, -\frac{1}{4}\right)$; $c' = -4$

3. A parabola   **4.** A hyperbola ; $\left(-\frac{11}{25}, -\frac{2}{25}\right)$; $c' = -46$

5. Two straight lines ; $\left(-\frac{11}{13}, \frac{10}{13}\right)$; $c' = 0$

6. A hyperbola; $\left(-\frac{41}{25}, \frac{1}{50}\right)$; $c' = -\frac{33}{100}$

7. $(2x + 3y - 1)(4x - y + 1) = 0$; $8x^2 + 10xy - 3y^2 - 2x + 4y = 0$.

8. $(y + x - 2)(y - 2x - 3) = 0$; $y^2 - xy - 2x^2 - 5y + x + 18 = 0$.

9. $(11x - 2y + 4)(5x - 10y + 4) = 0$;
$55x^2 - 120xy + 20y^2 + 64x - 48y + 32 = 0$.

10. $19x^2 + 24xy + y^2 - 22x - 6y + 4 = 0$;
$19x^2 + 24xy + y^2 - 22x - 6y + 8 = 0$.

12. $x^2 - y^2 = 4a^2$.   **13.** $(ax - by)^2 = (a^2 - b^2)(ay - bx)$.

14. $(x - y)^2 - 2(x + y) + 4 = 0$.   **15.** $(xy + ab)\tan(\alpha - \beta) = bx - ay$.

16. $\frac{x^2}{a^2} + \frac{y^2}{b^2} - 2\frac{xy}{ab}\cos(\alpha - \beta) = \sin^2(\alpha - \beta)$.   **17.** A point.

18. Two straight lines   **19.** A straight line and a parabola

20. A straight line and a rectangular hyperbola.

21. A circle and a rectangular hyperbola.

22. A straight line and a circle.   **23.** Two imaginary straight lines.

24. A circle and a straight line.   **25.** A parabola   **26.** A circle.

27. A hyperbola   **28.** An ellipse.

XLI (Pages 321–323)

7. $\left(\dfrac{-1503}{676}, \dfrac{-23}{169}\right)$ **9.** Two coincident straight lines

10. $\tan\theta_1 = -\dfrac{2}{3}$, $\tan\theta_2 = \dfrac{3}{2}$, $r_1 = \sqrt{3}$, and $r_2 = 4$.

11. $\theta_1 = 45°$, $\theta_2 = 135°$, $r_1 = \sqrt{2}$ and $r_2 = 2$.

12. $\tan\theta_1 = 7 + 5\sqrt{2}$; $\tan\theta_2 = 7 - 5\sqrt{2}$,

$$r_1 = \sqrt{\dfrac{-6}{5}(2\sqrt{2} - 2)}, \quad r_2 = \sqrt{\dfrac{6}{5}(2\sqrt{2} + 2)}.$$

28. 2.   **29.** $\dfrac{1}{50}\sqrt{3}$.   **30.** $\dfrac{5}{3}\sqrt{-3}$.

31. $\left(\mp\dfrac{2a}{3}\sqrt{\sqrt{10}+1}, \dfrac{4a}{3}\pm\dfrac{2a}{3}\sqrt{\sqrt{10}-1}\right)$; $\dfrac{1}{3}\sqrt{20+2\sqrt{10}}$.

32. $\left(\dfrac{a}{2}\pm\dfrac{a}{4}\sqrt{3}, \dfrac{3a}{4}\pm\dfrac{a}{2}\sqrt{3}\right)$; $\dfrac{1}{2}\sqrt{5}$.   **33.** $\left(-\dfrac{3}{2}\mp\dfrac{1}{4}\sqrt{6}, \dfrac{1}{2}\pm\dfrac{1}{4}\sqrt{6}\right)$; $\dfrac{1}{2}\sqrt{3}$.

34. $\left(-1\pm\dfrac{2}{3}\sqrt{6}, 1\pm\dfrac{2}{3}\sqrt{6}\right)$; 2.

XLII (Pages 329, 330)

1. (1) 3 ; (2) 3 ; (3) 4 ; (4) 2 ; (5) 4 ; (6) 3 ; (7) 3

10. $Ax + Hy = 0$ and $Hx + By = 0$; $H^2 = AB$, so that the conic is a pair of parallel straight lines.

11. $x(x + 3y) = 0$; $(2x - 3y)^2 = 0$.

XLIII (Pages 336, 337)

1. A conic touching $S = 0$ where $T = 0$ touches it and having its asymptotes parallel to those of $S = 0$.

A conic such that the two parallel straight lines $u = 0$ and $u + k = 0$ pass through its intersections with $S = 0$.

XLIV (Pages 348–350)

6. $(-1, 5)$ and $(4, -3)$.   **7.** $\left(-\dfrac{4}{5}, -\dfrac{3}{5}\right)$ **8.** $\left(\dfrac{-59}{676}, \dfrac{66}{169}\right)$

9. $(-4, -4)$ and $(-1, -1)$; $x + y + 7 = 0$ and $x + y + 3 = 0$.

15. If P be the given point, C the centre of the given director circle, and PCP' a diameter, the focus S is such that $PS \cdot P'S$ is constant.

16. If PP' be the given diameter and S a focus then $PS \cdot P'S$ is constant.

XLV (Pages 355, 356)

5. $6x^2 + 12xy + 7y^2 - 12x - 13y = 0$.

17. The narrow ellipse (Art. 408), which is very nearly coincident with the straight line BD, is one of the conics inscribed in the quadrilateral, and its centre is the middle point of BD. This middle point, and similarly the middle points of AC and OL, therefore, lie on the centre-locus.

XLVI (Pages 362–364)

7. Proceed as in Art. 413, and use, in addition, the second result of Art. 412, Cor. 2. From the two results, thus, obtained, eliminate δ.

9. Take $l_1x + m_1y - 1 = 0$ (Art. 412, Cor. 1) as a focal chord of the ellipse

14. If the normals are perpendicular, so also are the tangents; the line $l_1x + m_1y - 1 = 0$ is therefore, the polar with respect to the ellipse of a point $(\sqrt{a^2 + b^2}\cos\theta,\ \sqrt{a^2 + b^2}\sin\theta)$ on the director circle.

15. The triangle ABC is a maximum triangle (Page 217, Ex. 15) inscribed in the ellipse.

20. Use the notation of Art. 333.

XLVII (Pages 368, 369)

11. The locus can be shewn to be a straight line which is perpendicular to the given straight line ; also the given straight line touches one of the confocals and its pole with respect to that confocal is its point of contact ; this point of contact therefore, lies on the locus, which is therefore, the normal.

14. As in Art. 366, use the Invariants of Art. 135.

XLVIII (Pages 375–377)

5. Two of the normals drawn from O coincide, since it is a centre of curvature. The straight line $l_1x + m_1y = 1$ (Art. 412) is therefore, a tangent to the ellipse at some point ϕ and hence, by Art. 412, the equation to QR can be found in terms of ϕ.

XLIX (Pages 384–386)

1. $(by - ax - c)^2 = 4acx$,   **2.** $x^2 + y^2 - c(x + y) + \dfrac{c^2}{4} = 0$.   **3.** $\dfrac{x^2}{b^2} + \dfrac{y^2}{a^2} = 1$

4. A parabola touching each of the two lines.   **5.** A central conic.

6. A parabola.   **7.** $a^2x^2 + b^2y^2 = c^4$

19. The line joining the foci is a particular case of the confocals and the polar of O with respect to it is the major axis ; the minor axis is another particular case, so that two of the polars are lines through C at right angles ; also the tangents at O to the confocals through it are two of the polars, and these are at right angles. Thus, both C and O are on the directrix.

21. The crease is clearly the line bisecting at right angles the line joining the initial position of C to the position which C occupies when the paper is folded.

23. $\dfrac{l \cos \alpha}{r} = 1 - e \cos \alpha \cos \theta.$

Popular Series for
JEE (Main & Advanced)

All arihant books are available@www.arihantbooks.com

Classic Texts Series

New Pattern JEE Books

Problem Books/Irodov Solutions

Bridge Course Books for JEE

37 Years' Chapterwise IIT JEE Solved

IIT JEE Questions & Solutions (Yearwise)

*All arihant books are available@***www.arihantbooks.com**

Master Resource Books for JEE Main

Solved Papers & Mock Tests for JEE Main

40 Days Revision Books for JEE Main

Objective Books for JEE Main & Advanced

DPP Daily Practice Problems
for JEE (Main & Advanced)

Physics

Chemistry

Mathematics

Solved & Mock Tests for Engineering Entrances

Solved Papers & Mock Tests (2-Edge Series)

Andhra Pradesh

Bihar

Chhattisgarh Complete Success Packages

Solved Papers & Mock Tests

Delhi

Haryana/Jammu & Kashmir (Solved Papers & Mock Tests)

Jharkhand (Solved Papers & Mock Tests)

Kerala (Solved Papers & Mock Tests)

Karnataka/Maharashtra (Solved Papers & Mock Tests)

Uttar Pradesh (Complete Success Packages)

Solved Papers

West Bengal

Science & Mathematics Olympiads

NCERT Exemplar Solutions

Class XI

Class XII

The Complete Study Resources for
CBSE 11th & 12th

Class XI

Class XII

Handbook Series

Dictionaries

*All arihant books are available@***www.arihantbooks.com**